INTRODUCTION

Corporate Source II presents the latest innovations in corporate communications, with a focus on design, exhibit and display, photography and illustration. Here are samples of international quality from the top professionals working in Canada. In addition to a visual directory, Corporate Source II offers well researched, informative articles and actual case histories in which some of Canada's foremost communications specialists discuss their most successful projects. Beautifully designed with more than 3,000 colour illustrations and packed with useful information, Corporate Source II is a valuable resource that keeps pace with the rapidly changing international graphic communications scene.

Corporate Source II

An annual publication of

Wilcord Publications Limited

511 King Street West, Suite #110

Toronto, Ontario

M5V 2Z4

Tel.: (416) 599-5797

Fax: (416) 591-1630

Chairman: Peter Cordy

President: Geoff Cannon

Director of Finance: Brian Goffenberg

Publisher: Peter Cordy

Editor: Margaret Condy

Writer: Grant McIntyre

Rédacteur au Québec: Frédéric Simonnot

Database Co-ordinators:

Micki Leger, Richard Needham

Client Services Director: Marie MacDonald

Advertising Account Directors

Toronto: (416) 599-5797

Robert Carscadden

Bob Simms

Tracy Seki

Montréal: (514) 849-5812

Anna Gedalof

Vancouver: (604) 688-6819

Tom Davison

Cover/Book Design: Ove Design Toronto Ltd.

Design Co-ordination and Production:

King West Communications

Title Pages Photography: Michael Sandor

Editorial Photography: Paul Appleby, Casimir Bart

Editorial Illustrations: Brad Black, Philippe Béha

Copyright© 1990

Wilcord Publications Limited

ISBN 0-920986-18-8

ISSN 0709-7727

Printed in Hong Kong by Book Art

DESIGN, COMMUNICATIONS & SERVICES

Contents

◁ 1 ▷ Design

▷ 1.1 Designers

▷ 1.2 Sales Promotion

▷ 1.3 Advertising Agencies

▷ 1.4 Electronic Graphics and Services

▷ 1.5 Computer Film Recording

▷ 1.6 Film/Video/AV

◁ 2 ▷ Exhibit & Display

◁ 3 ▷ Photography

▷ 3.1 Photo Laboratories

▷ 3.2 Stock Photography

DESIGN

"To do good and to communicate forget not."

The Epistle of Paul to the Hebrews

CORPORATE STRATEGY BY DESIGN

➢ **Perhaps the most influential trend in graphic design as a tool of corporate communication is the notion that a designer can bring to a corporation much more than a system of decorative symbols and appealing brochures. When the designer's work is created as a communication of a corporation's objectives, personality and style, it has the power to dictate how the specific audience will perceive that company. As more buyers of design become aware of the strength of good design, more and more designers are being invited to participate as communication consultants while that corporate strategy is being developed.**

◆ ◆ ◆

This is a welcome change for designers who, for too many years, have been treated by many of their clients as visual artisans. Corporations are now coming to acknowledge that design fees are better spent when they are used to create a solution rather than decorate a problem.

Subjective tastes and an emphasis on aesthetics — which often results in the gratuitous use of flashy, gimmicky effects — as well as the corporate community's own reluctance to let designers in on the essential business plans of the corporations they are supposed to represent, have contributed to the customary relegation of designers to the sidelines of corporate strategy development.

Members of the international design community and observant corporate strategists cannot help but acknowledge the value of strategic design when they look at a well-known success story. Paul Rand's contribution to the success of IBM came about through the designer's thorough examination of his client's objectives, its position in the marketplace, its competition and the projected future of the industry. Rand was able to give his client much more than a logo. The company's vision and identity have become a visual paradigm of the value of design as an integral part of a corporate

strategy. This takes the designer's responsibility far beyond the decorative.

This breakthrough in design as a strategic tool occurred many years ago, and its benefits to IBM are still paying off. Apple, Olivetti and Braun are other names associated with successful acknowledgement of design's importance in overall corporate objectives. But this is by no means the norm. The message has yet to reach the majority of Canada's corporate community.

What are the benefits of treating design as an important part of corporate strategy, and how can more companies be brought to acknowledge this?

As Stephen Candib of Gottschalk+Ash International (Graphic Design Consultants) points out, "There is a cost involved in doing any work of a visual nature. While cost will be incurred regardless of the work's quality, there is a tremendous opportunity to capitalize on what has to be done and accomplish another goal. All the visual material that a company produces can be co-ordinated to communicate a message about what the company is, what it does and what it stands for."

The company's corporate identity should thus be viewed as a strategic tool with long-term impact as well as an aesthetic statement. Its visual qualities

"In addition to setting up a company to help people perceive it in a certain way, a properly implemented program can help clients from an operational point of view, saving them money as well."

Stephen Candib
Gottschalk + Ash

should endure for years, retaining relevance to the corporation and supporting the company's image. "In addition to setting up a company to help people perceive it in a certain way," Candib continues, "a properly implemented program can help clients from an operational point of view, saving them money as well."

And what can be more important in a corporate strategy than that? The designer's influence can be as nuts-and-bolts as selecting a method for affixing the company logo on its trucks. When you are dealing with a fleet that consists of thousands of vehicles, the designer's recommended method of implementing the identity — with paint or decals — can save hundreds of dollars per truck, which can translate into millions of dollars for the whole fleet. This is only one way to show how a designer's expertise can directly affect the bottom line.

It was an acknowledgement of the value of the designer's influence that allowed Ove Design Toronto Ltd. to save Canadian Airlines millions of dollars by developing a bilingual logo. When the corporation commissioned Ove to create a new identity for the airline, they brought the design team into the process of developing not a decorative, but a strategic design project.

"We were all sleeping in the same bed," Michel Viau, associate at Ove, metaphorically recalls of his close relationship with the company that selected his firm to create its new name and identity within a tight deadline.

The bright orange CP Air logo was familiar to every Canadian, and part of Ove's job was to erase that image from the national memory. The only way to do that was to create a new identity that went beyond aesthetics, and keep it visible wherever possible.

The aircraft of the former CP Air had a French logo on the left side of the plane and an English one on the right. "This meant they had to duplicate everything, and the question was often asked, 'Is the French on the left side for some hidden political reason?'" Viau comments.

The new logo is one word. Even though Canadian is spelled differently in French, Viau's design team ingeniously created a bilingual logo by substituting, with the symbol they had created, the single letter that varies between the two spellings, hence Canadi >n.

This saved the company millions in implementation costs. It also simplified the uniquely Canadian dilemma of bilingual signs, counters, ticket envelopes, stationery and all other

"Your basic marketing principle has to work hand-in-hand with your design principle. If it doesn't, you just have another product, another flyer for people to look at and throw in the garbage."

Your Guide to the World of SkyDome

Sky Elements

These graphic interpreta-
tions of the basic sky
elements: stars, clouds,
lightning and the moon are
used throughout the
SkyDome site. They should
also be used on promo-
tional pieces and licensed
products.

The sky
appear i
ways: as
shapes, as
and as phot

The use of the
is open to inter
The images on t
are only suggestio
Proposed designs
however, have to be
approved by SkyDome
management before the
designs are used.

For photographic applica-
tions, the SkyDome
resource center exists to
assist you, by providing the
use of its collection of
sky photos.

Not applicable

What Not to Do

PMS 116

PMS 116

PMS 293

Here are examples of
incorrect applications of
the SkyDome mark.

In text, always capitalize
the "S" and "D" in
SkyDome. Never use all
caps, and do not change
spelling or hyphenate.

.Skydome..
.SKYDOME.

Never attempt to make a
physical article out of the
"D" mark if it needs an
outline support (i.e. a pin,
etc.). The "D" mark should
never appear with this outline. Instead place "D" inside
a star, cloud, circle, etc.

Do not u
shapes. W
required f
etc., use a s
geometric
pages 7, 8, 1

Always use white or one
of the SkyDome spectrum
colours as a background
(never beige, brown, etc.)

PMS 293

PMS 293

PMS 348

PMS 514

PMS 348

PMS 307

PMS 348

PMS 345

PMS 293

PMS 307

PMS 348

PMS 307

PMS 293

PMS 307

PMS 266

**SkyDome corporate
identity manual created
by Gottschalk+Ash
International for the
Stadium Corporation**
♦ ♦ ♦

materials. After accomplishing these corporate objectives, the design also possesses aesthetic qualities of strength and elegance relevant to modern international air travel.

A solution as appropriate and cost-effective as Ove's Canadian Airlines identity does not come easily. The designers succeeded in establishing the company's identity within a severely limited time frame largely because the client had the wisdom to bring them into the project at an early developmental stage.

"It's really our role when we start a project for any large corporation to first and foremost let them understand what we can provide them with," Viau says. "We need to become involved in the early stages if only because we bring in another dimension. We impact on numerous facets of the whole, and in order for us to translate that whole into visuals that will carry the theme, we have to be a part of that theme. That's what we were able to do for the airline."

Ted Forrest

Ove Design

Ted Forrest, Ove's corporate communications director, emphasizes the importance of clear communication between client and designer. "To put as few restrictions on the designer as possible is the beginning of that communication. When you put too many restrictions on, you might as well do it yourself."

Too often, clients approach designers with briefs that are more like print specifications than strategic objectives: "It's an A4 format, eight-page, straight saddle-stitch..." That's where the designer should put up the red flag and start asking questions. What is the purpose of the project? What are you trying to achieve? What are the target markets, the distribution and any other considerations?

The designer might assess the client's objectives and recommend something other than the A4 format, eight-page saddle-stitch brochure. The function of the design firm is not to deliver products to the client's preconceived specifications, but to translate the company's overall objectives into communication.

"It is important," Viau observes, "when we start working on a project, not to talk in terms of specifications and guidelines. We speak more in terms of the general concept. We try to convey this in our proposal so that if we're asked to put some visuals together we will, but we always go to the extent of explaining what our research has turned up and for what reason. Your basic marketing principle has to work hand-in-hand with your design principle. If it doesn't, you just have another product, another flyer for people

"To put as few restrictions on the designer as possible is the beginning of that communication. When you put too many restrictions on, you might as well do it yourself."

Canadian

Canadian Airlines
corporate identity
program created by Ove
Design Toronto Ltd.
♦ ♦ ♦

Ted Forrest

Ove Design

to look at and throw in the garbage."

The economic benefits of fully utilizing a designer's expertise might not be as immediately measurable as is the performance of a retail advertisement, but on paper they can be clearly defined in dollars and cents.

A company recently commissioned Ove to re-create some product literature. Ove's research process put the design team in touch with the company president, the vice-president of marketing and the sales people who were using the existing brochures. This research revealed that, as a result of recent mergers, there was some confusion among the sales force as to the current company name. The president of the company was unaware of this embarrassing confusion.

Having identified a problem that extended far beyond the healing capability of a few brochures, Ove submitted a 25-page proposal calling for a complete corporate identity program as well as an internal employee communications program. What started out as a six-month project turned into a multiple-year commitment. This approach might scare away a less receptive client, but it is a way of investing a communications budget more effectively over the long term. Rather than spend

$70,000 this year on some brochures and the same amount next year, why not let the designer recommend a cost-effective five-year program based on the yearly budget?

It is important for the design firm to know the details of the corporation and its communication budget before it can recommend a long-term plan. If the client can only afford to execute a portion of the plan during the first year, the designer can then assist in budgeting for subsequent years.

This makes intelligent use of a budget the client was going to spend with or without a five-year strategy.

"I don't think anybody would have any trouble spending an entire budget," Forrest comments. "It's a matter of spending it more effectively."

It should be pointed out to cautious clients who don't want to have their companies re-invented by graphic designers that good designers don't make changes for the sake of change; they translate corporate objectives into visual communication. And they cannot recommend a tailor-made, cost-effective solution without a thorough understanding of the corporate spirit and vision.

The importance of design to a corporation cannot be limited to the two-dimensional. Some

"I don't think anybody would have any trouble spending an entire budget. It's a matter of spending it more effectively."

graphic designers, through their commitment to the overall corporate strategy of their clients, become involved in an entire system that extends into package design and the development of the products themselves. Very often the designers find themselves in an industrial design project in which their influence not only reshapes the look of the product but can redefine the product's three-dimensional presentation.

The name that springs to mind most readily to designers when this subject is brought up is Braun.

Stuart Ash, a founding partner of Gottschalk+Ash International, says the German appliance manufacturer "has been consistent with a certain attitude toward design and as a result has stood out in front of the masses."

Braun's use of design as an integral part of the overall product, and therefore the corporation itself, occurred at a time when "breakthrough" products were being introduced regularly. Consumers in those days based their purchases on the products' technology. As far back as the 1950s, Braun stood alone as a producer of unique products that had the added value of innovative design.

Today, whether a product originates in North America, Europe or Asia, the technology is very similar. "The differentiating factors are how the product is positioned, what it looks like and how it is presented to its respective audiences," according to Ash. Because of the common technology, "you position that product in the marketplace in a way that is going to give a perception of difference and an added value."

For that reason, Ash and other members of the international design community feel that design is poised to "take off."

As graphic design doesn't stop at the two-dimensional, neither does corporate communication restrict itself to brochures and conventional communication media. Ash recalls learning of the Japanese attitude to design in Tokyo, where he noticed great expense and thought had gone into the excellent design of a block of retail stores. A local businessman told him that design is recognized as a relatively small incremental cost in a country where land is scarce and everything else is expensive. "Why not spend a little more and do it well?"

This attitude toward design, as an inevitable expense that can be better invested as a part of the overall strategy, is growing in popularity, according to Ash. "Design is now filling a role on the other side of the balance sheet. It is a necessity that has to

"There has to be some truth about a corporation, what it is doing and its products. Visually, there is going to be a move back to the basics of trying to get the message across with integrity and simplicity."

Michel Viau

Ove Design

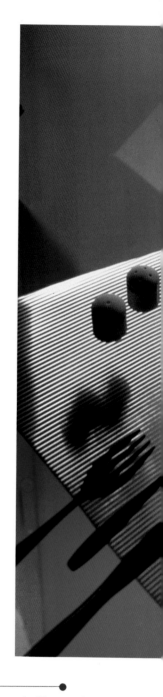

be included in the product. Companies now have more of a vision, a desire to make a statement that expresses a message of very high quality. Where IBM and Braun were the exception, now they are becoming more of the norm."

Canada, according to Ash, is about to enter a very exciting time in design. Environmental considerations have become the issues of the future, the next generation of ideas that will be important. "Places like Paris, New York and Tokyo can't achieve that. Thanks to our quality of life, we have an opportunity to bring this environmental consciousness into design."

An obvious example of this is the environmental trend in printed corporate communication, with annual reports being printed with environmentally friendly inks on recycled paper. "You can't have the finishes that you could achieve on coated paper, and there's a certain quality statement that goes along with that. As those issues become important they will bring with them a certain design aesthetic that is going to change the aesthetics of today."

Michel Viau agrees, calling this "a move away from glitz...maybe the whole industry will finally catch up to the philosophy that

Stuart Ash

Gottschalk + Ash

nature will eventually make us more sincere about life in general. We shouldn't be wasteful. We shouldn't be spending money like crazy just to show off.

"There has to be some truth about a corporation, what it is doing and its products. Visually, there is going to be a move back to the basics of trying to get the message across with integrity and simplicity."

The public's perception of quality is moving toward a less "glitzy" product as the audience becomes more sophisticated. Ash cites the example of Mercedes Benz, a high-end manufacturer that must stay in tune with its market's preferences. "No longer is wood veneer looked upon as something of high quality. Mercedes uses the best quality wood laminate because this adds an element of perceived quality. The old veneer doesn't cut it anymore; neither does French Provincial furniture."

This is indicative of the graphic designer's professional fascination with every aspect of design. It is a professional attribute that a good graphic designer can bring to every project when given the opportunity.

As a strong believer in the importance of a building's interaction with the public, Ash has demonstrated how the

"The differentiating factors are how the product is positioned, what it looks like, and how it is presented to its respective audiences,"

Table settings designed
for Canadian Airlines
by Ove Design Toronto
Ltd.

♦ ♦ ♦

graphic designer can complement the architect's efforts by making the building more accessible to the public. "The idea of a building being in scale to the pedestrian brings about a whole refocusing of relationship between the building and the pedestrian."

This kind of vision takes the graphic designer closer to the strategy that is put forward by the developer and executed by the architects and interior designers. Whether the objective is to create a corporate identity or lure the public to a building, the graphic designer's influence is most valuable when he is brought in at the conceptual stages.

Creating an identity for Toronto's SkyDome represented both a corporate and an architectural communications project. Gottschalk+Ash were called in at the conceptual stages of corporate strategy development to give the building an image that would become an integral part of the corporate strategy.

The designers had a mandate to generate activity in the stadium far beyond the baseball and football seasons. "Our objective was to attract other events and give the stadium its own kind of momentum."

This was the vision of Chuck Magwood, former president and

CEO of the Stadium Corporation. Magwood was responsible for co-ordinating the completion of the SkyDome and supervising the creation of an identity. He is the kind of client who knows how to get the most from the designers' contribution by bringing them in "before things get screwed up."

Magwood put together a team of people to generate ideas that would bring to life his vision of the Dome. "The idea was to incorporate the hotel, the fitness club, the bars and restaurants to give it a life that made it a city within a city," Ash recalls. "Fortunately, we were in a position where we could communicate our ideas in a creative environment. Chuck Magwood created a sort of synergistic atmosphere with the design team that bred creativity."

Magwood feels he brought about this environment unintentionally. "I love the creative side and I respect the people who provide that input.Coming from a development background, I respect the importance of creative touches and the personality and enthusiasm that the creative process thrives on."

This is how to let the designer create a solution that is a part of the corporate strategy itself: be a good client. Magwood, who acted as a buffer between the creativity and the budget,

SkyDome graphics
identity program
designed by
Gottschalk+Ash
International for the
Stadium Corporation
♦ ♦ ♦

displayed an uncanny ability to communicate complex ideas between the designers and the consortium.

"It wasn't a matter of 'Let's build a building,'" says Ash. "It was 'Let's build a great building.'"

From the midst of developing a corporate strategy, Ash and his team were able to identify three important points to be addressed in the Dome's corporate identity. Since the Dome was essentially an engineering concept, it didn't have a lot of aesthetic appeal. An identity had to be created that would give the public a perception of the building architecturally as well as from the corporate and marketing perspectives. Gottschalk+Ash International joined forces with the industrial design firm of Keith Muller Limited, forming a design consortium capable of quickly responding to the environmental design needs of the SkyDome.

The graphic system developed by Gottschalk+Ash International conveys the image of the Dome with a visual representation of the building's retractable roof. The symbol broadens itself into the concept of the sky and its related elements, with a spectrum of colours. "We came up with an idea that could be rendered in many different areas as a palette or a kit of parts which would give a common

visual feeling to the place," Ash explains.

Because this was a corporate communications project using an architectural medium, the graphic designers were given the responsibility of identifying opportunities to use graphic design as a way of making the exterior of the building more appealing to the public. Time constraints made for some innovative organizational planning, and the creative team was always looking for ways to do things both quickly and effectively.

When it was decided that the exterior of the building needed some colour for the opening, the idea of banners came up. "They gave out the assignment for each one of the design people to design one of the banners, which was the only way we could get it done in three days."

This brought the strategy of the SkyDome into the visual realm. But because the design team was involved at the early stages of the corporate strategy conception, its contribution goes far beyond the visual.

The design consortium was able to turn interior signage into a revenue-generating tool rather than a onetime expenditure, thus making a greater contribution to the corporation as a whole. This was done by incorporating advertising into the signage. The

Stuart Ash

Gottschalk + Ash

"It wasn't a matter of 'Let's build a building.' It was 'Let's build a great building.'"

designers also contributed to the development of a licensing program that turned the visual vocabulary of the Dome into salable products to further generate revenue.

Also inside the building, where the colour scheme visible on the outside was continued on the seating and the signage, another problem presented itself.

There was a need to cover up some of the mechanical, electrical and plumbing arteries that could still be seen from inside the stadium. The design consortium of Gottschalk+Ash International and Keith Muller Limited came up with a way of covering what he calls this "awful mess" with a revenue-generating solution. They created a "modesty screen" that, while following the colour scheme, incorporates advertising into a signage system that veils the once visible "guts" of the building.

These solutions go far beyond decoration and, like Ove's Canadian Airlines logo, will reflect on the corporation's bottom line for years to come.

The people who operate today's major graphic design firms have learned, from their own experience and from observing other successful international corporate communications programs, that the visual elements are the tools

of a larger corporate strategy.

Every company communicates, and can make the most of it by doing so deliberately and strategically. "Having a communication plan is absolutely critical," says Ian Tudhope, principal of Tudhope Associates Inc., a Toronto communications consultancy. If a Tudhope client doesn't have such a plan, "the first thing we do is help them structure one. Very few clients come to the table with a fully evolved communication plan. The more sophisticated clients will have a marketing and communication budget in place, but exactly how that money will be spent is frequently not known."

The company that doesn't have a communication plan can do worse than encounter a designer who will act as communication consultant and help create one that suits the client's objectives.

The first step, according to Ian Tudhope and his partner/brother, Bev, is to identify the client's communication objectives and the audience to whom that communication is directed. The role of the consultants is to recommend, based on their experience or market research, the most efficient way to fulfill those objectives.

"We're not just designers," Bev asserts. "We're communications

"Having a communication plan is absolutely critical. If a client doesn't have such a plan, the first thing to do is help them structure one."

Ian Tudhope
Tudhope Associates

Ian Tudhope
Tudhope Associates

consultants." This approach makes the visual expression secondary to the overall communication process. Identifying the idea that needs to be conveyed comes before the development of a means of expressing that idea. The content of the message itself is the critical, often elusive piece of information that the designer must find before thinking about execution.

Bev mentions a client who once commented that he loved working with his firm "because I can sit down and talk to you and you always give me what I want."

"But this client is often unclear in a briefing," Bev continues. How, then, do they get what they want? It is an uncanny ability honed through years of interpreting general briefings that has enabled the Tudhopes to "read between the lines and hear what the client isn't telling you, ignore certain things, sense what they really need, and come back with the appropriate response. The mark of a good design consultant is the ability to come back the first time with something that is very close to what the client has envisioned they want, but may have difficulty expressing."

But it's not as easy as it sounds. Before beginning to think about visual communication, the designer

must first gain a thorough understanding of the current and desired image of the company. Every time a receptionist picks up a telephone, a pedestrian looks at a storefront or a customer thumbs a brochure, a company is making a statement about itself. This is the image, the broad canvas upon which the designer's work will appear.

Image is largely a matter of differentiation, the perceived difference between one bank and another, one oil company and another, one product and another. The design consultant who wishes to contribute to the effective communication of that image must become immersed in the corporate culture, find out the expectations and objectives of the client and ask a lot of questions.

The briefing is a crucial stage in developing a communication project. This is where the patient tells the doctor where it hurts. Without a proper briefing that includes the client's articulating the company's overall objectives and that of the project at hand, the designer cannot begin to write a prescription.

Yet many clients still ask for an A4 format, eight-page, straight saddle-stitch brochure, when a written brief of the brochure's objective is what the designer needs. Ian Tudhope notes that clients' objectives are rarely

"We prepare a situation analysis, identify the communication objectives and target audience, determine a strategy for our approach, and outline a plan for implementation."

1325

AVENUE
OF THE
AMERICAS

"The mark of a good design consultant is the ability to come back the first time with something that is very close to what the client has envisioned they want, but may have difficulty expressing."

Bev Tudhope
Tudhope Associates

Leasing brochure for
1325 Avenue of the
Americas created by
Tudhope Associates Inc.
for J. Minskoff Equities,
New York
◆ ◆ ◆

1325
AVENUE
OF THE
AMERICAS

EXCEPTIONAL BUILDING

1325 Avenue of the Americas has strong visual and
textural impact. The tower exterior, clad in light, deer-brown
flamed granite, rises out of a podium of similar materials but
with a honed finish. Cornices and setbacks are given special
prominence by the use of Sardinian grey granite.

This design is translated from its exterior expression into its
magnificent entry lobbies facing West 53rd and West 54th
Streets. Spacious, semi-circular entrances, clad in high-honed
Crema Valencia marble, feature 27-foot coffered ceilings.
A spectacular main elevator lobby joins the two entrances, its
Tennessee pink and Rosso Antiquo marble walls and vaulted
ceilings emphasizing the classical treatment of both the
entry lobbies and the exterior.

Geometric patterns of Impala black granite have been set in
five colors of terrazzo on the lobby floors. The elevator cabs are
finished in Verde St. Nicholas marble which has been polished
to a mirror finish.

THE INTERIOR FINISHES
OF THE BUILDING ARE
AN ELEGANT COMPLE-
MENT TO THE EXOTIC
PALATE OF THE
EXTERIOR.

The superior quality of
design and finishes ensures that
the building will be an enduring classic.

documented. "We prepare a situation analysis, identify the communication objectives and target audience, determine a strategy for our approach, and outline a plan for implementation." This is an efficient way to get the client to agree to a plan of action from which the designer can begin developing a solution. This is the basis of a value-added approach.

From here, everything the designer presents to the client must in some way respond to the brief. Every physical, strategic and aesthetic element of the presentation is justified as a means of achieving the objectives articulated in the brief, which in turn harmonizes with the overall corporate strategy.

The nature of the brief depends on the client and the design consultant, and rigid rules of briefing could inhibit the success of the project. The main point is that the designer needs information and the client must be willing to provide it. "The briefing must come from a high corporate level," says John Taylor, a principal of the Taylor-Sprules Corporation. "And clients must be candid and honest about themselves and their competition, as well as their communication needs and long-range goals." But the briefing doesn't stop there, as Taylor explains. After the company has bared its soul, it is up to the designer to assess the accuracy of the client's subjective self-perception by researching the market, the competition and the targeted audience of the project.

A strong believer in research, Taylor emphasizes the value of focus groups for testing markets, particularly in product design projects. "Some designers like up-to-date, flashy stuff, but the market of a particular product is not always so sophisticated. You must test and target."

Taylor's research extends from the offices and boardrooms and into the retail environments themselves. Before beginning a package or product design project, the Taylor/Sprules design team examines the way competitive products are displayed in the stores to give a context for their design. This research also includes actually purchasing a competitive product to give them an experiential understanding of the industry and the market in which their design is expected to perform.

This way of strategic thinking can be particularly valuable in finding markets for high-technology products, according to Taylor. The designer can become involved in repackaging an existing product to position it in other markets. This is another way useful ideas can be brought to the table.

"Some designers like up-to-date, flashy stuff, but the market of a particular product is not always so sophisticated. You must test and target."

John Taylor,
Taylor/Sprules Corporation

Expo 2000 Canada book
developed by the
Taylor/Sprules
Corporation
◆ ◆ ◆

Tom Pigeon, head of the Thomas Pigeon Group, a Montreal firm specializing in package design, tries to narrow the briefing down to a specific format. The information the client supplies can "range from a verbal briefing to a 400-page presentation of Marketing 101. What we do is distill all that down into a document we call a Packaging Design Briefing Summary."

This five-page document outlines salient background information, current consumer purchase behavior, demographics and psychographics. It also projects future purchasers. "Who have you got now; who do you want to talk to?" Pigeon summarizes.

The brief must contain a maximum of five strategic communication objectives because, as Pigeon explains, "Any package that can achieve more than five broad objectives has to be six feet by six feet square." Narrowing the objectives to only five can be a difficult process, since, in a perfect world, the client would have it do 22. But Pigeon and his team consult on the five most important objectives and try to put them in order of priority before beginning the design process.

The importance of research in package design has become conventional wisdom, and Pigeon accepts his role as a translator of research findings into packaging objectives. Research takes many forms and at one time, it consisted entirely of walking into the supermarket and looking at the product displays. While this is still an important part of the process, the packaging strategy must also respond to the buying habits of the prospective consumers. How people use the retail environment is as significant to the package designer as the environment itself. Do they spend 15 minutes making a considered decision or 15 seconds making an impulse purchase? This depends largely on the store environment. And when the consumer makes the purchase, that part of the strategy has been achieved.

Another testimonial to the value of package design and marketer working as strategic design partners is the multi-year relationship Thomas Pigeon Design Group has with Julius Schmid of Canada.

"We've had the complete involvement of all management level from Murray Black, the president, on down," says Pigeon. "They've subscribed to our philosophy of strategic package design and it's helped them keep their leading edge."

When Julius Schmid commissioned the Thomas Pigeon Design Group to redesign

Tom Pigeon

Thomas Pigeon Group

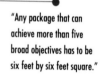

"Any package that can achieve more than five broad objectives has to be six feet by six feet square."

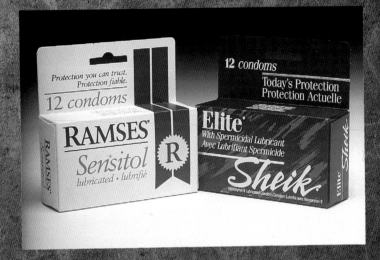

Package redesigns
executed by the
Thomas Pigeon Group
❖ ❖ ❖

their Ramses line of condoms, Pigeon was quick to survey and summarize the situation. "Clearly, AIDS had introduced a whole new market dynamic to the category." Condoms were no longer simply a promise of enjoyable sex without the fear of pregnancy. They had suddenly elevated themselves to the position of protection against death. Market players were changing; heterosexual females were buying more, gay males were purchasing when they hadn't before and heterosexual males were looking for added protection.

"I noticed that the 'grab and dash' attitude was present at the retail shelf," says Pigeon. "Additionally, most packs cleared the checkout counter upside down, concealing the more provocative photographic image of old. It was like watching someone buy *Penthouse*... it was somewhat embarrassing."

Research supported Pigeon's conclusions and led his firm to design the new package direction of "ethical confidence." Package graphics are discrete and understated and are much more responsive to the consumer and social dynamics of today.

Pigeon believes that package design should be regarded as a component of the overall corporate strategy rather than an isolated marketing exercise.

Louis Fishauf
Reactor Art and Design

"There is brand strategy and corporate strategy, and they overlap. When the senior people are committed to their corporate strategy and the brand packaging is part of it, you have a much better chance of weaving a whole thought process through the organization.

"There is no question that, because product managers are becoming directors and vice-presidents, there is more of a commitment to packaging as a strategic marketing tool or a component to the strategy."

Louis Fishauf, co-founder of Reactor Art and Design, stresses the importance of receiving the briefing from the right person. We have yet to find a designer who will dispute that "any designer who is working on a project needs to talk to the client directly. There's too much that can be lost in the translation if you have a person in the middle." That's why it is important to have one person on the client side who is qualified to make decisions at both the briefing and approval stages.

One of Reactor's most visible clients is Bata Shoe Stores. Although the corporation itself has a number of creative suppliers, one co-ordinator looks after the in-store signage, displays and retail advertising. Reactor has cultivated a strong relationship and good

"Any designer who is working on a project needs to talk to the client directly. There's too much that can be lost in the translation if you have a person in the middle."

**Point-of-sale posters
designed by Reactor Art
and Design for Bata
Shoe Stores**
◆ ◆ ◆

communications with this client in order to consistently create retail posters and advertising that are both pertinent and visually exciting. Fishauf refers to the posters as "one of the more fun aspects" of Reactor's five-year relationship with Bata. "There's been a certain amount of continuity; it's not as if we've had to deal with new people coming in and changing everything around."

Ric Riordon, principal, The Riordon Design Group Inc., agrees with the assertion that every company communicates whether it has a communication program or not. He observes that the most important purveyors of a company's image are receptionists, business cards and sales people. "These are what people in business will come in contact with before they actually meet you. It is a personality that the design helps to crystallize and solidify. Every company has a personality they're trying to put forth. The visuals reinforce it."

Riordon insists on working with a hard-copy briefing. The copy itself will raise questions from the designer's side, and it is the designer's responsibility to ask those questions and continue to consult regularly with the client throughout the process.

As an example, Riordon cites a logo he developed for Sandesign Homes, a Mississauga developer specializing in luxury houses. The design team created some themes for the logo, using pillars and gates as elements of the design. During a presentation of the project in progress, the client agreed with the use of type and illustration with an architectural style of graphics.

But the client had an idea. His own house, an English Tudor style home that was the company's first development, might make a suitable motif for the logo. Riordon agreed. "It was a brilliant input from the client and it worked beautifully."

Communication between client and designer "is important right from the ground level," he says, choosing an apt simile. "It's like building a house."

Leslie Sam Smart, of Leslie Smart & Associates Inc. Communication, believes design is still often thought of as "an appendage, a coat of paint on the house. If the designer were in early, he could help with the structure of the house."

Even when the designer is called in to follow explicit instructions, his expertise can be beneficial to the client. When Smart was asked to produce some material for Foster Parents Plan International, one of his instructions was to leave the logo — a symbol showing two children — exactly as it is.

"But the reproduction quality

Ric Riordon

Riordon Design Group Ric

S·A·N·D·E·S·I·G·N·H·O·M·E·S·I·N·C

"It is a personality that the design helps to crystallize and solidify. Every company has a personality they're trying to put forth. The visuals reinforce it."

"If you can make the solution something other than aesthetic, if you do even a partial job of getting some sort of measurement other than the visual interest, that is a plus."

Sam Smart

Leslie Smart & Associates

Corporate identity
designed by the
Riordon Design Group
Inc. for Sandesign
Homes

♦ ♦ ♦

Album covers designed
by Leslie Smart &
Associates Inc. for the
Canadian Broadcasting
Corporation

♦ ♦ ♦

Catherine Haughton
Haughton Brazeau Design

of the little stick legs didn't carry well, particularly on faxes," Smart says. He exceeded his mandate by presenting a modification of the logo, which the client accepted.

"If you can make the solution something other than aesthetic, if you do even a partial job of getting some sort of measurement other than the visual interest, that is a plus."

Catherine Haughton of Haughton Brazeau Design Associates Ltd. emphasizes that the design process is one of constant checking and re-evaluation. "There are many meetings and different phases during the course of the project which serve as a double-check measure to make sure we're staying on track."

This is particularly important in projects that extend over many months when, in today's fast-paced corporate climate, mergers and other changes can alter the corporate objectives. Often the designer will have to stop in midstream and re-assess the project to make sure the objectives are still being met.

The preliminary and continuing research needed to keep the design project in line with the corporate objectives ensures that, in spite of the client's personal aversion to the colour green, the project will be on target come presentation time.

"If you've got a good, strong solution, you can rationalize it by doing your homework," says Haughton. "If you have solid reasons for doing something a certain way, there should be no disputing." While a designer should always remain open to criticism, Haughton believes a presentation backed up by hard, rational evidence should override any matters of taste.

Design is just one form of communication, according to Jim Hickman, president and creative director of King West Communications Inc. "A design firm should not think of itself as a design firm but as a communications company."

He cites the example of oil companies that now call themselves energy companies, avoiding the limitations that a label can instill in the market's perception of the enterprise.

This helps encourage the client to be receptive to the communications company's recommendations. In order to help the client accomplish its objectives, the communications company can "take the client beyond the briefing and guide them into the right communications vehicle for the job."

Ted Larson, president of Oasis Creative Group Inc., puts it this way: "The client may think they

"The client may think they need a 24-page booklet or a corporate profile, but maybe they would be better off with some other method of reaching their market. It's good to be there while they're starting to think and formulate their ideas, so you can be formulating with them."

"There are many meetings and different phases during the course of the project which serve as a double-check measure to make sure we're staying on track."

Ted Larson
Oasis Creative Group

Markborough Properties Inc.
Annual Report 1989

Annual report designed
by Haughton Brazeau
Design Associates Ltd.
for Markborough
Properties Inc.
♦ ♦ ♦

Brochure developed
by the Oasis Creative
Group for the
Lester B. Pearson
International Airport
♦ ♦ ♦

need a 24-page booklet or a corporate profile, but maybe they would be better off with some other kind of folder or with some other method of reaching their market. Certainly, we should be in at the beginning."

Oasis has executed corporate and government projects such as the new corporate product portfolio image for UNITEL and the complete graphics for the World Conference on "The Changing Atmosphere" for Canada's Ministry of the Environment.

"It's good to be there while they're starting to think and formulate their ideas, so you can be formulating with them," he says. "It's a dialogue between two or more of you and you can work back from that to satisfy all the different criteria you've dealt with."

When the Ontario Ministry of Industry, Trade and Technology had the goal of getting 12- and 13-year-olds interested in entrepreneurship, they presented this objective to King West Communications. Without preconceptions about print specifications or even a name for the program, the ministry asked King West, "How can we introduce something as esoteric as entrepreneurship to children in a way that gets them interested?"

Jim Hickman and the King

Jim Hickman

King West Communications

West team had the opportunity to work with the client to formulate a strategy.

The program included speaking engagements in which entrepreneurs were invited to address the students in schools across the province. The name "Visions" was created to unify the program; kits were produced for the speakers and teachers involved in the presentations. A poster was created and decals produced for the children. "We were involved right from the very beginning as an integral part of the whole project," Hickman says. "That's why it was a success."

When C-I-L, the venerable Canadian division of one of the world's largest chemical companies, had to be brought in line with a global unification of its U.K.-based parent, Imperial Chemical Industries PLC (ICI), King West was given the task of helping to implement the change.

For almost 130 years, C-I-L had been a familiar name in Canada, with a long-living orange oval logo that identified the brand to consumers on millions of paint cans. ICI had instituted a global identity policy, which meant bringing all its operations — manufacturing facilities in over 40 countries and sales in 150 — under the ICI umbrella.

The first step was to give the Canadian company a new name. Director of corporate affairs Pat

"A design firm should not think of itself as a design firm but as a communications company. A communications company can take the client beyond the briefing and guide them into the right vehicle for the job."

Material developed
by King West
Communications for ICI
Canada's Human
Resources Information
System

Preston proposed ICI Canada Inc. She brought King West Communications in to create a Canadian version of the graphic standards manual as well as a complete communications package.

"King West were my outside consultants in managing that whole process," Preston recalls. King West consulted on all aspects of the changeover process and implemented everything "right down to the business cards," according to Preston.

Although King West was working within a palette of existing graphic elements, its role as a communications consultancy was important to the project's success. "Because this was part of a multinational, worldwide group, we needed information from every level of the company," Hickman observes. "A lot of research and the use of focus groups were involved. Our relationship with ICI Canada is very strong; we have a lot of respect for some of the people there because we worked so closely with them from the beginning."

Indicative of the shifting attitudes toward design as a strategic tool is the renewed emphasis on corporate identity. Much more than a graphic symbol accompanied by logotype, identity has come to signify a

company's projected image and its strategy.

Because the logo itself must express information and a feeling about the company and its personality, it must possess pertinence, longevity and the aesthetics to communicate the company's message.

Jim Donoahue has designed some of Canada's most visible logos. And he says that, as with any corporate communications project, creating a logo requires thorough briefing, contact with the decision maker and a receptive client.

One of Donoahue's most famous projects is the TSN logo. When the all-sports cable television network was well into its developmental stages, the network's advertising agency attempted to created the logo itself. Having come up dry, the agency called Donoahue to help them meet the deadline. "They called and said, 'You've done a couple of good television graphics. Have you got time? We need it in a week.'"

Donoahue was the agency's first choice because he had already created two successful television graphics — for the Global Television Network and First Choice.

The problem the agency had encountered was not an easy one to solve. How do you encompass all sports in one mark? It is one

Jim Donoahue

Jim Donoahue and Associates

"When a designer creates a corporate logo, there are many considerations. It has to look good wherever it's going: on a cheque, on a truck or on the side of a building. And it has to stand on its own, so the company can wear it for decades to come."

Ydessa
Gallery

A selection of
corporate logos created
by Jim Donoahue &
Associates

◆ ◆ ◆

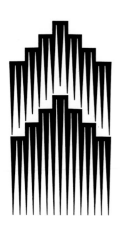

A selection of
corporate logos
created by Taylor &
Browning Design
♦ ♦ ♦

thing to create a logo that relates to hockey and another that works for baseball or football, but how do you find a concept common to all sports — perhaps some sports that the network will not know it is going to telecast until years later?

Donoahue, although severely constrained for time, had the advantage of contact with the network president, the ultimate decision maker. He also describes an exercise in presenting a client with the ideas that led to the designer's recommended solution.

"I took him through the steps," Donoahue says of the presentation he made to the client. He showed some possibilities that were workable, but they weren't winners, demonstrating the nature of the problem to the client. "Now you see the problem," he told him. "To cover all sports, you need a logo that is common to all sports."

One thing that is common is the scoreboard. The final page of the presentation showed the now famous TSN logo, lit up by scoreboard bulbs. "It was so obvious," Donoahue comments, "and it can never be done by anyone else."

Paul Browning of Taylor & Browning Design Associates believes corporations that acknowledge the value of

strategic design are "few and far between." It is important for the designer to be included at the very beginning of the project, because "the most successful projects are created when it's a team approach and you're part of that team from the very beginning. This lets you influence the strategic criteria."

One such opportunity presented itself when Taylor & Browning were approached to create a brochure for Menkes Developments Inc., an industrial and residential developer that has since entered the commercial real estate market. Browning explains that a brochure can be designed "to reflect the company as it is at that moment, or you can help the company communicate its vision of where it is leading — in other words, you can help the company achieve its strategic objectives."

John Sleeman needed more than a brochure from Taylor & Browning. His goal was to revive the defunct brewery once operated by his great-grandfather. He brought Taylor & Browning into the initial stages of developing the product and its look.

There were already a handful of small breweries in the marketplace, so the objective was to give this new, local brew an image that would position it strategically in the Ontario market.

"The most successful projects are created when it's a team approach and you're part of that team from the very beginning. This lets you influence the strategic criteria."

Corporate brochure
developed by
Taylor & Browning
Design Associates
for Menkes
Developments Inc.

◆ ◆ ◆

The brewery had many archival elements left over from its previous incarnation. Bottles and cases as well as photographs of other components were made available to the designers to help give them a feel for the old brewery.

"If you see a photograph of what these components look like," Browning explains, "the beer bottle was an embossed bottle and it had a certain shape. The strategy was to retain the character, the quality, the historic values."

But a 19th century design won't get very far in the final years of the 20th. The historical character of the product had to be presented in a way that would appeal to the current market. This meant creating a logo and a packaging system that spoke of tradition and history, yet did so in a way that was pertinent and communicated in a language today's consumers would respond to.

Because the designers contributed to the strategy development, the design became the marketing strategy. The Sleeman Brewing and Malting Company program included embossed bottles and caps, cases, signage, trucks and promotional items. And, to demonstrate the success of the design in tangible terms, this upstart brand almost immediately captured one

percent of the huge Ontario beer market.

It is widely agreed among designers that there is still a lot to be done to educate the corporate community on the critical role design can play in business. In the United Kingdom, where the fundamentals of design are taught in primary school, there is a much stronger appreciation of the importance of design in everyday life. Although we don't yet have such an early start in design literacy in North America, times are changing.

One promising sign of the marriage of design and corporate stategy is the recent introduction of design as part of the curriculum at the Harvard Business School. What better place to educate future MBAs and CEOs — the corporate communication buyers of tomorrow — on the value of design than in the continent's most respected school of business?

This development began as a result of a case study being presented at the school in 1989. Students were examining the case of the Watt Group, a Toronto-based international planning and design consultancy headed by Don Watt. In the course of analyzing the Watt Group, the Harvard study also looked at some of the design

Don Watt

The Watt Group

"When you find the opportunity, marrying business with design, it's like cutting butter with a wire. You get so far so fast because the rest of the world is standing still."

Graphic design and retail
packaging created by
Taylor & Browning Design Associates for
Sleeman's Brewing & Malting Co. Ltd.
◆ ◆ ◆

projects the company had undertaken. These included an effort to revitalize a then slumping Kraft brand image in Canada; a redesign of D'Agostino's, a New York supermarket chain; and the redefinition of the Loblaws image from the 1970s to the present. The Harvard case study of a successful Canadian company whose business was strategic design led to a detailed study of the design strategies themselves.

Don Watt, head of the Watt Group, was asked by Harvard professor Ray A. Goldberg to present these cases himself. This was an opportunity for the designer to actually profess, in bottom-line terms and to a captive audience of astute business minds, the value of strategic design in the corporate world.

"I've been very insistent at the business school that design is a part of the process," Watt says. "In the agribusiness school, people understand biotechnology, pesticides, control of the environment for growing the products and feeding the animals, and how to take the products through and process them."

But packaging, distribution and communicating to the consumers are equally important. Goldberg brought Watt and his techniques into the curriculum to help the graduate students and CEOs understand the important role design plays in the process of selling the goods. Or, as Watt puts it, "You can't just dump the grain on the shelf."

When Harvard was teaching the Loblaws case, Dick Curry, president of Loblaw Companies and a Harvard Business School graduate himself, pointed out that design had symbolized all the company's strategies.

Watt's involvement with the Loblaws case goes back to the early 1970s, when his vision of the successful retail environment led him to recommend to another, erstwhile supermarket client that a cohesive system encompassing store design, retail display, packaging and advertising formats would turn the company into a powerful retail mechanism. Although he had never undertaken the building of an entire store himself, Watt had observed several retailers in Europe who had succeeded with less comprehensive harmonization of the elements. "But no one in the world had put together the total package in such a forceful, cohesive way," he reflects. He was convinced that the company that used design to unify the entire retail package would be the leader of the industry.

The construction manager of the former client was

Don Watt

The Watt Group

"The company that used design to unify the entire retail package would be the leader of the industry."

Loblaws graphics
identity program
designed by
the Watt Group

♦ ♦ ♦

unresponsive to this opportunity. He told Watt to come back when he had "built a few stores."

So the Watt Group built a few stores for Loblaws.

In the 1970s, Loblaws experienced a severe identity crisis. Some ineffective measures, such as hiring a small advertising agency to create a multicoloured signage logo, did not save the business from its declining sales.

Watt recommended to the new Loblaws management team, which now included Dick Curry and David Nichol, that a concurrent retail refurbishment and a product development program would be required to turn the business around. The client agreed.

But three weeks into the project, Watt was fired. Some Weston executives from England had changed the mandate, which had become "just tell us what colour to paint the walls, what colour the drapes should be, and maybe put a sign on the store," as Watt recalls.

But Watt was rehired when he convinced the client that anyone who agrees to do the drapes is not worth listening to. So what is held to be, in the opinion of the Harvard Business School, one of

the world's landmark business turnaround cases was allowed to proceed.

Watt shared with the Loblaws team his idea of bringing all the visual elements together to not only heal the struggling supermarket chain's ills, but place it at the forefront of the industry in Canada. The strategy was to differentiate the business from the competition by giving the visual identity a common thread. Product development and packaging, architecture, store layout, promotions, product mixes, advertising — all points of contact with the public — would become reflections of the store's personality.

Loblaws was receptive. Watt proposed a new concept in food retailing, a symbolic environment with huge photo enlargements of fresh produce to attract shoppers from other areas of the store. Instead of offering the customers the "jumbled mess" Watt says exists in most retail outlets, every square foot of the Loblaws store would reflect a common visual theme.

According to the Harvard study, Loblaws management set up a design competition between the Watt Group and the Loblaws

Loblaws

Kraft

in-house designers. Each was assigned a store refurbishment project, and the success of each design would be measured in sales. The Loblaws-designed store was by no means a failure, recording a modest 15 percent increase in sales. But it didn't come close to Watt's results — two prototype stores each showing immediate increases of 60 percent to 65 percent.

Within four years, half of Loblaws stores had been designed by Watt.

Part of the success of these designs lies in anticipating the concerns of the market. The first phase of the redesign had an image that reflected the consciousness of economy-minded consumers in the throes of a recession. Yellow, the colour of economy and thrift, dominated the exterior of the stores. And inside, yellow spoke out from the "No Name" product labels, a private brand developed by Dave Nichol and packaged by Watt.

As the economic climate improved, Watt gave Loblaws another face-lift, this time appealing to a more affluent, selective market. Gone is the yellow and the exterior is now a muted gray. The Loblaws

environment has become one of upscale quality. With that shift of attitudes came "President's Choice," another David Nichol brand, which broke ground in giving a private label the image of quality once exclusive to national brands.

To Don Watt, the power of the brand cannot be underestimated. It was brand thinking on the part of Loblaws that played a large part in the company's turnaround. His latest brand, Green products — in distinctively communicative packaging design by Watt's wife, Patty — again addresses the current concerns of the consumer.

Placing Loblaws at the top of its industry came as a result of astute decisions made by an intelligent management team. This included the use of strategic design as a vehicle of business. Don Watt's vision was instrumental in turning the conceived solution into a workable process. He summarizes the success this way: "When you find the opportunity, marrying business with design, it's like cutting butter with a wire. You get so far so fast because the rest of the world is standing still."

As more and more examples of

design working at the foundation of corporate strategy bring success to those companies, more corporations should be catching on to the value of design. The bottom line is that good design gives a better bottom line. There are more case histories around the world of design as a corporate policy bringing success to the corporations that use it. The message should be getting through.

Whether one is talking about a logo, a poster, a machine, a building or an entire city, it can be argued that design is the seed of every human accomplishment.

Design is communication. And what organization could last a single day without communication?

Graphic design can create a visual system that brings order to otherwise disparate elements of an organization. A business card, a truck, a line of products, an invoice, a building. When design is fully utilized and accepted as a powerful tool of business, a struggling airline can return to being a world leader, as British Airways did in the 1980s. Design can be a critical part of the process that turns the name of a computer company into a household word and turns the computer into a household appliance.

While design is not a magic wand, it is undeniably a powerful tool when used as a cornerstone of business. It doesn't have to cost any more to use design effectively than it does to apply it as an afterthought. When design is introduced at the foundation of corporate strategy, it becomes, rather than an expense, an investment whose dividends will pay off for years to come.

Corporate Source talked to numerous members of the design community, and not one disagreed that they can give more value to a company when they are allowed to contribute to the corporate strategy. Not one designer chose to speak about the aesthetics of design; graphic designers feel that good aesthetics are expected, and their most important task is to help their clients communicate.

The process of effective communication is a complex one, yet solutions often seem surprisingly simple. From a single logo to a complete program, every design project presents an opportunity for client and designer to bring success to a company. Design goes far beyond the two-dimensional, and the corporations that recognize design as an important element of the whole strategy today will succeed tomorrow.

As successful companies have learned, good design is simply good business.

MERGING DESIGN AND BUSINESS:

THE NEW ROLE OF THE DESIGNER

The public's perception of the graphic designer is changing dramatically. The image of the scruffy, long-haired creative type who spends day after day in his paint-splattered studio creating crisp comprehensive layouts and ornately hand-lettered trademarks is giving way to another, more updated version.

But the graphic designer as trendy creative type who spends day after day in his floppy-disk-littered studio coming up with new extended typefaces and innovative ways to render them illegible with spot varnishes and glosses is equally inaccurate.

Graphic design is a widely misunderstood profession. Because the designer's work is seen as a matter of visual creativity, it is often judged on purely aesthetic merits. Design is incorrectly regarded as a decorative, rather than a strategic discipline and is still often commissioned based on subjective selection from speculatively submitted visual presentations.

The question of whether design is a profession or a business is almost debatable when one considers that many corporate buyers treat design as a decorative afterthought. These buyers should consider the importance of design in everyday living as well as the power that good design has to improve a company's image, its position and its profits.

Reputable graphic designers don't want to sell aesthetics. Cognizant of the success they can bring to a project by analyzing its objectives along with those of the corporations they serve, graphic design consultants can contribute

to the success of a business with sound communications solutions.

It would be easier on the buyer if it were true that all graphic designers share the same level of qualifications and professionalism. But a problem arises when some designers respond to the aesthetic thinking of prospective clients by applying for work on aesthetic terms. This results in the folly of speculative work, in which eager designers make aesthetic presentations in hopes of winning the contract.

Catherine Haughton of Haughton Brazeau Design Associates Ltd. feels that designers are largely responsible for the image that is cultivated within the buying market. "Some clients are ignorant of the importance of design, the significance of the designer's role in solving the problem," she observes. "At the same time, designers are negligent in communicating the value of their services."

Some clients will use the cost factor as a way of measuring and evaluating the performance of the project "instead of actually looking at credible examples of what designers have contributed to corporations."

Shopping for design services by price ignores the value of the designer's influence on the whole corporate strategy.

"It is a lack of understanding as to what is good value, what is bad value, for the money," Haughton's partner, Philip Brazeau, comments. He describes the speculative pitching process. When a company is searching for design firm to create an annual report or a brochure, it will look at three or four candidates. "They'll call us in and then want us to go back and do some designs. This becomes an evaluation of aesthetics, which is quite contrary to what we believe our whole effort is all about."

"So many designers are out selling a product," Haughton adds. "That's the problem. They're selling a pretty picture, a nice logo, nice stationery. When they're selling a product, the client is buying on that basis. But we don't even take samples with us when we go out on a sales call. We sit down with the client and tell them what we can do to achieve their marketing objectives."

Why not show fabulous photographs and great illustrations?

The client should expect good-looking work from a good firm. Aesthetics are a given. The buyer should be shopping for a communications strategy that works.

To describe graphic design as a profession leads to comparisons with other professions. A corporation will choose its lawyers and accountants, for example, very carefully. The individuals with whom a corporation's legal and financial matters are entrusted must be qualified professionals. There is always an assurance that these people have spent the years in university to earn the degrees, the initials after their names, to legally qualify them to practise. Even plumbers have to be licensed.

But graphic design has no such requirement. Anyone can open up a studio, and confusion results when a designer who offers simply aesthetics is selling to the same market as graphic communications consultants who provide complete strategic services.

The confusion would be easy to sort out if buyers knew the importance of differentiating between professional design consultants and aestheticists. Quite simply, the designer who shows an interest in contributing to the client's business objectives by asking questions and speaking in terms of communication, isolating audiences and positioning is more likely to add value to the corporation than the one who tries to impress the client with visuals.

Does graphic design need to be regulated to keep unqualified people out? For most professions, charters are established to protect the public from dangerously shoddy work. Imagine the consequences if a profession such as structural engineering were without regulation. The public would be constantly in danger of falling bricks from collapsing bridges and crumbling buildings. The risks of an unregulated graphic design community can only go as far as ineffective corporate communications, missed opportunities and lost market shares. No fatalities, but both design and business could benefit if they were protected from the maladies of mediocrity.

John Taylor of Taylor-Sprules Corporation wonders, if a charter were created to regulate graphic design, "would it be to protect the public or ourselves?"

In the absence of such a charter, the graphic design community's best assurance that it is providing valuable service to its corporations is to develop a more knowledgeable client base.

FOR DESIGN'S SAKE, OR FOR BUSINESS' SAKE

Spreading the message that design is a corporate profession begins within the design community itself. "We tell the juniors joining this firm to remember that this is an applied art," says Bev Tudhope of Tudhope Associates Inc. "You're not an artist. You're someone who is applying an artistic talent to a business purpose. It's art in the service of business. It's design that's serving a particular function, not design for design's sake."

Most awards competitions for graphic design are judged by

designers. The works are assessed on their aesthetic rather than functional merits.

"A client's priority may not always be the same as that of the designer," says Louis Fishauf of Reactor Art and Design. "Designers often design for themselves and for other designers."

Stephen Candib, account manager for Gottschalk + Ash International, wears a suit to work and, in a way, he wears two hats. Both a qualified graphic designer and an MBA, Candib embodies the marriage of design and business in his training and the way he approaches the profession.

"Design is a way of thinking," he says. "It can be as narrowly defined as having a problem to solve. If the problem is defined, we can think in terms of design. If it hasn't been defined, then let's figure out what the problem is while applying some design thinking."

It takes a knowledge of both business and design to be able to identify a problem and give it a solution that works for the benefit of the corporation.

Candib speaks of the traditional rift between creative people and those who run the business side of things. Citing the classic advertising agency stereotypes, he talks about "the people wearing suits and the person who is very much not wearing a suit. I've seen certain situations where clients want and expect to have this crazy looking guy in the room with them and they feel disappointed if they don't get that."

Because a lot of design thinking is concerned with organization and composition, a balance between organizational skills and creativity is essential to the design profession.

Creative and business functions have always been viewed as two separate entities.

"You have people who are trained in the design profession and people who are trained in the business profession," says Ian Tudhope. "East is east and west is west. One of the things that we're all about is trying to bridge that gap."

Michel Viau tries to accomplish this with the kind of employees he hires. "We're looking at people who have a strong technical background; people who have a good understanding of not only design, but also some of the business of design. There is a certain ethic to be followed. They will at one point find themselves in the boardroom and all that goes together."

HOW MUCH IS THAT LOGO IN THE WINDOW?

A Toronto design firm once received a phone call from a naive prospective client who was shopping by phone for services. The caller asked for the price of a logo. The designer responded, "We're having a sale this week only; two for the price of one."

Jim Donoahue designs a lot of logos, and he too would be hard pressed to give this caller a straight answer. "A small company that needs a logo will shop around and get it done cheap," he admits. "But a problem common throughout logo design is that there's a lot of stuff out there that's awful—not carefully done and not thought out. A kid in school will jam some letters together and he's done a logo. But there's no thought, no concept."

He notes that in many cases, such as the familiar IBM example, a logo may well last 20 or 30 years. So the importance of logo design, even to a relatively small company, cannot be over-emphasized.

He suggests that the wide disparity of pricing may be confusing to some clients. "A kid out of school might do a logo for $200, while a serious shop could charge $200 an hour."

Are hacks posing a threat to the business? Some designers hesitate to agree, insisting that the kind of client they work for is in a different ballpark. But Donoahue admits that underqualified designers "aren't helping the profession."

Donoahue, who has designed

logos for some of Canada's largest and most visible corporations, would rather design a logo himself than "see another piece of junk out there on the street. I'd rather you wore something I was proud of."

Perhaps he is speaking for the entire design community when he insists that money is not the issue. What is at issue here is the apparent belief among buyers that design is a product to be purchased from the lowest bidder. As Ian Tudhope says, "People should understand they're not buying design services as a commodity. It's not like buying bushels of wheat, and if this supplier is five cents less, then let's go with him. There's an added value component to creative services, and that's where the corporation has to choose their consultant on criteria that are not strictly financial."

HAVE COMPUTER, WILL TRAVEL

New computer technology makes it easier for designers to practise their professions while also making it easier for people without design training to produce their own graphic work. Desktop publishing has been around long enough for professional designers and non-designers to know its benefits and limitations.

But a so-called designer with access to the latest computer programs can pose a problem to unsuspecting clients.

"There's an increasing trend toward smaller shops," says Philip Brazeau, "because of the advent of technology that allows this to happen. 'Have computer, will travel.' Anyone who has even an inclination toward design can start their own business and sell to the corporations. Corporate buyers are now being barraged with very conflicting messages."

But as Jim Hickman, president and creative director of King West Communications, says, "The computer is a design tool in the same way as a paintbrush is a tool."

Louis Fishauf also sees the computer as a useful instrument of design. "One of my enthusiasms is computer technology and how the computer is having an impact on the design business." As a designer who has always struggled with what he perceives as a great expense of time and energy in producing comprehensives for presentation, Fishauf now welcomes the technology that enables him to utilize his company's time more effectively. "With the computer, you can produce comps easily. You can change things and show things to people on the screen."

The computer needn't be a threat to good designers as long as their clients understand the limitations of the technology.

Paul Browning of Taylor & Browning tells of a way in which a client was able to benefit from both an in-house desktop publishing system and a good relationship with a design firm.

"Part of the designer's role is to help the client in any way he

can," he says. Acknowledging that there is an element of pride inherent to a corporation producing some of its internal communications in-house, Browning explains that the idea of an employee newsletter being employee-produced makes a valuable contribution to the company spirit.

When TransCanada Pipelines decided its employee newsletter needed a face-lift, Taylor & Browning redesigned the house organ and produced its first issue on the company's new computer system. The design firm then consulted on the second issue and, with the look, grid and specifications in place, left the trained staff members to produce subsequent issues on their own, with the design firm on standby should they encounter any problems.

But in this case, the onus was on the client to recognize that a new design was needed and to use a professional design firm to fulfill that need. This client got the best of both worlds: a professionally designed newletter that is now produced by its own employees.

A NEW VOICE FOR DESIGN IN BUSINESS

Debbie Azulay, executive vice-president of the Michael Peters Group (Canada) Inc., believes strongly that speculative work is detrimental to both the

design community and the businesses it serves.

"There are a number of design companies that will happily pitch speculatively for business," she says, "who won't just write a proposal and explain their theory and strategy, but will actually do the work."

This kind of practise tosses out all hopes of accomplishing a corporate objective. It puts design back into the realm of the decorative, where the designer with the most attractive visual presentation—in the eye of the client—gets the work.

When a design firm is investing precious hours in a job it isn't even sure it has, the clients are not going to get the work they deserve, according to Azulay. "If we know we're not being paid to do it, then we're not going to give them the kind of creative

understanding and detail that they're going to get if they're paying us for it."

What should clients expect from competent, professional designers who are pitching for work?

The effective way to present a design solution to a client is to submit a proposal, a fee quotation based on extensive discussion, and in-depth research into defining what the client corporation's objectives are. Matters of aesthetics are at this point irrelevant.

In an effort to improve the image of various design professions, a number of designers in disciplines including architecture; graphic, industrial and interior design; and landscape architecture have formed the Group for Design in Business (GDB).

Azulay, a founding member of the GDB, says that, although the abolition of speculative work was not the primary objective of GDB, "anyone who is a member of the Group for Design in Business will not pitch speculatively. It's the unwritten as opposed to the written rule."

The GDB was founded to "initiate ways and means by which design in Canada can begin to realize its potential as a critical ecomomic force domestically and internationally." The group's strategy is to unite the design profession to speak as one voice to the Canadian government and corporate leaders. As Azulay puts it, one of the GDB's main objectives is "making sure business understands that graphic design is a business tool; making sure that government accepts that good design can actually increase your exports."

SHOPPING FOR DESIGN SERVICES

When clients understand that they are not hiring decorators when they commission graphic designers, they are equipped to make an intelligent and profitable choice. Finding the right professional to handle one's business affairs is not to be taken lightly. And selecting a designer based on one's visual preferences has little or nothing to do with assessing the value a designer can bring to a corporation.

Philip Brazeau concedes that it is difficult for a client to pay substantial fees for something he cannot see. "You can't kick the tire," he says. An element of trust is necessary in order for a client to get the most from a designer, and those who do instill trust in their clients can do the most effective work.

That trust can directly reflect on the quality of the project. If you believe that at the very least your designer will ultimately make the visual manifestation of his or her ideas aesthetically pleasing, this can save on costly comprehensives and presentations. That money can be invested in the project itself—in location photography or illustration, for example.

John Taylor recommends a method for selecting a graphic designer. First, talk to the prospective designers and define the task, isolating your need. Don't shop for price; look for a designer you are going to be comfortable dealing with. Talk to some of the firm's other clients and find out how the designer has met their objectives. Also, make sure the designer's expertise matches your needs. It is a true professional who will refer a client to a firm better suited to serve its requirements.

Louis Fishauf puts it this way: "If somebody came to us wanting a Taylor & Browning annual

report, I'd say 'Go to Taylor & Browning.'"

Ted Larson of Oasis Creative Group notes that anyone in business knows that there is a certain amount of risk involved in hiring a consultant. Some people like to take bigger risks than others, but the more you know about the kind of person you are dealing with, the more likely you are to make a good choice. "What you should look for is somebody you know you're going to have a good relationship with for some time, which can be difficult to find in some large firms."

Leslie "Sam" Smart of Leslie Smart & Associates agrees. According to Smart, you have made the wrong choice "if you get the best designer in the world and the chemistry isn't right."

Ultimately, the graphic designer functions as problem solver—in the broadest sense of the term. Reaching far beyond the role of simply creating aesthetically pleasing images, today's designer has a well-earned place in boardrooms where corporate strategies are formulated.

Given the opportunity to work with the client as a strategic communication consultant, the designer is then in a position to make a valuable contribution to the company's accomplishment of its goals—and the success of its business. ◁

ONCE A YEAR

The annual report is probably the most important statement that a company makes to the outside world. Its use as a strategic corporate tool is the subject of constant discussion among graphic designers and the corporate community. What can this yearly financial document accomplish, and what functions are better left to other communications vehicles?

Pose this question to any graphic designer with annual report experience and you will probably get a similar answer: "It depends on the company."

The designer who is committed to providing the most accurate and relevant visual manifestation of the client company's goals can only begin to create a book when the objectives are clearly communicated to him. Beyond that, the client company's attitude toward corporate communication will have a strong bearing on the process and the ultimate success of the project. Some companies still regard the annual report as a mandatory expense, a printing job whose delivery into the hands of shareholders is required by law. Others look at it as part of an overall communications program, one that is carefully designed to embody not only the business activities of the company but its spirit, personality and ambition. These are the companies that utilize the annual report as an investment toward their success.

As a means of communication, the annual report has followed an evolutionary development over the years. Even when it consisted entirely of typed numbers, the annual report did have the distinction of clearly and unwaveringly fulfilling its terse mandate of reporting those figures.

The idea of using this opportunity to communicate other information — about products, the industry, employees, the corporate vision — ushered in a new era. Creativity, colour and visual stimulation made the reporting of financials more palatable to the shareholder, and the use of high-quality papers added an element of substance and refinement to the report. But along with that came some redundant gimmickry. In many annual reports, aesthetics ruled the day, and varnishes, small type and postage-stamp photographs — not to mention hefty printing bills — became pitfalls.

The addition of creative flair to an otherwise stodgy document was indeed a great idea. But like all great ideas, it is worthless unless it satisfies its objective. The purpose of an annual report is first and foremost to communicate. And in order for that communication to succeed, the creators of the book must clearly understand the message to be imparted.

The days of glitz are passing (alas, the printing bills are here to stay) as designers and their clients are working together to pinpoint exactly what they want from their annual reports.

"There is a re-look to annual reports and an awareness of using it more as a strategic tool," says Jean-Pierre Lacroix, president of Boulevard Communications. "Historically it has been used to sell shares in the company and heighten awareness. In the past 10 years, the visual impact and the amount of time and money that are spent on annual reports have increased dramatically."

The annual report is used now for a variety of functions beyond reporting financial information and soliciting investment. Integrating the function of a capabilities brochure into the book has become somewhat of the norm. This has turned the annual report into a showpiece for soliciting business, carrying the corporate image, boosting employee moral and even recruiting new personnel.

The annual report can succeed at achieving all these goals. But to some companies, each of these functions can mean addressing a different audience. And with each audience a different type of message and language — both visual and verbal — might apply. It takes a skilled communications consultant to engineer a printed piece that effectively conveys the appropriate messages to the respective audiences.

The success of the annual report, as with any communications project, hinges on the briefing between client and designer. The designers cannot begin to consider ways of addressing audiences until they have a thorough understanding of the project's mandate. This begins with the client familiarizing the design team with the company.

Cliff Atkins of the Spencer Francey Group says that during this stage "we find ourselves asking provocative questions because it is important for us to solicit as much information as we possibly can." When interpreting this information, the designer must exercise caution because, perhaps unlike any other piece of documentation the company produces, "the president attaches his name firmly to an annual report."

According to Philip Brazeau of Haughton Brazeau Design Associates, many companies have yet to understand what a briefing is. Some briefings are as detailed and enlightening as "We need an annual report — 35,000 copies, 5,000 in French. Here's what we did last year. Go!"

Perhaps an extreme example, but a credible one. The annual report may be the single most direct contact a CEO will make with his constituents or shareholders, yet the system of protecting the chief executive from inquisitive designers in some companies would do the Secret Service proud.

If the CEO is not available or prefers not to get involved in the process, it is very important that the people who are involved carry considerable decision-making authority. It is their understanding of the chief executive's vision that will form the basis for the book.

Paul Browning of Taylor & Browning Design Associates has found that people placed lower on the corporate ladder sometimes lack the confidence to carry a good, innovative idea through. "Access to the top decision maker is very important in getting across a different strategic concept," he says.

The briefing stage requires an open and honest flow of information. This is the data that will be translated into an overall communication style to form the basis of the book. Long before the designers begin to think visually, they must know who the client is, who its competition is and conditions in the market, as well as the history, the present and the projected future of the organization. But it is not always easy for a company to bare its corporate soul to an outside consultant.

"You want to know the doctor before you take your clothes off," Jean-Pierre Lacroix remarks. "To a certain degree, the design process follows a consistent pattern." The client has a problem and enlists the services of a designer for guidance toward a solution.

How much information the client should give the designer is always an issue of considerable concern, according to Lacroix.

But there are, as Lacroix points out, extensive and binding contracts of confidentiality that can be used to protect the client from irresponsible use of information. It is always in the best interest of the client that the designer know as much as possible and is a part of the process from day one.

A good way for the designer to start gathering information is by conducting interviews with management. There can be a number of different versions of the company vision within one management team. The chairman and the president will be approving the project, but the people below them also have to feel they are a part of the process. Some designers also like to speak to the employees to get a perspective the managers might not be able to see. This variety of viewpoints can give the designer an accurate profile of the company, its people and their perception of the corporate spirit.

According to Paul Browning, asking questions allows designers to begin assessing which direction the annual report should take. "Not many companies look at design communication as a culture and how it affects their company." Corporations are beginning to see the strategic value of the annual report as they start to understand that design can become an important asset in their business strategies.

"There are various internal and external audiences, and sometimes the annual report has to communicate to different audiences," Browning asserts.

Cliff Atkins prefers to keep in touch with the original function of the annual report. "The designer's responsibility is to accurately reflect the corporate message principally to shareholders and analysts. Defining and prioritizing the main objectives of the document establish the report's target audience. For example, besides private shareholders and analysts, to what degree does one want to address employees, institutions or the media? Information requirements, image requirements or a combination can then be decided. In this way, the corporate image in relation to the target audience and objectives becomes clear as well as the appropriateness of mixing the annual report information with themes from the corporate brochure.

"The annual report should function and operate effectively within the total corporate communications program. If it is

Rogers Communications Inc. annual report designed by Taylor & Browning Design Associates
♦ ♦ ♦

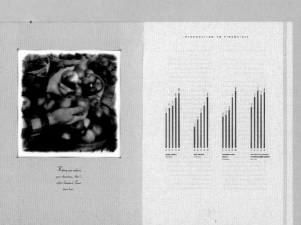

Standard Trust annual report designed by Haughton Brazeau Design Associates
♦ ♦ ♦

to serve a dual function, easy-to-find, well-ordered information should clearly define these areas. The success of the report is based on sound business understanding translated into creative design solutions. Reading it, one should be able to gauge the target audience as well as grasp the company's structure and offer.

"An annual report is often confused with a corporate capabilities brochure. We believe they can and should, in most instances, remain separate vehicles."

Of course, there are exceptions. On some occasions, a company will need to demonstrate its capabilities in a marketing sense rather than as purely financial information, which is often the case with a young company.

At this point, the process has reached a delicate crossroads if the designer feels a theme or concept is appropriate. Perhaps a mining company should depart from photographs of heavy equipment and underground shafts and adopt a more accessible theme, such as teamwork. Or a financial institution might be advised to personalize its message with employee profiles or photographs illustrating its contributions to local communities.

But how do you spring an innovative, albeit relevent concept on a conservative client?

"We're prepared to listen to all the considerations from the client's perspective," says Ian Tudhope of Tudhope Associates Inc. "We listen, assess and make our statement. There is a rationale for everything we present, with established, objective criteria for the validity of the presentation. If someone comes in and says they don't like a certain colour, it's often dismissed out of hand because the objective criteria are much more meaningful."

The success of any conceptual representation, no matter how justifiable and relevant to the objectives, can be aborted by an unreceptive client. Some clients want to do it their way or not at all. "If that's what they want to do, we as designers feel that solves only one side of the problem," Paul Browning observes. "The most successful jobs are the ones that meet both the client's and the designer's criteria."

Browning isn't talking about aesthetic success. The designer's criteria are strategic and reflect a recommended method of addressing the audience in a way that achieves the company's goals. Many clients feel that they appreciate good design, yet have difficulty differentiating between effective and ineffective design. "A lot of people might think, 'Boy, that looks great,' but until you qualify it and tell them what it accomplished and explain how it achieved actual results, they don't fully understand."

Why are thematic annual reports gaining in popularity among more progressive companies? People are becoming more interested in the culture of the company and how it thinks in addition to its year-end earnings, according to Jean-Pierre Lacroix. "People now judge companies' earnings not just based on performance but on who delivered it and how."

Prevalent issues invariably sneak into corporate communications when they are high on the public's priority list. Corporations proudly include members of visible minorities in their employee and customer photographs. Environmentalism is also a large enough concern to make its mark on the annual report. This again comes back to analyzing the functions of the report and the concerns of the audiences it will reach.

If one of the functions is as a recruitment vehicle, the goal should be high-quality applicants rather than vast quantities of job applications. If issues like ecology, equal opportunity and daycare are perceived as important reflections of a potential employer's integrity, Lacroix feels that the annual report is an effective way to communicate this. "Getting good people is going to become harder and harder," he adds, "and the annual report is an excellent vehicle in which to talk about the corporate spirit and its philosophy," instead of straight business.

A company is a living entity, according to Lacroix. More than a building with assets, a corporation lives, breathes, eats and sleeps. While people are focusing on the wellness of the environment and their own personal health, they are also paying attention to the wellness of the corporation and how it ties in with the whole community.

When it is appropriate to carry a visionary or conceptual message in the annual report, designers can have difficulty convincing a client of its strategic advantages. One role the thematic report fills is as a vehicle for differentiating the client from the competition. Again, the appropriateness of adding this function to the annual report as opposed to a separate capabilities brochure should be analyzed by the designer. But by its nature, the annual report can benefit by differentiating itself even as a way of performing its most fundamental functions. Keeping shareholders informed and soliciting investment can be done more effectively when the company presents itself as a leader, a strong performer or an organization embodying other qualities that set it apart from its competition.

The banking industry best exemplifies what Bev Tudhope calls a "mind-numbing parity of product type," where only image can differentiate one company from another.

Tudhope Associates Inc. has been designing annual reports for the Canadian Imperial Bank of Commerce for five years. Ian and Bev Tudhope feel they have been able to contribute valuably to the corporate effort by working with a responsive and innovative client. In the most recent CIBC annual report, the client agreed with the efficacy of expressing five abstract concepts throughout the book. The designers suggested a symbolic representation of these concepts, and the client financed top-notch location and studio photography using professional models, custom-built sets and props. Each picture tells a story related to an area of the company's business, and does so with the utmost professionalism.

Bev Tudhope attributes the success of this project largely to the client's marketing people. "When the client believes in your concept, then you can go ahead and execute it. Other clients would have said, 'No, that's just

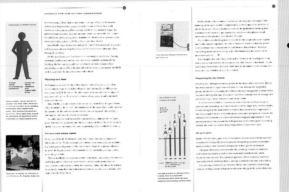

Ontario Hydro annual report designed by Tudhope Associates Inc.
◆ ◆ ◆

Tridel Enterprises Inc. annual report designed by Boulevard Communications
◆ ◆ ◆

too wild for us.'"

Debbie Azulay, executive vice-president of the Michael Peters Group Canada, says that companies accustomed to their own status quo can be expected to have difficulty accepting a sharp departure from tradition.

First of all, the need for a change must be verifiable. Designers who arrive at the conclusion that a dynamic report is strategically justified should be able to support this claim with research. When these findings are presented to the client, he can then be more receptive to the designer's ensuing recommendation. As Azulay puts it, "You can't just waltz in and show the client complete revolution, because he'll panic, understandably. You go through the process of showing the evolutionary steps that led to the revolution."

Azulay was involved with an annual report project in England that she says revolutionized the medium in Europe. The Burton Group is a large organization that, among other interests, owns chains of clothing stores throughout the U.K. and around the world. The company produced an annual report every year, at great expense, because they had to. Until 1986, the Burton Group annual report was a statistical booklet of interest to accountants.

When the company went to Michael Peters for their next report, the design firm recognized the marketing and employee morale-building potential of the project. Because the book is sent to the company's tens of thousands of employees every year, Azulay felt that this was an opportunity to show the check-out girl in Birmingham what a great company she works for. "You're sending it to her anyway; why not send her something she'll read?"

That year, the Burton's annual report was presented as a fashion magazine. Not an annual report with fashion photographs next to the financials, but a visual parody, right down to the type faces and a masthead, of a specific women's magazine.

Azulay admits that, while this report set the European standard for appropriate thematic innovation in annual reports, Canadian designers had been creatively ahead of the European annual report industry years before then.

"It's theming, but not just for the sake of theming," Azulay observes.

Themes are great for the fashion business, but what about a less accessible, more technical industry? Photographs of equipment alongside highly technical copy can make for a very dry book. The Michael Peters Group Canada recently took on the annual report of Unitel, the former CNCP Telecommunications.

The client wanted to reinforce its repositioning and its new identity with a report that was a departure from those of previous years. "They needed to reassure loyal CNCP consumers, shareholders and employees that the world isn't changing — we're just getting better; and also to attract new business."

The theme in this case had to parallel the telecommunications industry, not as masses of wires and computerized equipment, but as an integrated system that is orchestrated to enhance our quality of life.

While the client was understandably expecting last year's book with a different cover on it, the Michael Peters Group conceived a hardcover, accordion-fold publication that presented telecommunications as a parallel to music. Music connects people; music is something people understand irrespective of their language; music comes from beautifully handcrafted instruments of old and computerized synthesizers. The possibilities are plentiful.

The theme worked because it was relevant to the company, its industry and its message at the time. But a theme only works, says Azulay, "if we give them a parallel readers can relate to. You want them to feel about the piece exactly the way you want them to feel about the company."

But how they already feel about the company can be determined by other corporate communications the company has issued. It should always be remembered that an annual report is not a singular event, according to Catherine Haughton of Haughton Brazeau. "Whether it is positioned as a marketing tool, an internal communication or a positioning document, it is an integral part of the overall communications program: the consumer, customer service and staff motivational strategy."

This makes the piece a part of a larger whole. And it stands to reason that an annual report conceived and developed in harmony with existing communications strategies can be much more effective than one created in isolation.

Annual reports are read in stacks of three or four as often as they are looked at singly. For that reason it is very important for designers to have access to many reports from previous years when researching a new client. This also suggests that a sense of continuity can be a valuable element to a series of annual reports.

One way to retain this continuity is to commission a design firm for a multiple-year assignment. This can save a lot of time in research after the initial briefing is completed, as much of one year's research can be applied the following year. It can also help to unify the thematic concepts from one year to the next. When a designer recommends a visual concept, he can immediately start thinking about expanding on that theme for subsequent reports.

For example, this year's book might focus on the human side of the corporation with innovative employee photographs. Next year's can continue the theme by highlighting customers in a similar way. Or companies with more abstract business activities might symbolize their theme with impressionistic illustrations.

This has led many clients to assign their annual reports in three-year terms. The designer gets the opportunity to develop a strong knowledge of the spirit and strategies of the company, while the client benefits from appropriate and intelligent visual translations of the corporate message.

The annual report is, for public companies, a legal obligation. When regarded as a vehicle for expressing the corporate vision in new ways that convey the message clearly and with appropriate style, the annual report becomes a great strategic opportunity. ◁

Burton Group PLC annual report designed by the Michael Peters Group
♦ ♦ ♦

GEAC annual report designed by King West Communications
♦ ♦ ♦

DESIGN INDEX

	Phone	Page	Art Direction (1)	Computer Graphics (2)	Corporate Communications (3)	Corporate Identity (4)	Display & Exhibit Design (5)	Environmental Design (6)	Industrial Design (7)	Packaging & Brand Development (8)	Product Design (9)	Publication Design (10)
Designers/Graphistes												
AM Studio	(416)486-6279	D-74,75	◆	◆	◆	◆	◆	◆	◆	◆	◆	◆
Apple Tree Creative Services	(416)881-0137	D-66,67	◆	◆	◆	◆						◆
Ara No'vo Design	(514)849-2375	D-148	◆	◆	◆	◆		◆		◆		◆
Beakbane Marketing Inc	(416)787-4901	D-68	◆	◆	◆	◆				◆		
Belair Creative Concepts	(416)654-2160	D-69	◆	◆	◆	◆				◆		◆
Bentwater Creative Services Inc	(416)778-4600	D-70,71	◆	◆	◆	◆				◆	◆	◆
Bossardt Design Ltée	(514)849-3776	D-145	◆	◆	◆	◆						◆
CDA Industries Inc	(416)752-2301	D-122					◆		◆			
Cranwell Pietrasiak Design Associates	(416)975-1699	D-121	◆		◆	◆				◆		◆
Design Partners	(416)368-3800	D-65		◆	◆	◆		◆		◆		
Desjardins, Hubert et Associés	(514)934-4762	D-149	◆	◆	◆	◆				◆		◆
Falcom Design & Communications Inc	(416)467-0090	D-80	◆	◆	◆	◆						
Gottschalk + Ash International	(416)963-9717 (514)844-1995	D-81-88	◆			◆		◆		◆		◆
Greaves & Allen Studios Limited	(416)474-1666	D-76,77	◆	◆	◆	◆	◆			◆		◆
GSM Design Inc	(514)288-4233	D-154,155	◆	◆	◆	◆	◆					
Jars Design	(514)844-0530	D-150,151		◆		◆						◆
King West Communications	(416)591-8822	D-97-104	◆	◆	◆	◆	◆	◆		◆		◆
Lalonde Pedriks Budd Design	(514)939-1582	D-127	◆	◆	◆	◆	◆	◆				
Le Mot Dessiné	(514)485-1800	D-128			◆	◆		◆		◆		◆
Legoupil Communications et Associés	(514)939-3379	D-146,147	◆		◆	◆				◆		◆
Marketing F/X Limited	(416)862-0861	D-92	◆		◆	◆	◆			◆	◆	◆
Marko Creative	(416)756-0171	D-90,91	◆	◆	◆	◆				◆		◆
MCG Graphics	(416)593-1375	D-89	◆		◆	◆	◆			◆		◆
Méloche, Robert	(514)878-1001	D-158	◆	◆								◆

INDEX DE DESIGN

			Direction artistique (1)	Graphisme par ordinateur (2)	Communications Institutionnelles (3)	Image de marque (4)	Design d'exposition (5)	Design d'environnement (6)	Design industriel (7)	Emballage et développement de marque (8)	Design de produit (9)	Graphisme d'édition (10)

	1 Art Direction	2 Computer Graphics	3 Corporate Communications	4 Corporate Identity	5 Display & Exhibit Design	6 Environmental Design	7 Industrial Design	8 Packaging & Brand Development	9 Product Design	10 Publication Design	Page	Phone	Company
	◆		◆	◆	◆	◆		◆		◆	D-93-96	(416)516-0927	Moniz Design Group Inc, The
	◆		◆	◆	◆	◆	◆	◆	◆	◆	D-105-108	(416)423-6228	Ove Design Toronto Ltd
	◆		◆	◆	◆					◆	D-110,111	(416)964-6991	R.K. Studios Limited
	◆	◆	◆	◆			◆			◆	D-72,73	(416)673-2416	Riordon Design Group Inc, The
			◆	◆					◆	◆	D-152,153	(514)935-7098	Schell, Wolf Design & Associates1
	◆	◆	◆	◆	◆	◆		◆		◆	D-113-120	(416)927-7094	Taylor & Browning Design Associates
	◆		◆	◆				◆		◆	D-123-126	(416)924-3371	TDF Artists Limited
			◆	◆				◆	◆		D-129-144	(514)875-6844 (416)947-0304	The Thomas Pigeon Design Group Limited
	◆	◆	◆	◆				◆		◆	D-57-64	(416)366-7100	Tudhope Associates Inc
	◆	◆	◆	◆		◆		◆	◆	◆	D-156,157	(514)277-5552	Vasco Design International
	◆	◆	◆	◆						◆	D-78,79	(416)920-3397	Wittick & Wittick Communications Inc

Sales Promotion/Promotion

	1	2	3	4	5	6	7	8	9	10	Page	Phone	Company
	◆	◆	◆	◆				◆			D-162	(416)787-4901	Beakbane Marketing Inc
	◆		◆	◆	◆	◆		◆	◆	◆	D-160,161	(416)484-1840	Ocean Boulevard

Advertising Agencies/Agences de publicité

Page	Phone	Company
D-164,165	(416)362-6545	Aggressive Creative

Electronic Graphics & Services/Infographie

Page	Phone	Company
D-167	(416)863-9900	Ariel Computer Productions Inc
D-170	(514)931-4221	Dignum Infographie
D-168-169	(514)762-0785	Grafnetix

Computer Film Recording/Enregistrement Film

Page	Phone	Company
D-172	(416)863-9900	Computer Imaging Services

Film/Video/AV – Film/Video/Audiovisuel

Page	Phone	Company
D-175	(514)725-5915	Les Productions Imagique
D-174	(416)977-9880	Toronto Creative Centre

Colonnes (1-10):
1 Direction artistique
2 Graphisme par ordinateur
3 Communications Institutionnelles
4 Image de marque
5 Design d'exposition
6 Design d'environnement
7 Design industriel
8 Emballage et développement de marque
9 Design de produit
10 Graphisme d'édition

INDEX DE
DESIGN

Society of Graphic Designers of Canada

Société des Graphistes du Canada

The Society of Graphic Designers of Canada (GDC) is the only national association of professional graphic designers in Canada.

Find out about the benefits of joining the GDC by contacting your local chapter today.

Atlantic
P.O. Box 1533, Station M
Halifax, NS B3J 2Y3
(902) 425-0015

Ottawa
P.O. Box 2245, Station D
Ottawa, ON K1P 5W4
(613) 238-7108

Ontario (Toronto)
Adelaide Street P.O., Box 813
Adelaide St. E., Toronto, ON M5C 2K1
(416) 420-6962

Alberta
c/o University of Alberta
Department of Art and Design
3-98, Fine Arts Bldg.
Edmonton, AB T6G 2C9
(403) 492-3456

Manitoba
c/o Circle Design Inc.
601-63 Albert Street
Winnipeg, MB R3B 1G4
(204) 943-3693

British Columbia
VMPO, P.O. Box 3626
Vancouver, BC V6B 3X6
(604) 254-3210

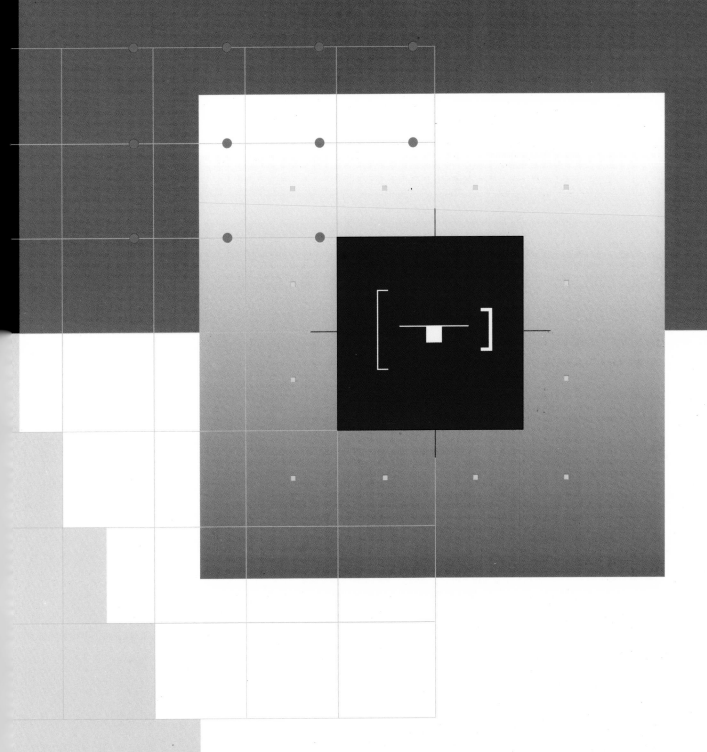

TUDHOPE ASSOCIATES INC

COMMUNICATION & DESIGN

CONSULTANTS

THE DISCIPLINED

IMAGINATION

THE DISCIPLINED IMAGINATION ™

Tudhope Associates Inc. is one of Canada's most innovative communication and design practices. Since 1984, we've been in the business of helping major corporations apply imagination and judgement to their communication opportunities. These pages show the scope and quality of work we have undertaken for a few of many exceptional clients.

IDENTITIES

TORONTO ARTS AWARDS

FUSION CANADA

BAY ADELAIDE CENTRE
FUSION CANADA
THE LMI GROUP
TORONTO ARTS AWARDS

BAY ADELAIDE CENTRE

THE LMI GROUP

APPROPRIATE INNOVATION

THE DISCIPLINED IMAGINATION—OUR CREDO AND MODUS—IS CONSTANTLY BALANCING THE APPRO-
PRIATE AND INNOVATIVE. WE DON'T DESIGN FOR DESIGN'S SAKE. WE COLLABORATE WITH CLIENTS
TO CHANGE HOW THEIR WORLDS ARE PERCEIVED. THAT CAN BE AS SUBTLE AS A COMMA, AS OBVIOUS
AS A NEW IDENTITY. APPROPRIATE AND INNOVATIVE COMMUNICATION CAN BRING ABOUT A DESIRED
PERCEPTION IN THE MINDS OF OUR CLIENTS AND THEIR AUDIENCES.

WHY ARE WE HERE?

THE PROJECTS WE'VE SHOWN HERE ARE THE OUTCOME OF A PROCESS OF THOUGHT, 'ANALYSIS, IMAGINATION AND JUDGEMENT THAT WE USE IN HELPING A CLIENT DERIVE THE MOST FROM THEIR PROJECT AND BUDGET. WE WORK HARD TO UNDERSTAND EACH CLIENT'S SITUATION, OBJECTIVES AND AUDIENCES, AND DEVELOP A STRATEGY TO ENSURE THAT THE COMMUNICATION WILL SERVE THE DESIRED PURPOSE. THAT'S AS TRUE OF SIGNAGE AS IT IS OF AN ANNUAL REPORT.

ADVERTISING

COLLEGE PARK

QUEEN'S QUAY TERMINAL

THE CONTEXT! THE CONTEXT!

WE EMPLOY CONTEXT AS A DISCIPLINE FOR IMAGINATION. THE BENEFIT TO OUR CLIENTS IS TANGIBLE. GOOD COMMUNICATION PREDISPOSES A CUSTOMER OR STAKEHOLDER TO RECEIVE A PARTICULAR MESSAGE BECAUSE IT IS DELIVERED IN A WAY THAT HAS MEANING FOR THEM. WE BELIEVE THAT THIS IS WHAT MAKES OUR APPROACH MORE THAN SIMPLY VISUAL ENGINEERING. WHEN FORM REFLECTS MEANING, CLIENTS ARE WELL SERVED.

TECHNO-TOOLS

OUR BUSINESS, LIKE OUR CLIENTS', HAS BEEN INFLUENCED BY MASSIVE INFORMATION GROWTH. WE HAVE EQUIPPED OUR CREATIVE TEAMS WITH THE LATEST COMPUTER-ASSISTED DESIGN TOOLS THAT SAVE TIME AND MONEY FOR OUR CLIENTS AND THE FIRM. WE DON'T CONSIDER TECHNOLOGY A REPLACEMENT FOR THE JUDGEMENT AND IMAGINATION THAT RENDERS THE CREATIVE IDEA IN THE FIRST PLACE. IT IS TECHNOLOGY IN THE SERVICE OF EXPEDIENCY.

OFFICE LEASING BROCHURES

1325 AVENUE OF THE AMERICAS,
EDWARD J. MINSKOFF EQUITES INC.

ARCHITECTURAL GRAPHICS

SIGNAGE PROGRAMS

MARKETING CENTRES

NATIONAL GALLERY OF CANADA
BANKERS HALL,
TRIZEC EQUITIES LIMITED
CANARY WHARF,
OLYMPIA & YORK COMPANIES (U.S.A.)

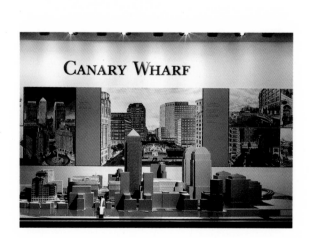

QUALITY OF ACCOUNTABILITY

OUR CLIENTS HAVE TAUGHT US A GREAT DEAL OVER THE YEARS ABOUT THE QUALITY OF ACCOUNT-
ABILITY THEY REQUIRE. IN RESPONSE, WE HAVE DEVELOPED PROCEDURES THAT ALLOW US TO DELIVER
PROJECTS MORE EFFECTIVELY ON THE COMPETITIVE DIMENSIONS OF COST, QUALITY AND TIMELINESS
THAT AFFECT ALL BUSINESSES. THIS ASSURES CLIENTS THAT THEY WILL OBTAIN A CREATIVE PRODUCT
THAT MEETS OR EXCEEDS THEIR EXPECTATIONS ON ALL BUSINESS MEASURES.

PROJECT TYPES

Annual Reports

Corporate and Capability Brochures

Real Estate Marketing Programs

Corporate Identity Programs

Project Identity Programs

Development and Financial Proposals

Direct Mail and Promotional Design

Advertising Campaigns

Packaging Design

Exhibit Design

Signage Programs

Architectural Graphics

CAPABILITIES

Communication Strategy and Planning

Writing and Editorial Consultation

Corporate and Project Positioning

Motivational Research

Public Relations

Two- and Three- Dimensional Design

Art Direction of Photography
  and Illustration

Detailed Design/Artwork

Production Coordination
  and Supervision

SELECTED CLIENTS

Abitibi-Price Inc.

BASF Corporation

Bramalea Limited

Cadillac Fairview Corporation Limited

Canadian Imperial Bank of Commerce

CIBC Development Corporation

Davies, Ward & Beck, Barristers & Solicitors

Hewlett Packard Canada Ltd.

Miller Thomson, Barristers & Solicitors

National Gallery of Canada

National Trust

Ontario Hydro

Olympia & York Developments Limited

Olympia & York Companies (USA)

Rice Brydone Limited

Royal Bank of Canada

Toronto College Park Ltd.

Toronto Stock Exchange

Trizec Corporation Ltd.

We would be pleased to discuss your requirements, and our approach to the business of communication and design, at your convenience. Please contact Bev or Ian Tudhope.

Tudhope Associates Inc.

284 King Street East

Toronto, Ontario

M5A 1K4

Tel. (416) 366-7100

Fax (416) 366-7711

DESIGN PARTNERS

DESIGN FOR FINANCIAL SERVICES MARKETING

Corporate Identification Systems

Corporate Communications

Signage

Annual Reports

Credit and Transaction Cards

Promotional Design

Graphic Standards and Guidelines

For credentials presentation contact
Michael Butler, President
Design Partners
282 Richmond St.East,
Suite 200
Toronto, Ontario M5A 1P4
Telephone (416) 368-3800
Fax (416) 368-9710

AppleTree Creative Services
30 Wertheim Court, Unit 19, Richmond Hill, Ontario L4B 1B9
Telephone (416) 881 0137

AppleTree Creative Services is a comprehensive communications facility which operates on strict design disciplines. By following defined objectives and agreed-upon strategies, AppleTree can help you 'say' all the right things to your audience, and stay within your budget and timetable.

The operating principles of AppleTree are based on 20 years of experience in typography, advertising, art direction, editorial and graphic design. However, today they are supplemented by the latest computer technology and software.

The combination results in graphic communications of the highest calibre.

During the past year, AppleTree Creative Services created and produced a complete identity system for the exclusive Founders Club at SkyDome – starting with the traditional heraldic logo.

In addition to stationery, the package included an introductory brochure, as well as menus, wine list, guest introduction cards, signage, internal forms, a newsletter, and invitations to the inaugural dinner. The nature of the program

and its intended audience dictated exceptionally high standards of design and production, while the fixed timelines required considerable project management experience. AppleTree was able to provide both for its client.

AppleTree

1

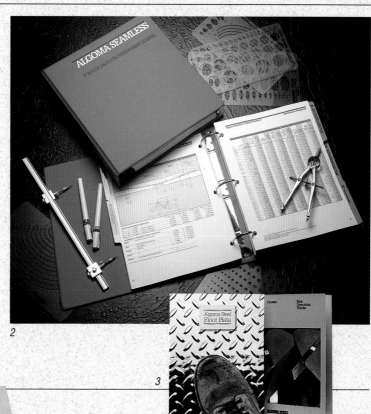

2

Algoma Steel
Floor Plate

3

4

Marchand Pétroleum

5

TIVOLI GARDEN

6

7

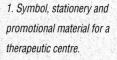

8

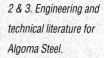
GOBEIL

9

10

THE
DUCHESS
FINE FARE
of
MARKHAM
FULLY LICENSED

11

12

1. Symbol, stationery and promotional material for a therapeutic centre.

2 & 3. Engineering and technical literature for Algoma Steel.

4. More than just a card. The 1989 AppleTree Christmas promotion.

5. Part of a visual identity program for Petro-Canada's Eastern partners.

6. Unpublished menu cover for a hotel Cafe / Bistro.

7. Logo for Griffin Workshop – fine art publishers.

8. Logo for Amiga Developers Forum – a software developers group

9. Logo for Gobeil Publishing – producers of specialist accounting software.

10. Logo for System Directions – a computer consultancy.

11. Design of logo and painted wood sign for Markham's local pub.

12. Printers colophon based on the initials MBL.

MAIN PHOTOGRAPHY. RUDY VON TEIDEMANN / FOCUS STUDIO.   PHOTOGRAPHY OF THE FOUNDERS CLUB LOGO: WAYNE SPROULE / AGS PHOTOGRAPHY   COLOUR SEPARATIONS AND FILM STRIPPING: IMAGE DYNAMICS CORP

Beakbane
Marketing Inc.

**130 Bridgeland Ave., Suite 314
Toronto, Ontario M6A 1Z4**

Trade
& Consumer
Communications

Colourgraph, for cleaner colours and brighter whites

Image technology is constantly changing. The picture on the left, from the 1960s, now looks tired and dated. The colours are soft and un-convincing, but when it was printed it was state-of-the-art.
We are leaders in colour technology. Whether it's the simple or the ex-traordinary, we create images where the colours are lifelike, the action

seamless, so your image climbs from the page, to arrest your viewer and deliver your message.
We created the above precipitous scene from four feet-on-the-ground shots and by scaling new heights of electronic composition.
So if you need a cleaner, brighter image and don't like taking risks, call us.

Colourgraph   *Colour separations you can count on.*

Colourgraph Reproduction Systems Inc., 90 Floral Parkway, Toronto, Ontario M6L 2B9   **Call:** (416) 245-2526   **Fax:** (416) 245-3035

When one of Toronto's top separation companies wanted to communicate their skill, who did they ask to create a campaign? Beakbane Marketing Inc. because of our knack for coming up with attention-getting images.

How do you successfully launch a brand with no advertising into a competitive market? First create an eye-catching pack that immediately communicates the end benefit: smooth, sensuous skin. Then reinforce that theme in trade and consumer brochures.

How did Apple Computers Inc. impress printing professionals? They got Beakbane Marketing Inc. to create a brochure. Every page shows what can be achieved with technology and ingenuity.

More than good R.O.I.

Leadership in computer artwork matched by solid marketing strategy are the reasons Beakbane Marketing Inc. creates trade and consumer communications that give more than a good return on investment.

**Phone:
(416) 787-4901**

**Fax:
(416) 787-9665**

D-68

Belair Creative Concepts

P.O. Box 174
Postal Station L
Toronto, Ontario M6E 4Y5
Telephone: 654-2160

Belair Creative Concepts is an advertising and graphic design company whose originators have over twenty years experience dealing with national and retail accounts. Each one of our highly trained associates is thoroughly knowledgeable in business procedures as well as applied arts. Belair Creative Concepts is dedicated to helping you reach your target market.

Advertising campaigns
Sales promotion materials
Corporate identity programs
Photography
Illustration
Camera ready art preparation
Flyers
Brochures
Annual reports
Posters
Logo design
Desktop publishing

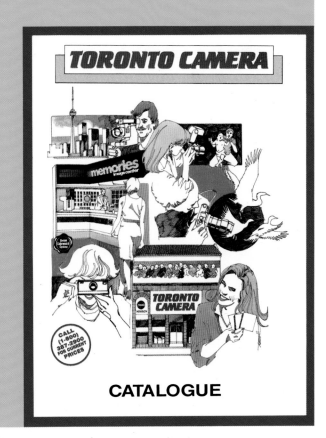

CATALOGUE

Honey I'm home; Yabadabado!; Don't leave home without it; Life, Love & Liberty; Cheeseboiger,

Cheeseboiger; Far Out; Decent; Yummy yummy yummy I've got love in my tummy; One Small Step

for Man...; Groovy; Plop, Plop, Fiss, Fiss, oh what a relief it is; Excellent; I dream of Jeannie; The wet

head is dead; Like No Waaye, Oh my Gaud; The Aqua Velva Man; Peace; As the world

turns...Band Aid; Aids; Bell Bottoms; Rock Lobster, Down, Down, Down; Let them eat cake; The

Jetsons; Free Love; Of sound mind and body.   Bentwater.

THE

RIORDON

DESIGN

GROUP

INC

✉ The Airway Centre

5945 Airport Road, Suite 195

Mississauga, Ontario, Canada L4V 1R9

☎ (416) 271 0399 / 673 2416 FAX (416) 271 0256

children's store symbol

full page trade ad

display panels

full page consumer ad

brewery hockey poster

designer watch

lifesize / P.O.P.

new package design poster

entertainment sponsorship symbol

corporate capabilities booklet

nutrition guideline booklets

direct mailer

full page consumer ad

children's clothing line symbol

health conference poster

designer t-shirt

designer sweatshirt

turkey producers' newsletter

vehicle graphics

reduce, reuse, recycle booklet

calling card

catering service logotype

consumer food magazine

promotion package

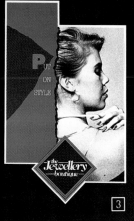

*T*he Greaves & Allen Studios —
your advertising and marketing
support specialists since 1978. We
transform ideas into effective
creative solutions.

As a full service advertising studio,
Greaves & Allen is capable
of creating

☐ corporate brochures
☐ retail identity packages
☐ marketing and sales promotions
☐ print advertising
☐ point-of-purchase programs
☐ package design
☐ direct mail

and other forms of printed media for all
your marketing and sales-related needs.

Energetic, responsive and highly
motivated, our team is committed to
producing superior results on time,
every time.

The Greaves & Allen Studios limited

One Fifty One
Esna Park Drive
Studio Thirty
Markham, Ontario L3R 3B1
(416) 474-1666
(416) 474-9890 (FAX)

1   Nestea Promotional Campaign —
Nestlé Enterprises Ltd.

2   3-Dimensional Christmas P.O.P. —
Consumers Distributing

3   In Store P.O.P. Program —
The Jewellery Boutique

4   Corporate Brochure —
CP Express & Transport

5   Corporate Identity and Stationery Package —
Town & Country

6   Direct Mail —
Imperial Oil Ltd.

7   P.O.P. Signage —
Toy City

8   Policy Guide Package —
United Steelworkers of America

9   Sales Conference Materials —
Consumers Distributing

10   Resource Binder Program —
Town & Country

7

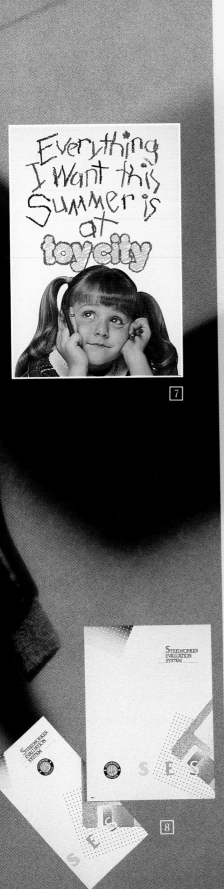

Steelworker
Evaluation
System

8

9

10

D-77

D-78

Introducing Wittick & Wittick and Mac®, the new advertising and promotion whiz-team.

With design, copywriting and account service experience of no less than 15 years each, only seasoned professionals work on your account.

And wait till you see what state-of-the-art technology brings to the party. With over 1,000,000 glorious colours, more than 200 typefaces, and outstanding artistic talents, SuperMac® makes innovative solutions surprisingly cost effective.

We have ready access to media and broadcast services, and can provide you with a full range of advertising options. Whether it be print ads, promotional material, corporate logo design, annual reports, presentations or brochures, give us your next job.

See for yourself just what Wittick & Wittick can do with a little help from their friend, Mac®.

WITTICK AND WITTICK COMMUNICATIONS INC.

174 MacPherson Avenue, Toronto, Ontario M5R 1W8

Telephone or Fax **(416) 920-3397**

2116 Canterbury Drive, Burlington, Ontario L7P 1N8

Telephone or Fax **(416) 332-6369**

FALCOM

DESIGN & COMMUNICATIONS INC.

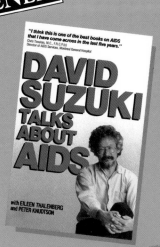
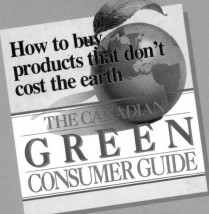

Gottschalk
+Ash
International

Design Consultants   Montréal
Conseillers en design   Toronto
Zürich
Milano

What is good design?

It is the process through which ideas
are communicated and products developed.
Good design is innovative, motivating and
persuasive.

Qu'est-ce qu'un bon design?

C'est le processus qui permet de réaliser
l'adéquation entre les idées et leur représentation. Un bon design est novateur,
motivant et convaincant.

SKYDOME

Environmental wayfinding integrates function and aesthetics to make a space work and give it a special identity. Gottschalk+Ash International begins with an analysis of the practical requirements and the needs of each user group.

With the industrial design firm of Keith Muller Limited, we have successfully resolved these design challenges into a comprehensive signage and wayfinding program for Toronto's SkyDome, incorporating advertising as a revenue generating opportunity.

Le design environnemental étudie la configuration d'un lieu, les contraintes matérielles et les besoins de chaque groupe d'usagers pour créer une signalisation fonctionnelle et distinctive.

En collaboration avec la société de design industriel Keith Muller Limited, Gottschalk+Ash International a réalisé la signalisation et l'affichage au SkyDome de Toronto, intégrant avec succès les diverses exigences de cette tâche, tout en utilisant la publicité comme source de revenus, pour créer un environnement accueillant, stimulant et sécuritaire.

Canadian Pacific Forest Products Limited

Union Gas

THE GLOBE AND MAIL

ROGERS

CANTEL

Canadian
Museum
of Nature

Musée
canadien
de la nature

The identity of an organization is the result of its name and related visual elements working together to produce a unified image of its essential characteristics.

We believe that the elements of corporate identity, from type to symbols, must be consistent with corporate image strategy. As well, they must communicate the positioning of the organization - what it is, what it does and what it stands for.

L'identité d'une entreprise résulte de l'utilisation de sa raison sociale et des éléments visuels qui s'y rattachent en vue de projeter une image cohérente.

Chez Gottschalk+Ash International, nous croyons que tous les éléments d'identification de l'entreprise, du graphisme aux symboles, doivent mettre ses caractéristiques essentielles en valeur et communiquer clairement la nature de ses activités.

1

2

3

4

1 PETRO-CANADA
2 AIR CANADA
3 CANADIAN PACIFIC
4 SCOTIA BANK

Gottschalk+Ash International designs, writes and produces all types of corporate publications, and helps organizations set and manage their corporate communication goals. Those goals become the guidelines for integrated, coordinated communication that builds unified messages over time. Annual reports, corporate brochures and newsletters are some of the forms of print communication typically used.

Gottschalk+Ash International aide les entreprises à établir et à réaliser leurs objectifs de communication. Ces objectifs sont les lignes directrices sur lesquelles nous nous fondons pour mettre en place une stratégie de communication intégrée et efficace au service du message de l'entreprise. À cette fin, nous concevons, rédigeons et produisons diverses publications, dont des rapports annuels, des brochures et des bulletins d'information.

ANDRÉS WINES
VINS ANDRÉS

From concept to final implementation, Gottschalk+Ash
International helps companies
reposition products through
their packaging. The challenge
in today's markets is to attract
and maintain attention for
products in crowded and cluttered communication channels.
With innovative design solutions derived from product
strategies, brands can achieve
an enduring individuality that
contributes directly to the
bottom line.

De la conception initiale
à l'élaboration définitive,
Gottschalk+Ash International
travaille avec ses clients à la
commercialisation des produits
par leur conditionnement.
Le défi dans les marchés actuels,
où les canaux de communication
sont plus nombreux et plus en-
combrés que jamais, est d'attirer
et de retenir l'attention. Le design
créateur confère aux marques une
identité propre à leur assurer une
présence durable et, par consé-
quent, concourt directement aux
résultats de l'entreprise.

ENICHEM
ELASTOMERI SpA

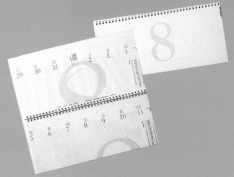

Consistent reinforcement and implementation of corporate identity is important to ensure the long-term success of any organization's image. Nomenclature must be standardized, formats, sizes and colours applied in a systematic manner. Combined with good design, this approach has proven successful for our clients, regardless of national standards, languages or cultural requirements.

La reconnaissance de l'image de l'entreprise ne peut se faire sans le renforcement constant de son identité visuelle. Des normes strictes doivent régir de manière systématique les caractères graphiques, les couleurs et les supports matériels utilisés pour la diffusion de cette identité. Cette approche, appuyée par un design de qualité, a réussi à nos clients, quelles que soient leurs caractéristiques nationales.

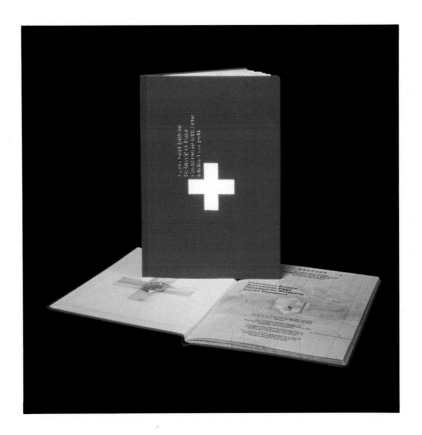

SWISS PASSPORT
PASSEPORT SUISSE

Strategic print communication design encompasses a wide range of applications, from corporate print applications to postage stamp design. In designing the Swiss passport, Gottschalk+Ash International had to deal not only with rigorous design standards but also with unusual security requirements.

La conception graphique touche de nombreuses applications, des communications d'entreprise au dessin d'un timbre poste. Pour la conception du passeport suisse, Gottschalk+Ash International a dû se conformer non seulement à des normes strictes, mais également à des exigences très particulières reliées à la sécurité.

Montréal

2050, rue Mansfield
Montréal, Québec
H3A 1Y9

Tel 844-1995
Fax 844-9530

Toronto

11 Bishop Street
Toronto, Ontario
M5R 1N3

Tel 963-9717
Fax 963-9351

Zürich

Sonnhaldenstrasse 3
Postfach 105
8032 Zürich

Tel 252-5042
Fax 252-5136

Milano

Via Revere 16
20123 Milano

Tel 469-4769
Fax 498-9469

Gottschalk+Ash International has become known for design that is strategically bold, creatively powerful and uniquely yours.

Gottschalk+Ash International est reconnu pour ses designs audacieux, créateurs et uniques.

Montréal

2050, rue Mansfield
Montréal, Québec
H3A 1Y9

Tel 844-1995
Fax 844-9530

Toronto

11 Bishop Street
Toronto, Ontario
M5R 1N3

Tel 963-9717
Fax 963-9351

Zürich

Sonnhaldenstrasse 3
Postfach 105
8032 Zürich

Tel 252-5042
Fax 252-5136

Milano

Via Revere 16
20123 Milano

Tel 469-4769
Fax 498-9469

G R A P H I C S

A FULL SERVICE STUDIO

▲

DESIGN, TYPESETTING, ASSEMBLY, ILLUSTRATION, RENDERING, COMPS, STATS, TRANSFERS, ELECTRONIC PUBLISHING,
SALES PROMOTION, PRINT MANAGEMENT

MCG GRAPHICS
88 UNIVERSITY AVENUE, TORONTO, ONTARIO M5J 1T6 (416) 593-1375 FAX # 593-6837
A Member of The Marketing Communications Group Inc.

Illustrations by Emilio Bandera

Airbrushed background by Paul Chen

FRESHNESS GUARANTEED

©1990 RICHARD BROWN

FROM CORPORATE COMMUNICATION

PROGRAMMES AND PACKAGING DESIGN TO

CONVENTION PLANNING AND STAGING,

AT MARKETING F/X IDEAS AND SOLUTIONS

DON'T COME PRE-PACKAGED.

MARKETING
F/X
LIMITED

205 CHURCH STREET
SUITE 100
TORONTO, ONTARIO
M5B 1Y5
TEL: 862-0861
FAX: 862-2798

INTEGRATED MARKETING COMMUNICATION AND CORPORATE DESIGN

CORPORATE IDENTITY

BROCHURES

PROMOTION

ANNUAL REPORTS

PACKAGING

ENVIRONMENTAL

EXHIBITS

The

MONIZ
DESIGN
GROUP
Inc

THE MONIZ DESIGN GROUP INC.
219 Dufferin Street, Suite 306B
Toronto, Ontario, Canada, M6K 1Y9
Tel: (416) 516-0927

Film/Separations: Colour Innovations Inc.

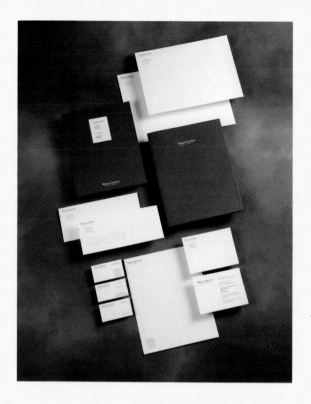

This brochure was targeted to Canadian businesses involved in the preparation of in-house visual presentations . Printed in four-colour process, with gloss and matte varnishes throughout, the brochure was both visually intriguing and informative. Polaroid received a high rate of response from the information request card attached to the brochure.

Warren Shepell Consultants Corporation is a Toronto-based company providing Employee Assistance Programs to small, mid-size, and large corporations across Canada. The new look reflects the com- pany's leading position in the industry. The identity was applied to stationery (includ- ing 4 business card variations), pocket folders, proposal covers, and signage at the company's new head office location.

THE MONIZ DESIGN GROUP INC.

This newsletter was designed to inform professional photographers and photo schools across Canada of the latest advancements in Polaroid instant film production. Formerly an 8-page booklet, we suggested the change to a 4-page tabloid format to reduce costs. Printed in 2 colours, it proved very successful and quarterly publications are being considered.

The Polaroid Birthday Party Planner Kit, consisting of a mural, souvenir cards, planner, and die-cut window matte, was a promotion attached to consumer-line cameras in retail outlets across Canada. Bright intense colours were used to convey the playful nature of the kit, yet a slightly sophisticated design appeals to the adult organizing the child's birthday party.

THE MONIZ DESIGN GROUP INC.

Discovering Spadina is an exhibit, produced in collaboration with Wojtek Janczak, for the Toronto Historical Board explaining the origins and history of one of the city's historic landmarks. Located in the basement of the house, the exhibit- which consists of 12 information panels and 2 showcases- was designed to complement the rustic and unfinished look of the building's foundation while enhancing the many artifacts and photos displayed.

The Moniz Design Group is a multi-disciplined, complete creative design service handling such diverse projects as corporate identities to exhibit design. We work with our clients to first determine their visual communication/marketing require-ments and then plan out a strategy to fill those needs. We oversee the project from the concept stage through to the finished printed or fabricated component.

THE MONIZ DESIGN GROUP INC.

Strategic creative. It provides the spark to truly *communicate* and not merely inform. Organized thinking solves problems and meets marketing objectives.

Like putting a new face on an old, respected company — when C-I-L Inc. became ICI Canada Inc. Corporate identity on a massive scale, where everything had to be redesigned: from stationery to signs, packaging to vehicles.

Disciplined imagination manifests itself in a strong, logical concept, yet one that's unique and innovative; clever, concise copy inextricably linked to the visual presentation; and graphic design so fresh and bold it burns the message into the mind.

This is what it takes, regardless of the medium. The results speak for themselves. A successful recruiting campaign that "humanized" a bank to university graduates. An award-winning marketing display exhibit used worldwide for a packaged-goods giant. A hard-hitting employee video explaining the facts of company life in the '90s.

The tools may have changed, but the aim remains the same. Since 1980, as the Saturday Night Group and now as King West, our mission has endured: to produce the most effective, creative communications anywhere. Over the years we have held fast to our credo. Now, equipped with powerful new tools, we still accept no limitations. Ours was the first full-color consumer publication to be produced straight to final film from an Apple Macintosh disk.

Annual report for Wardair

New corporate identity for ICI Canada Inc. (formerly C-I-L)

Spread from recruiting literature for
the Toronto Dominion Bank

Corporate book for
Enterprise Property Group

Strategic creative. What's integral is a keen sensitivity to public concerns, such as the portrayal of women and visible minorities. Or how best to communicate issues that shape attitudes.

Cases in point: a promotional campaign for the Ontario government to interest 12- and 13-year-olds in entrepreneurship opened young minds to a vision of alternate career paths. Or, at the other end of the spectrum, the chilling reality of sexual assault represented with a tactful but trenchant edge.

When the concept is focused, the results can transcend borders. Like a complete redesign of tourism publications, to market Ontario all over the world. Designing a mammoth international engineering trade fair in India, when Canada was host country. Project manager of the Ontario Pavilion at the Francophone Summit in Quebec City.

Getting the message across appropriately is just as important as getting it across.

Effective vehicles for marketing and corporate communications are the result of much more than simply creative inspiration. They have to be researched, developed and produced too. That's why account management is so vital to King West, for intelligent, experienced liaison and translating clients' needs to the creative staff. The same holds true for our production department, which is supported by a computerized docket-management system.

Detail from a poster for the Ontario Pavilion
at the Francophone Summit

Campaign to increase awareness of entrepreneurship in schoolchildren

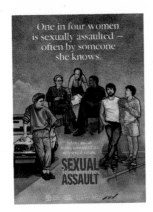

Poster for a campaign by the
Ontario Women's Directorate

Part of a package for the Premier's Council
conference on global competition

Strategic creative. The accord of ability, experience and clear, fresh thinking results in communication that consistently meets or even exceeds a client's objectives.

Like *Scorebook*, the finest magazine of any American League baseball team. Each issue, half of its 200-plus pages are bursting with national advertising, as well as enough explosive graphics to excite any Blue Jays fan. Or the *Royal Bank Reporter*, with an image that's always at the forefront, reflecting the company's leadership role among Canada's financial institutions.

An unconventional catalogue for the Royal Ontario Museum, which helped precipitate a dramatic rise in sales. For Gemstone Productions, a successful campaign to promote their impressive television mini-series.

A well-thought-out strategy and imaginative concept, skillfully executed and exactingly produced, provide the complete solution to any marketing and communications challenge.

Whether or not awards really attest to anything more than conversion of the already converted is debatable. But we at King West are proud of the recognition conferred upon us by our peers, as well as others. A Gold Quill from the International Association of Business Communicators; 37 Art Directors' Club awards; first prize from the Printing House Craftsmen; and numerous others from the National Magazine Awards Foundation to the Canadian Direct Marketing Association.

Mail-order catalogue for the
Royal Ontario Museum shops

Scorebook, the official magazine of the Toronto Blue Jays

Directions, a manual of courses available through
the Scarborough Board of Education

Technology issue of the *Royal Bank Reporter*,
a publication distributed across Canada

KING WEST

**KING WEST
COMMUNICATIONS INC.**

511 King Street West
Suite 100
Toronto, Ontario
M5V 2Z4
(416) 591-8822
Fax: (416) 591-1630

Ove

THE ART OF COMMUNICATION LIES

IN THE ABILITY TO TRANSLATE

THOUGHTS INTO IMAGES AND

IMAGES INTO THOUGHTS

▪ OVE DESIGN TORONTO LTD. ▪ 302-73 LAIRD DRIVE ▪ TORONTO, ONTARIO ▪ M4G 3T4 ▪ TEL. (416) 423-6228 ▪ FAX (416) 423-2940 ▪

D-106

UNIQUE IN CANADA

The place to be
The place to visit

Centre International de Design

▶ 150 exhibitors on 100,000 square feet

▶ A second phase of 150,000 square feet under construction

▶ 400 parking spaces

▶ A reference centre with the products of more than 2000 companies

▶ Multi-media hallroom

CENTRE INTERNATIONAL DE DESIGN

D D D D D D D D
D D D D D D D D
D D D D D D D D
D D D D D D D D

M O N T R É A L

85, RUE ST-PAUL OUEST
MONTRÉAL, H2Y 3V4

(514) 842-4545
FAX: 848-9730

D-109

Woodwin
Renovations Contractors

Woodwin handles all stages of development and construction. Working for the home and institutional market, Woodwin completes its assignments from concept development through to the finishing touches.

The Canadian Autoworkers

On December 1, 1984, the Canadian UAW Council approved a recommendation from UAW Director for Canada Bob White that unless the UAW in Canada was able to achieve complete autonomy within the International Union, two separate and distinct unions should be structured, one in the U.S. and one in Canada.

National Forest Congress

The National Forest Congress was planned to act as a catalyst for the development of policies to meet the challenges facing Canada's forest sector through the Eighties and the Nineties, and into the 21st century.

Toronto
Arts Against Apartheid
Festival Foundation

The issue of apartheid in South Africa first received attention in 1962 when Nelson Mandela was imprisoned on charges of conspiracy and sabotage. The Festival was planned to use public support, to encourage corporate support, government endorsement and political action.

THE
PAY EQUITY
COMMISSION

Ron Kaplansky believes that good design requires time and communication with the client at the concept stage. His sensitivity and intuition, combined with a solid background in graphic design, direct you to the best visual approach for your needs.

You'll exchange ideas and discuss concrete visual suggestions. When the approach has been agreed upon, Ron will complete all phases of production including printing supervision, if required.

Ron's work, which has included annual reports, educational displays, posters, large and small publications, and advertisements, is distinguished by its simplicity and clarity.

The Pay Equity Commission

As of January 1, 1988 employers in Ontario are legally bound to set up pay equity plans to make sure that their salary and wage scales are based on the value of work performed – regardless of the sex of the person doing the work.

Imperial Pipe Corporation

Imperial Pipe Corporation is a manufacturer of plastic piping. It transforms Low, Medium and High Density Polyethylene Polypropylene and ABS resins into finished pressure piping.

Metro World 1991

Metro World 1991 is being planned as a coordinated response to the urgent environmental issues arising in world metropolises. Our ability to respond to these urban challenges will determine, in large part, the global quality of life for the 21st century.

Ron Kaplansky
Graphic Designer
R.K. Studios Limited
309 Wellesley Street East
Toronto, Ontario
M4X 1H2

Tel: (416) 964-6991
Fax: (416) 964-8900

L'Association des illustrateurs et illustratrices du Québec (AIIQ) est une association fondée en 1983 dans le but de veiller aux intérêts des illustrateurs. L'AIIQ offre à ses membres l'information essentielle à la pratique du métier, concernant les questions éthiques et légales. Elle représente également ses 310 membres auprès des gouvernements et de l'industrie des communications.
Le répertoire annuel des membres, édition 1990, regroupe les œuvres de 195 illustrateurs en 304 pages, dont 192 pages couleurs. Le Répertoire 90 (19,90$ + 2,60$ pour frais postaux) ainsi que d'autres publications de l'AIIQ sur le droit d'auteur et la tarification sont disponibles à nos bureaux.

The Quebec Association of Illustrators (AIIQ) was founded in 1983 to promote the interests of illustrators. The association provides its members with information concerning legal and ethical questions, business practices and promotion. The AIIQ represents its 310 members in an official capacity to government and the communications industry.
Our annual visual directory of members, the "Répertoire", at 304 pages — 192 pages in color, includes the work of 195 illustrators. The Répertoire ($19.90 + $2.60 post) as well as other AIIQ publications concerning copyright and fee schedules is available by writing or calling our offices.

AIIQ

Association des illustrateurs et illustratrices du Québec, 19, cours Le Royer, O., bureau 305, Montréal, Qc H2Y 1W4 (514) 499-1799 fax (514) 866-4020

ANNUAL REPORTS

THE FUNCTION OF GRAPHIC DESIGN IS TO EXPRESS INFORMATION AND IDEAS IN A

PACKAGING

COMPELLING WAY. OUR CONCERN ISN'T JUST AESTHETICS – ALTHOUGH GOOD DESIGN IS

SIGNAGE

ALWAYS PLEASING TO THE EYE – RATHER IT IS TO HELP OUR CLIENTS COMMUNICATE

BROCHURES

CONVINCINGLY WITH SPECIFIC AUDIENCES. IN CONCEPT AND EXECUTION, EVERY PROJECT WE

EXHIBITS

UNDERTAKE IS UNIQUE. BUT OUR OBJECTIVE NEVER CHANGES: TO CREATE DESIGN SOLU-

PROMOTION

TIONS THAT ARE STRATEGICALLY TARGETED TO SUPPORT OUR CLIENTS' BUSINESS GOALS.

CORPORATE IDENTITY

**TAYLOR & BROWNING
DESIGN ASSOCIATES**

**DESIGN & MARKETING
CONSULTANTS**

**TORONTO
10 PRICE STREET
TORONTO, ONTARIO
CANADA M4W 1Z4
416 ■ 927 ■ 7094**

**CALGARY
221 10TH AVENUE S.W.
STUDIO 1
CALGARY, ALBERTA
CANADA T2R 0A4
403 ■ 237 ■ 5151**

ROGERS COMMUNICATIONS INC. ■ For its 1989 annual report Rogers Communications Inc. wanted to present bo

its past accomplishments and its present innovations in a single document. To meet the challenge of blending the tw

themes into a visually attractive whole, we dedicated single pages to photographic montages that illustrate the ma

breakthrough technologies that have brought success to this Canadian communications conglomerate. Seconda

photographs and illustrations – each with a stand-alone caption – highlight major events of the past and are integrat

with the text. Dominant colours in the primary photographs were repeated in bar charts to sustain visual continuit

SHERIDAN COLLEGE ■ As one of Canada's top educational institutions, Sheridan College wanted to present a strong and consistent visual identity. Working with an already established symbol and logotype, we compiled an extensive graphic standards manual for the college's departments and faculties. The manual provides a flexible framework while ensuring consistent applications of the identity. As part of the overall program, we also created a promotional campaign for the 1990-91 school year. Using a series of lively illustrations by Joe Fleming, a Sheridan graduate, the different components are visually expressive to help communicate the college's many educational programs.

"TAYLOR & BROWNING'S CONCEPT FOR THE BRAZILIAN BALL WAS SUPERB." THE FIRM'S QUALITY OF DESIGN SET THE TONE FOR A FIRST-CLASS EVENT."

ORGANIZER
BRAZILIAN BALL

Strong visual images and contemporary design helped turn the Royal Canadian Mint 1989 annual report into an

effective corporate brochure. ■ The prestige location of Campeau Corporation's Water Park Place called for an

innovative promotion and leasing program. ■ The real estate development company, Herity Corp called on Taylor &

Browning to design a distinctive brochure that would position the company apart from its competitors. ■ To support an extensive leasing program for Cadillac Fairview Corporation's many shopping centres we designed a massive

portfolio to showcase each centre. ■ For TransCanada PipeLines' desktop-published newspaper, Taylor & Browning

designed formats, layouts and typography entirely by computer. ■ To communicate employee benefits to its partners

and staff, Peat Marwick Thorne commissioned us to create a flexible information package that could be easily updated.

NORGRAPHICS ∎ As part of a plan to communicate its capabilities as a high-quality sheet-fed printer, Norgraphics (Canada) Limited recognized the importance of graphic designers and art directors as a target audience. We recommended that the company produce a brochure to showcase Norgraphics' printing capabilities. Because of the audience's high expectations, it was paramount that the brochure be exceptional in its creativity. Its theme – the glittering pop images of Las Vegas – is interpreted by 13 of North America's foremost photographers and illustrators, and its production values demonstrate state-of-the-art techniques to achieve stunning graphic effects.

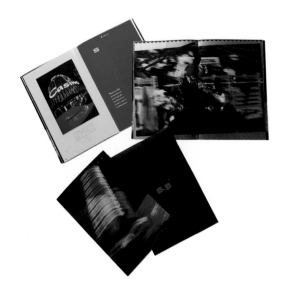

MAZOLA MARGARINE ■ When Ault Foods decided to launch a new margarine made of 100 percent Mazola corn oil, it turned to Taylor & Browning to create package designs, labels and collateral promotional materials that would portray Mazola margarine as a healthy, premium quality brand within its product category. Our objective was to achieve maximum impact on the store shelf and to position the new margarine against competitive brands while reinforcing the Mazola brand name. In designing the new packaging we combined bold, contemporary graphics, and strong colours with the traditional expression of quality represented by the Mazola wordmark and corn symbol.

"TAYLOR & BROWNING HAS CONTRIBUTED GREATLY TO THE MARKETING OF OUR ORGANIZATION. THEY EXCEL IN EVERYTHING THEY DO, AND THEY HELP US GET RESULTS."

DIRECTOR MARKETING COMMUNICATIONS THE CADILLAC FAIRVIEW CORPORATION LIMITED

BRAZILIAN BALL ■ Toronto's premier fund-raising event has also become a mainstay of the city's social calendar. The annual Brazilian Ball is a gala evening whose proceeds are used in aid of The Hospital for Sick Children. For the 1990 Brazilian Ball Taylor & Browning created a pictorial motif that evokes both the joy of a child's spinning top and the frentic tempo of Rio de Janeiro's famed Carnival. To heighten public awarness the intense primary colours of the computer-designed illustration are repeated on a variety of promotional items – invitations, tickets, posters, programs, banners, T-shirts, signs, and carry-bags. The promotion helped the hospital raise a record $710,000.

Cranwell & Pietrasiak
DESIGN ASSOCIATE

Annual Reports

Corporate & Product Identity

Packaging

9 Hazelton Avenue

Third Floor

Toronto, Canada

M5R 2E1

PH: 1-(416) 975-1699

FX: 1-(416) 975-4031

P.O.P.

Burst into the market place with displays from CDA and discover the creative edge.

We can offer an abundance of creative, cost effective solutions to your specific needs in a spectrum of materials. Wood, metal, wire, card and vacuum forming, all under one roof.

For over 35 years, both national and international advertisers have entrusted CDA to design and manufacture their P.O.P. displays...with stunning results. Call us today and we'll show you the diversity and expertise that has made us Canada's largest P.O.P. manufacturer.

"Member P.O.P.A.I.".

CDA

ILLUSTRATION
GN · PHOTOGRA
ION · VIDEO PRO

TDF ARTISTS LTD.

LAYOUT
DESIGN
TV STORYBOARDS
ILLUSTRATION
PHOTOGRAPHY
PHOTO RETAIL

PHOTO FASHION
PHOTO LABS
RETOUCHING
TYPOGRAPHY
VIDEO PRODUCTION

ILLUSTRATION

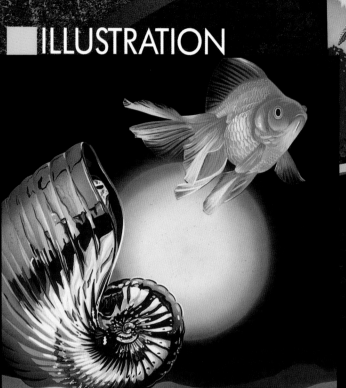

LA

RETAIL

PHOTOGRAPHY

■ FASHION PHOTOGRAPHY

■ TYPOGRAPHY

TYPOGRAPH
TYPOGRAPH
LAYOUT · D
RETAIL · FA

ZOO
ADVENTURE

OCEAN
Reef

VHS
VIDEO

WONDERFUL
WEEKENDERS
Better than Basic Brunches

NUMBER
5
IN THE INSTANT GOURMET SERIES

VHS
VIDEO
COLOUR RECIPE CARDS ENCLOSED

■ VIDEO

PRODUCTION

TDF Pictures, our video production division, provides a wide range of services to corporate and agency clients.

From sales, training, and corporate productions, to commercials, PSA's programming, and packaged videos for home viewing, TDF Pictures, (recipient of numerous awards), brings many years of expertise to every production, from the most straightforward to the more elaborate.

SILENT PARTNER
TOM PEDRIKS
MARTIN BUDD

MONIT

BUREAUX
À
LOUER

933 3000

LALONDE (SILENT PARTNER)

PEDRIKS

AND BUDD

DESIGN

MONTREAL

514 939 1582

PACKAGING

CORPORATE COMMUNICATIONS

SIGNAGE

CORPORATE IDENTITY

BROCHURES

SUPERIOR

LE MOT DESSINÉ INC.
COMMUNICATION GRAPHIQUE

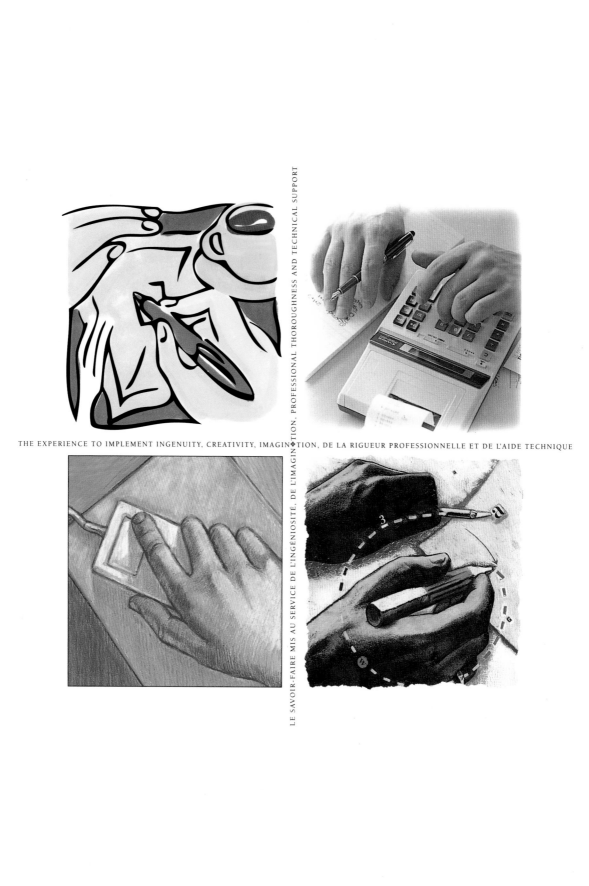

THE EXPERIENCE TO IMPLEMENT INGENUITY, CREATIVITY, IMAGIN◆TION, DE LA RIGUEUR PROFESSIONNELLE ET DE L'AIDE TECHNIQUE

PROFESSIONAL THOROUGHNESS AND TECHNICAL SUPPORT

LE SAVOIR-FAIRE MIS AU SERVICE DE L'INGÉNIOSITÉ, DE L'IMAGINATION,

5890, AVENUE MONKLAND ❖ BUREAU 401 ❖ MONTRÉAL (QUÉBEC) CANADA ❖ H4A 1G2 ❖ TÉLÉCOPIEUR (514) 485.3034
TÉLÉPHONE (514) **485.1800**

Humpty Dumpty wanted to introduce a new premium popcorn into the market. The Group was commissioned to design high shelf impact graphics. An illustration of a corn husk was utilized to highlight the natural baby corn aspect of the popcorn. The added feature of white cheddar cheese was strongly bannered in the descriptor. The look being premium and "fun", befitting the inherent qualities of the product, contributed to position sales growth.

HUMPTY DUMPTY

Humpty Dumpty voulait mettre en marché un nouveau maïs soufflé de qualité. Le Groupe fut donc désigné pour créer des graphismes particulièrement percutants. L'illustration amusante d'un jeune épi de maïs souligne l'aspect «tendreté» du maïs soufflé. Le cheddar blanc ajouté est fortement présenté dans le descripteur. L'image de qualité et d'amusement répondent parfaitement aux caractéristiques du produit et ont ainsi contribué à augmenter les ventes.

The Group was commissioned to revitalize Champagne's packaging. A strong, bold centre positioning of the Champagne logo was used to ensure higher visibility. A halo effect was created to spotlight the brand itself. Top down photography was utilized to shift from the traditional landscape approach used by competitors. Recipes were developed and managed by the design firm and a dietician, to reflect ideal usage for the various flavours and to suggest reasons to purchase extra flavours.

CULINAR

Le Groupe a reçu la mission de rafraîchir l'emballage dont l'ancien emballage était quelque peu terne. L'emballage devait traduire l'idée de qualité supérieure pour refléter le positionnement. On a recommandé de centrer de façon provocante le logo Champagne pour en améliorer l'impact visuel. On a également créé un effet de halo pour faire ressortir la marque elle-même. Une approche photographique de style «direct» a été utilisée pour se distinguer de l'approche «horizontale» des concurrents. La firme de concepteurs ainsi qu'une diététicienne ont mis au point des photographies et des recettes pour expliquer l'usage idéal des différentes saveurs et pour fournir aux consommateurs les raisons d'acheter des saveurs supplémentaires.

Before/Avant

Joseph E. Seagram commissioned The Group to create the brand personality for its new premium wine entry... Masson Import. The company had identified a need for higher quality wines within the grocery-dépanneur system and elected to assume the leadership position to capture that niche. Masson Import was conceived to incorporate the classic virtues of the Old World, while meeting the contemporary consumers' taste expectations and demand for a greater variety of premium products at an affordable price. Brand names were developed to capture the personality of the country of origin. As a premium priced wine, the graphics on the package combined with the unique logo style with heraldic roots underline that proposition.

JOSEPH E. SEAGRAM & SONS

Le Groupe a reçu le mandat de créer une personnalité de marque pour son vin de qualité supérieure Masson Import. Seagram avait identifié un besoin pour des vins de dépanneurs et épiceries et décidé de se positionner à la tête de ce segment de marché. Le produit a été conçu afin d'incorporer les valeurs traditionnelles du vieux monde tout en répondant au goût du consommateur et à la demande d'une plus vaste gamme de produits de qualité supérieure. Des noms de marque ont été développés afin de traduire la personnalité du pays d'origine. Le graphisme de l'emballage combiné avec un logo unique de style héraldique reflète bien l'image d'un vin de qualité supérieure.

The packaging of Social Tea needed a more contemporary look and a strong injection of appetite appeal. The Group chose as a theme the "tea occasion". The black and white silhouette portrays the social nature of a friendly pause-café type situation. The roses inject an elegant feel as well as adding a feminine touch, women being the primary consumer. The product was subsequently flavour extended into lemon and orange, with design elements remaining consistent while flavour coding was addressed in the brand and in the photography.

CULINAR

L'emballage des biscuits Thé Social avait besoin d'être modernisé et devait rendre le produit plus appétissant. Le Groupe décidait d'exploiter le thème «c'est l'heure du thé». La silhouette en noir et blanc reflète l'idée d'une pause-café amicale. Les roses ajoutent une touche de beauté et d'élégance ainsi qu'un contexte féminin, les femmes étant les principales consommatrices de ces biscuits. Par la suite, on a ajouté d'autres saveurs au produit, soit le citron et l'orange en faisant en sorte que les éléments du design soient les mêmes et que le codage de la saveur soit retransmis par la marque et la photographie.

Before/Avant

Culinar markets a line of bread sticks under the Grissol banner. The packaging was somewhat dated, and it was felt an image upgrade was required to revitalize the brand. The product proposition was that bread sticks were a tasty snack to nibble on at anytime of the day. Through the use of elegant yet simple photography the product proposition was communicated in a contemporary manner. The small staff of wheat communicates the healthy aspect of the product. The extensive use of white was used to convey elegance and specialness to the product, while the flavour differentiation is treated through the strong use of colour.

CULINAR

Culinar possédait sur le marché une marque de pains bâtons appelée Grissol. L'emballage était quelque peu démodé et une amélioration de l'image se faisait sentir pour revitaliser cette marque. Le message était qu'il s'agissait de pains bâtons, un amuse-gueule qu'on pouvait déguster à n'importe quelle heure du jour. Grâce à une photographie simple et élégante, on a réussi à communiquer cette idée de façon très moderne. Le petit amas de blé transmet la notion de produit nourrissant. On a utilisé abondamment le blanc pour donner l'idée d'élégance et d'unicité dun produit. D'autre part, la différence de saveur est communiquée par une harmonisation hardie des couleurs.

Before/Avant

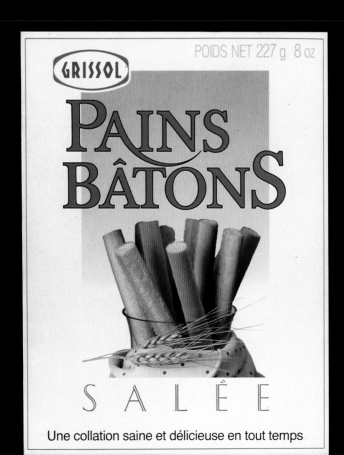

Before/Avant

Kraft General Foods wanted to create a premium image with a new package targetted to adult tastes, as they were seeing significant growth in this market segment. A key benefit of the product was that it had 40% more cheddar than regular process cheese food slices. To emphasize the benefit, The Group proposed as a central graphic a wheel of cheddar cheese with the slices tumbling out of it. The 40% cheddar benefit is aggressively communicated by a colourful flash. Linking the look with the older packaging, a rich blue background was used. The use of a metallic gold ink as well as "deluxe" typography further enhance the premium aspect of the brand.

KRAFT GENERAL FOODS

Kraft General Foods désirait créer l'image d'un produit de qualité supérieure par l'intermédiaire d'un nouvel emballage visant les acheteurs adultes, ce segment du marché s'avérant fort prometteur. Une des caractéristiques principales du produit était qu'il contenait 40% de plus de cheddar que les tranches de fromage fondu ordinaires. Pour mettre l'accent sur cette caractéristique, le Groupe a proposé le dessin d'une meule de fromage cheddar dont on verrait les tranches se détacher. Le contenu de 40% supérieur en cheddar est communiqué de façon dynamique par un «tape-à-l'oeil» coloré. Pour faire le lien avec l'ancien emballage, on a largement utilisé un arrière-plan bleu, renforçant ainsi l'homogénéité. L'utilisation de la couleur or métallique et une typographie de style «de luxe» viennent rehausser l'image de qualité supérieure de la marque.

The Group was commissioned to take the personality of Super Mario of Nintendo Corporation fame and recreate the character in the form of a glass jar. Working within the constraints of "fillibility" and "moldability" the final form evolved from a series of concepts developed by the design firm.

Kraft General Foods a demandé au Groupe de prendre le célèbre personnage Super Mario du jeu Nintendo et d'en traduire l'image à l'aide d'un contenant de verre. La forme finale est le fruit d'une série de concepts dont les paramètres étaient la capacité de remplissage du bocal ainsi que les possibilités de travail du verre.

KRAFT GENERAL FOODS

The Group was charged with the responsibility of leveraging the image and the brand equity of Cheez Whiz process cheese in a jar, into a new category of cheese sauces being introduced. The link with the base brand was maintained through the use of colour, the Cheez Whiz logostyle, and by retaining the red and yellow colour signature. These visual links to the brand heritage inspired confidence adding to the quality promise of a new microwaveable product. The new packaging format responds well to a more mobile society.

Le Groupe a été chargé de promouvoir une nouvelle catégorie de sauce au fromage en se basant sur la popularité du fromage fondu en bocal Cheez Whiz. Le lien avec la marque de base a été établi par les couleurs, le logo Cheez Whiz ainsi que par l'utilisation des couleurs rouge et jaune bien connues. Les liens visuels avec la marque de base inspirent confiance tout en promettant la qualité d'un nouveau produit pouvant être utilisé dans un four à micro-ondes. Ce nouvel emballage répond parfaitement aux attentes d'une société plus mobile.

Before/Avant

Culinar was concerned the existing packaging on their Strawberry Tarts had become dated. The Group developed a basket-weave texture for the biscuit, reminiscent of home-made strawberry pie. Photography was used to give a crisp, clean image of the cookie on the principal display panel. Fresh, lifesize strawberries were featured near the cookie, to strongly reinforce flavour. The brand name was redesigned in a "strawberry" green, with a graphic device of an illustrated sprig of strawberries dripping from the brand copy in both the French and English principal display panels.

CULINAR

Culinar estimait que l'emballage de leurs Tartes aux fraises était désuet. Le Groupe a donc conçu un motif à texture pour le biscuit, avec gros plan sur le tressage, pour rappeler les tartes faites à la maison. Sur la face principale de la boîte, la photo crée une image vibrante du produit, et des fraises fraîches, grandeur nature, déposées près du biscuit, renforcent l'idée de la saveur. Sur les rabats supérieurs et inférieurs, dans les deux langues, le vert couleur «fraises» souligne le nom de la marque auquel s'accroche un graphisme de fraises rattachées par leur queue.

D-137

Yogourt has evolved into an extremely segmented marketplace. Agropur asked The Group to design packaging for their "stirred" brand. Fruit flavour differentiation was featured around the container edges to visually illustrate the stirred benefit. Equity elements of logo style and white background were maintained to keep the family look of Yoplait. Subsequently the look was extended into an exotic flavour offering of fruit and floral combinations based on the success of the European experience.

AGROPUR

Le yogourt a évolué sur un marché extrêmement compartimenté. Agropur nous a donc demandé de concevoir un emballage pour leur marque de yogourt «brassé». Sur le bord du contenant, les différentes saveurs de fruit sont mises en valeur pour bien illustrer le yogourt brassé. Toutefois, pour conserver l'unité visuelle de la famille de produits Yoplait, les éléments similaires comme le style du logo et l'arrière-plan blanc sont demeurés les mêmes. Par la suite, l'image a été adaptée à une saveur exotique, un mélange de fruit et de fleurs, en se basant sur le succès de cette saveur en Europe.

Before/Avant

Originally branded under 3 separate names ; Riviera, Parade and Normandie ; an opportunity arose for Culinar to link the three flavours under a common banner - Normandie. Through the use of strong, crisp photography on the principal display panel individual flavours were identified to enhance appetite appeal. Also, the use of a more traditional illustration was recommended to link each flavour and to develop a brand personality for the umbrella brand, Normandie, reinforced by the typical Normandie style cottage.

CULINAR

À l'origine, la marque portait trois noms différents: Riviera, Parade et Normandie. Culinar a eu l'occasion de regrouper cette gamme sous un seul vocable, Normandie. Les saveurs individuelles furent identifiées sur le panneau principal de présentation grâce à des photographies percutantes et appétissantes qui rehaussent l'attrait du produit. On a également recommandé d'utiliser une illustration plus classique pour relier chaque saveur de façon à typifier la marque commune, soit Normandie, renforcée par l'image d'une maison normande traditionnelle.

Before/Avant

McCAIN FOODS

McCain Foods felt that a revamping of the packaging would assist them in achieving their sales objectives. Within the aseptic juice marketplace, most of the competition lacked differentiation, as they all tend to feature pictures of fruit. The design firm isolated the prime proposition of **blend** and linked it more aggressively with the brand name McCain. A line of dynamic illustrations were commissioned from one of Canada's top illustrators, which captured the element of the blend of fruits in a visually strong manner. The resulting design creates a highly synergistic look on shelf, while still featuring clear product differentiation within the family of flavours.

McCain Foods a décidé que l'emballage devait être retravaillé de façon à leur permettre d'atteindre leurs objectifs de vente. Parmi le marché des jus aseptiques, la plupart des produits concurrentiels se distinguaient mal en ce sens qu'ils présentaient tous des photographies de fruits. La firme de concepteurs a mis en évidence le concept de **punch** et l'a rattaché de façon plus dynamique à la marque McCain. On a demandé à l'un des meilleurs illustrateurs canadiens de fournir une série d'illustrations frappantes transmettant la notion de mélange de fruits avec un impact visuel hardi. Le dessin obtenu confère au produit un aspect hautement synergique en étalage tout en le différenciant clairement à l'intérieur de la gamme de saveurs.

Claritin had been a prescription product, which was being introduced in an over-the-counter format. It benefited from its relationship to Chlor Tripolon, a well-known medication within this group, as well as the additional feature of being non-drowsy. A certain lethargy existed within the shelf appearance of antihistamines. Schering wanted a confident, trustworthy contemporary look for its packaging. The new design, with its bold and distinctive blue sky package, suggests hay fever relief, and is also unique in the category. The Claritin branding is aggressively billboarded on the package.

SCHERING CANADA

Autrefois médicament sur ordonnance, Claritin est devenu un produit accessible à tous les consommateurs. Claritin possédait un avantage dû à sa relation avec le Chlor Tripolon, un médicament bien connu du même genre qui ne provoque pas de somnolence. La présentation des antihistaminiques sur les tablettes ne faisait pas preuve de grande originalité. La compagnie Schering désirait que l'emballage dégage une image de confiance, de fiabilité et de modernité. Le nouveau design d'emballage a fait appel à un ciel bleu caractéristique. Ce design unique en son genre transmet l'idée que ce médicament soulage le rhume des foins. La marque Claritin apparaît massivement sur l'emballage.

F.W. Horner felt their existing packaging was recessive on shelf and The Group was commissioned to revamp the design. The new package with the bold and distinctive blue pack graphics has tremendous on-shelf presence and arrests attention. This look is unique within a somewhat staid category and has contributed to a positive sales increase for the brand.

HORNER

La compagnie F.W. Horner trouvant que l'emballage de leur produit était plutôt faible, demanda au Groupe d'actualiser le design. Le bleu percutant du nouvel emballage se distingue nettement sur le linéaire et capte l'attention. Ce concept unique, dans un secteur plutôt pondéré, contribua à faire augmenter les ventes de la marque.

Before/Avant

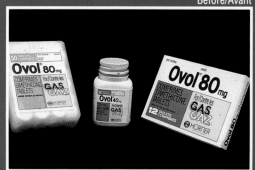

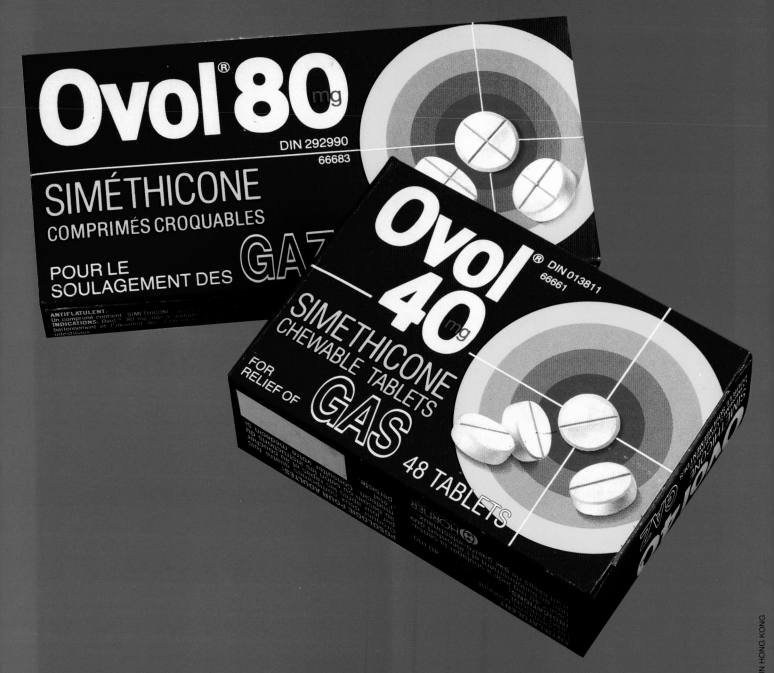

PRINTED IN HONG KONG

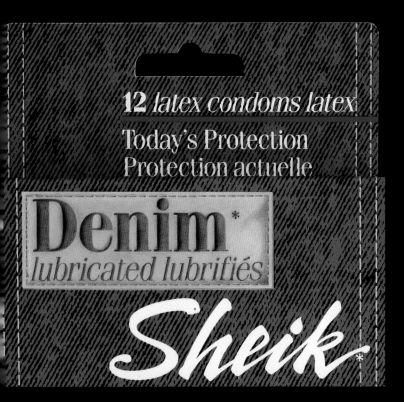

Before/Avan

The Group was commissioned by both Julius Schmid of Canada and Schmid Laboratories in the U.S. to redesign its line of Sheik Products. Driven by a concern over sexually transmitted disease, the condom market has undergone significant changes. The promise of enjoyable sex and protection against pregnancy, although still concerns, take second place against a desire for protection against AIDS and other sexually transmitted diseases. The packaging was somewhat neutralized from its male/female orientation. An aggressive use of colour with a contemporary feel make the brand stand out in an exciting fashion against competitive entries.

JULIUS SCHMID

Le Groupe a été chargé par Julius Schmid du Canada et Schmid Laboratories des États-Unis de refaire la conception de la gamme de produits Sheik. Le marché a subi d'importantes modifications suite aux inquiétudes de la population concernant les maladies transmises sexuellement. Les notions de protection contre la grossesse et de plaisir sexuel restent importantes, mais sont au deuxième plan après la protection contre le sida et les maladies transmises sexuellement. Le message masculin/féminin de l'emballage a été quelque peu dilué. On a utilisé agressivement la couleur dans un contexte moderne de façon à rendre la marque attrayante par rapport à ses concurrentes

The Thomas Pigeon Design Group

Strategic Design Consultants

For over 10 years we have been satisfying the strategic package communication needs of Canadian and international marketers.

Our expertise rests in translating brand strategy into enticing, communicative package expression which elicits purchase.

Our team of creative marketing and design professionals forms the nucleus of a service and creative proposition that is truly hard to beat.

With an acute ability to quickly comprehend and visually articulate brand strategy coupled with our total immersion in the bicultural reality of Canadian packaging, we are eminently well placed to serve your marketing needs.

Conseillers en design stratégique

Nous répondons, depuis plus de dix ans maintenant, aux exigences des spécialistes en marketing canadiens et internationaux.

Nous nous spécialisons dans la traduction des stratégies de marque en

Montréal

Le Groupe Design Tho

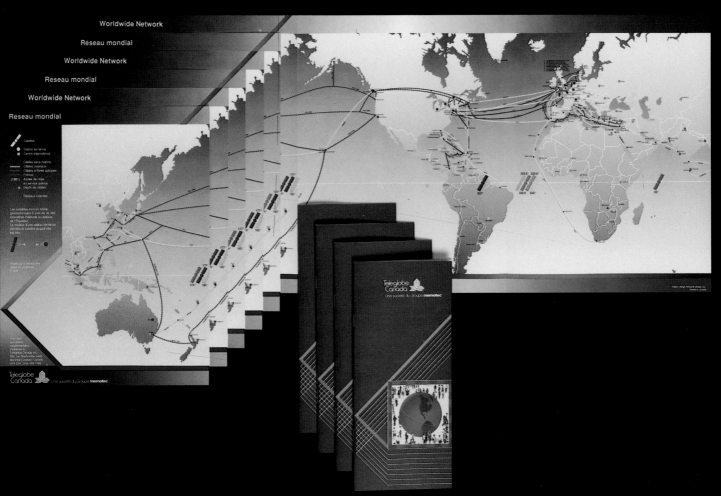

Annual Reports   Corporate Identity   Marketing Communication   Packaging   Illustration

JEUX DE LA FRANCOPHONIE   JUILLET 1989

DENISE FALARDEAU

Solidaires dans l'action

D-146

RICHARD ADAMS
Gâteries

BACCHUS

QUALITÉ EN PRIORITÉ
DOMTAR

Photos: l'ami Jac Mat

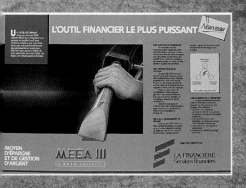

LEGOUPIL
COMMUNICATIONS

424 RUE GUY

BUREAU 200

MONTRÉAL, QC.

H3J 1S6

FAX : 939-3628

TÉL. : 939-3379

"Quel est votre style?"

On nous pose souvent cette question.

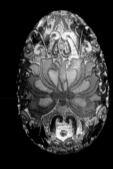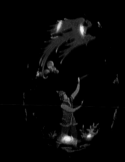

Notre réponse est toujours la même:

"Quels sont vos objectifs?"

ARA NO'VO DESIGN

La réflexion d'abord

Découvrez la philosophie d'ARA NO'VO DESIGN sur la communication graphique en lisant notre brochure corporative ARA NO'VO PRÉSENTE ARA NO'VO.
Pour obtenir cette brochure, communiquez avec Julie Séguin en composant le (514) 849-4065.

CATHERINE THIBAULT   JEAN-DANIEL NOLIN   MARTHE BOLDUC   GUY HUBERT   CHARLES DESJARDINS   SYLVIE NOLIN   TOM LEWIS   MARIE-JOSÉ LEGAULT

WITH US, **THE DIFFERENCE IS YOU.** AND YOU IS YOUR COMPANY, YOUR WAY OF

DOING BUSINESS. THE DIFFERENCE IS THAT WHICH SETS YOU APART... OR SHOULD.

AND THE DIFFERENCE WITH YOU IS **THE DIFFERENCE IN OUR DESIGN WORK.**

WE DESIGN IN AND SPELL OUT EXACTLY WHAT MAKES YOU DIFFERENT. AND IN SO

DOING WE MAKE YOU LOOK GOOD. WHICH IS GOOD FOR BUSINESS. YOU CAN SEE

THE DIFFERENCE WE MAKE BY ASKING FOR A COPY OF OUR

BROCHURE. OR BY CALLING US IN TO DISCUSS YOUR NEXT

PROJECT. **DESJARDINS HUBERT ET ASSOCIÉS INC.**

1222 MACKAY, MONTREAL, QUEBEC, H3G 2H4

TELEPHONE (514) 934-4762   FAX (514) 934-2334

DESJARDINS HUBERT
DESIGN MARKETING

D-149

DANIEL JALBERT, **JARS DESIGN INC.** 10, RUE ONTARIO OUEST, BUREAU 903, MONTREAL (QUEBEC) H2X 1Y6 **(514) 844-0530** FAX (514) 844-6002

IDENTIFICATION VISUELLE ET PRODUCTION

Wolf Schell & Associates Inc. ist eine Design Agentur
zu deren Hauptarbeitsgebieten neben der Entwicklung von
Corporate Identity Programmen auch die Konzeption und
Durchführung aller kommunikativen Massnahmen gehören.

1220 Mackay, Montréal, H3G 2H4, tél 514 935 7098, fax 514 935 8794

Wolf Schell+Associates Inc.

Wolf Schell et associés se spécialise dans l'image et la communication corporative. Que vos besoins relève de design, direction artistique ou d'illustration, nous avons l'expertise pour y répondre de façon intégrale.

Wolf Schell & Associates Inc. specializes in corporate image development and visual communications for business. We provide turnkey service for needs analysis, concept and design with innovative computer assisted production technology.

GSM DESIGN

317 Place d'Youville, Montréal, QC, Canada H2Y 2B5
Téléphone (514) 288 4233, Fax (514) 288 3820

Exposition Domicile: Montréal
affiche / poster

GSM Design / Aménagement, communication visuelle et exposition inc.
GSM Design / Interiors, Visual Communication and Exhibition Inc.

GSM DESIGN

317 Place d'Youville, Montréal, QC, Canada H2Y 2B5
Téléphone (514) 288 4233, Fax (514) 288 3820

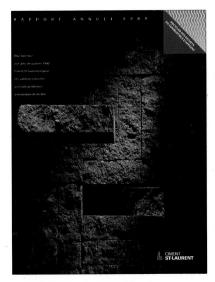

Ciment St-Laurent, rapport annuel
St. Lawrence Cement, annual report

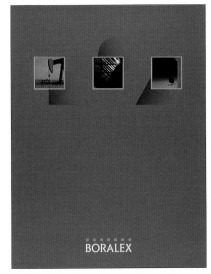

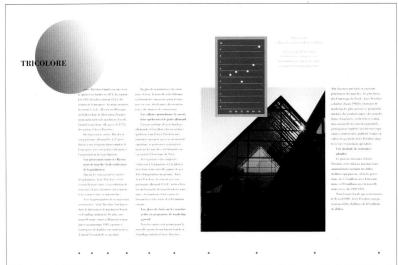

Boralex inc.
brochure corporative / corporate brochure

La Société immobilière du patrimoine architectural de Montréal
image de marque / corporate image

GSM Design / Aménagement, communication visuelle et exposition inc.
GSM Design / Interiors, Visual Communication and Exhibition Inc.

Assurance·vie Desjardins

BANQUE NATIONALE

BANQUE NATIONALE
Notre banque nationale

Vasco

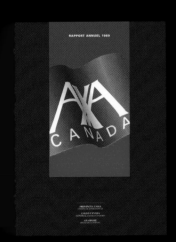

*design
graphique*

multimedia

**Des chercheurs
de formes,
de couleurs,
de textures,
d'émotions.**

**Des designers
graphiques
d'une créativité
nouvelle et d'un
impressionnisme
saisissant.**

**Une technologie
informatique
de pointe,
une représentation
internationale et
une qualité
exemplaire
depuis 21 ans...**

45, avenue McNider
Outremont (Québec)
Canada H2V 3X5
Fax: (514) 277.27.37
Tél.: (514) 277.55.52

esign

White page syndrome ?

Mind your creative, call the best!
Robert Meloche
(514) 878-1001

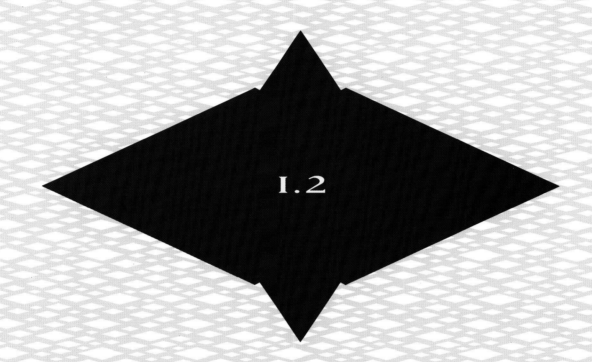

1.2

SALES PROMOTION

SET THE OCEAN IN MOTION

D-161

Beakbane Marketing Inc.

130 Bridgeland Ave., Suite 314
Toronto, Ontario M6A 1Z4

**Trade
& Consumer
Communications**

Can a simple sales brochure really make a difference? Ask a company that knows: Nabisco. The brochure on the left generated sales increases in the double digits.

Labatt's wanted to stimulate trial on a new brand. Beakbane Marketing Inc. created a unique miniature fridge with a pop-up bottle that helped break the ice.

When Duracell asked "How can we demonstrate our concern for the environment?" Beakbane Marketing Inc. helped create an event that clearly communicated Duracell's position on this complex issue.

More than good R.O.I.

Leadership in computer artwork matched by solid marketing strategy are
the reasons Beakbane Marketing Inc. creates trade and consumer communications
that give more than a good return on investment.

**Phone:
(416) 787-4901**

**Fax:
(416) 787-9665**

D-162

1.3

ADVERTISING AGENCIES

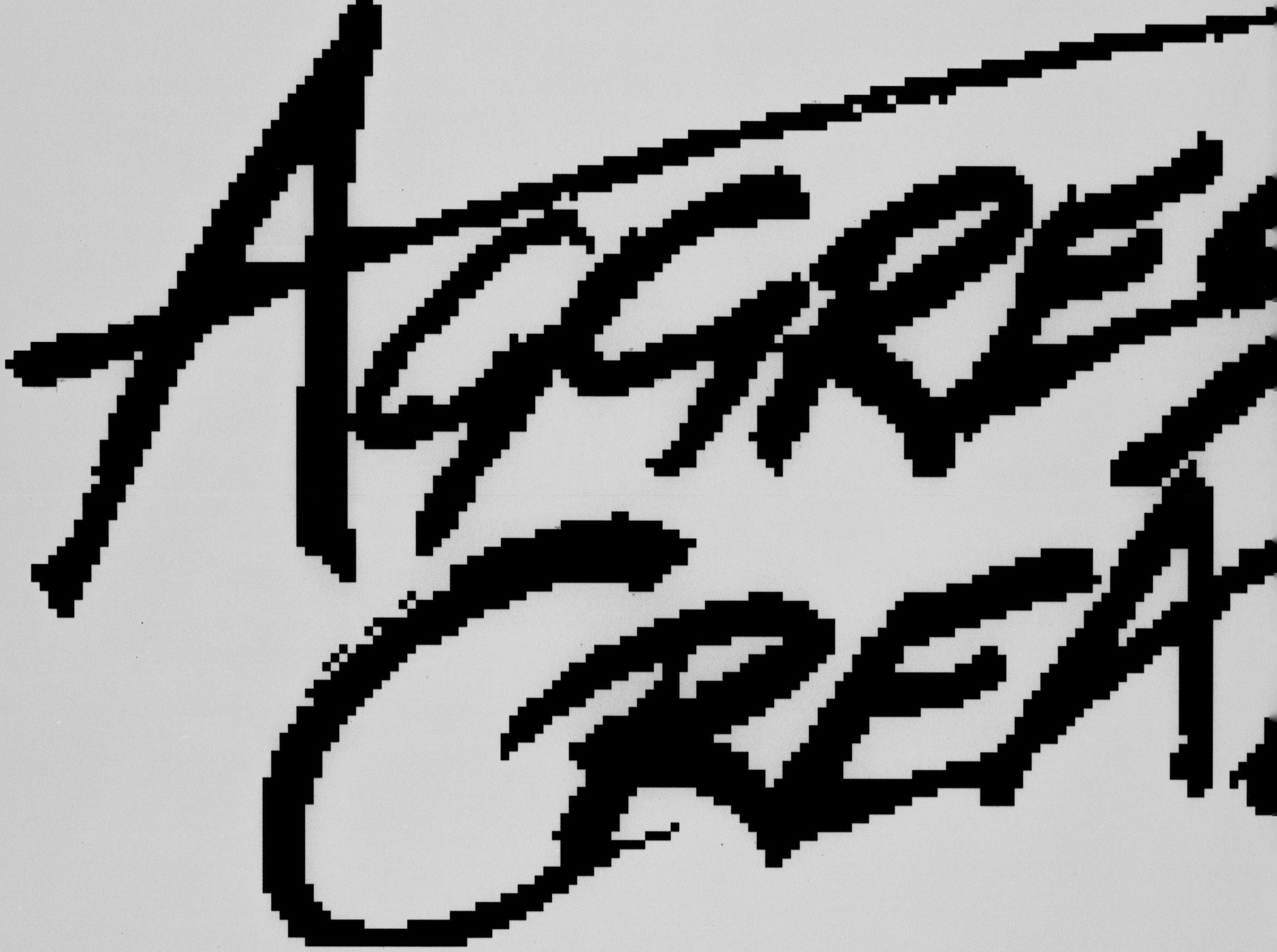

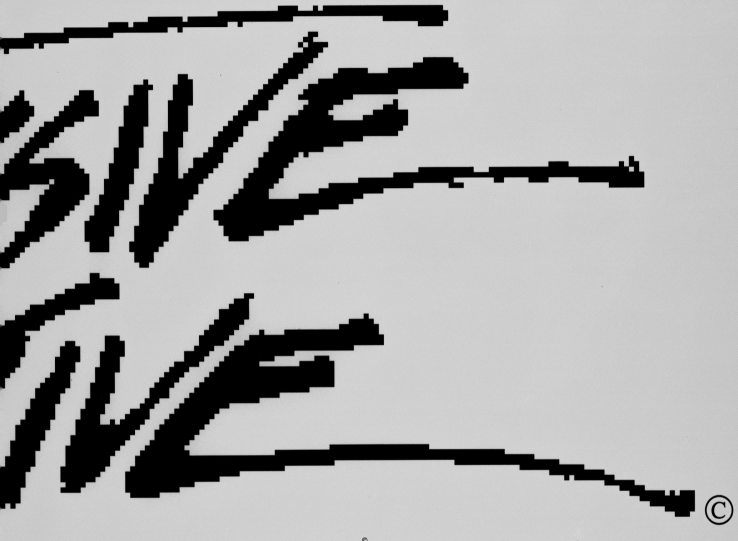

Aggressive Creative© summarizes what effective marketing communications are all about.; the aggressive execution of aptly original creative ideas.

Our creative approach presents the perceived benefits of your product or service in a simple, clear way, using images and phrases that are relevant, appropriate and proprietary.

Our aggressive execution delivers your message to your target market in a daring, original way, which will dominate the selected media — unforgettably.

Call, write or Fax us for our thought provoking Video; "Listen, It's How You Look At It".

Aggressive Creative© 1987, John D. Brooke Advertising Inc.
27 Longboat Avenue, Toronto, Ontario M5A 4C9, Canada
Telehone: 416-362-6545 Fax: 416-368-3126

I.4

ELECTRONIC GRAPHICS & SERVICES

from speaker support slides to multi-image and video

from business cards to posters

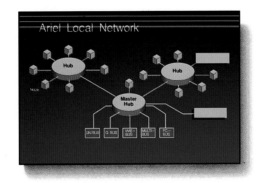

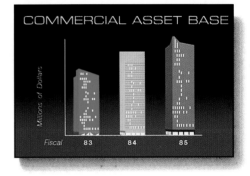

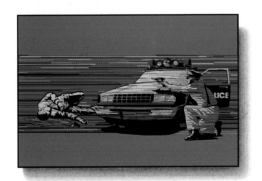

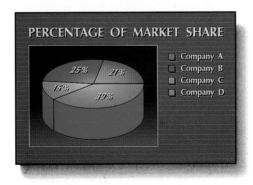

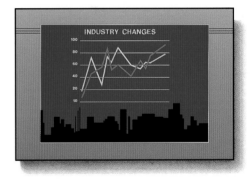

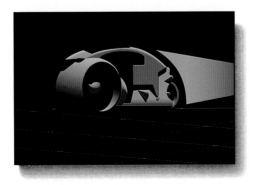

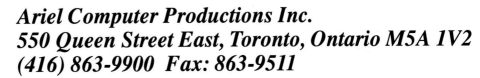

Ariel Computer Productions Inc.
550 Queen Street East, Toronto, Ontario M5A 1V2
(416) 863-9900 Fax: 863-9511

L'avenir est plein de promesses!

Aux professionnels de l'édition, de l'imprimerie et de la publicité,
GRAFNETIX livre des solutions informatiques qui tiennent leurs promesses.

Grafnetix

DIGNUM ANIMATION 3D

514 931 4221

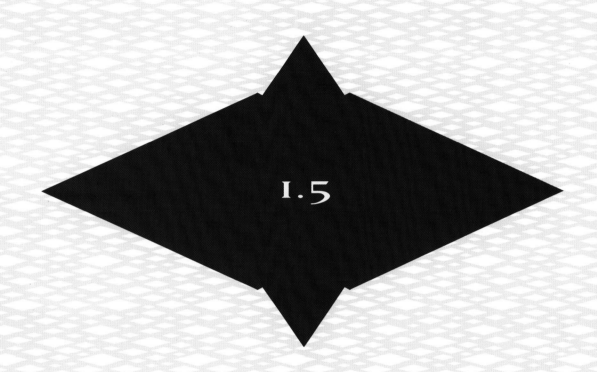

1.5

COMPUTER FILM RECORDING

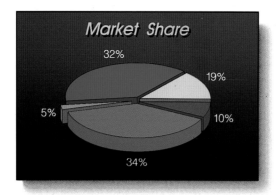
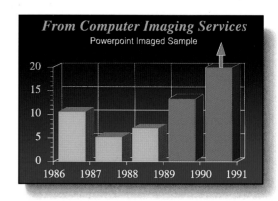
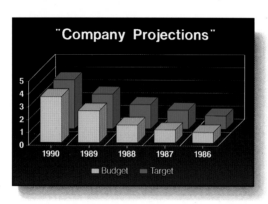

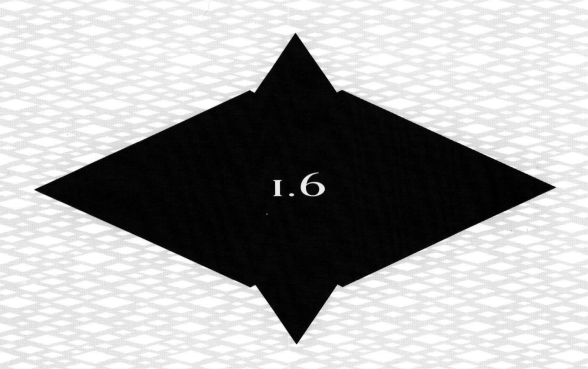

1.6

FILM/VIDEO/AV

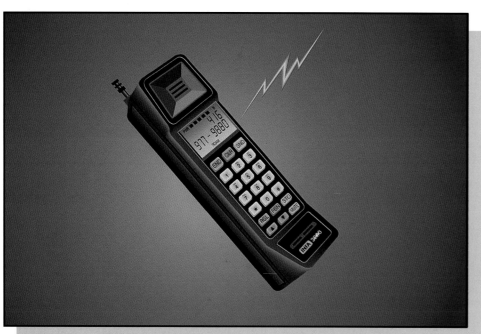

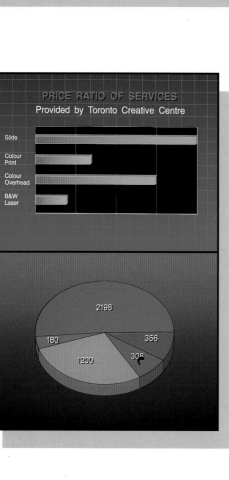

PRICE RATIO OF SERVICES
Provided by Toronto Creative Centre

Slide
Colour Print
Colour Overhead
B&W Laser

2198
180
356
1200
308

Business Graphics and
Slide Imaging for all your
Presentation needs.

*Let us help you present your
best image!*

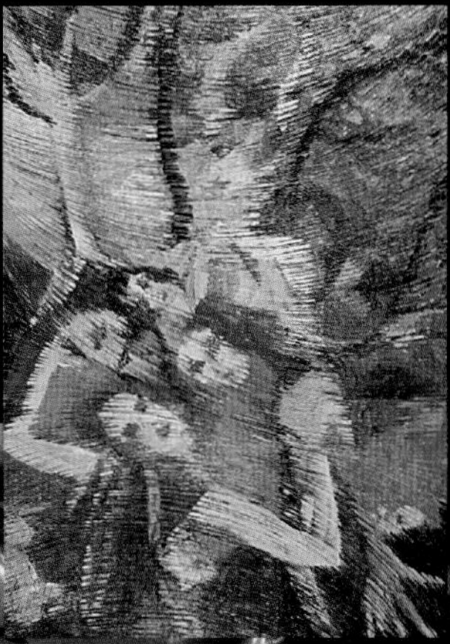

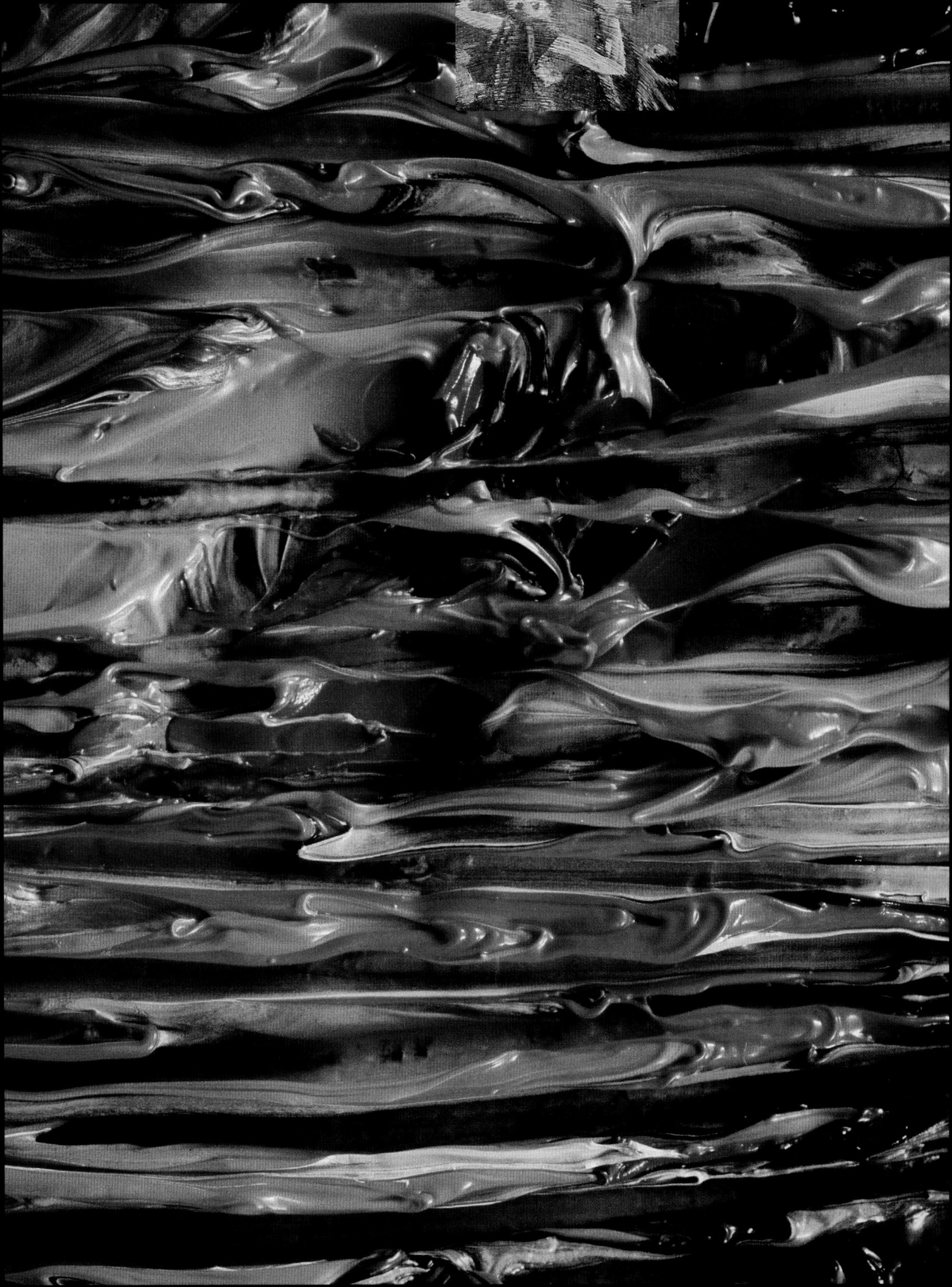

EXHIBIT & DISPLAY

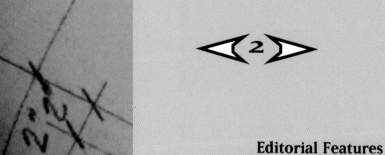

"I am from Missouri. You have got to show me."

Willard Duncan Vandiver

FROM CONCEPT TO SALES

THE SUCCESSFUL TRADE SHOW PROGRAM

➤ Some companies still think of
trade shows as a secondary,
obligatory supplement to their
sales and marketing program. They
will allot multi-million-dollar
budgets for media advertising and
other marketing programs, yet
trade shows — one of the strongest
of marketing media — are too
often relegated as an afterthought
to junior personnel, with minimal
budgets and very little planning.
The companies that use trade
shows as a powerful sales tool have
a different attitude. The trade
show is, after all, the only selling
medium that is as old as
selling itself.

◆ ◆ ◆

The concept of exhibiting has been with us since the ancient Egyptian days, and soliciting business in an open market in the tradition of the bazaar has been practised for thousands of years — because it works.

At a trade show, as in a market, vendors can meet their clients in person, in many cases let the customers see and touch their goods, and find out exactly what the competition is up to. The trade show presents sales opportunities found nowhere else, in which qualified leads and even signed sales agreements can be obtained.

There are two ways to miss out on the powerful marketing potential of trade shows. The cheap way is to not participate at all. The more expensive way is to exhibit ineffectively.

When a company decides to cash in on exhibiting opportunities by planning a trade show program, there are many options to be considered. What is a reasonable annual trade show budget? How many shows should we enter? What size booth should we use? Who will design our booth and help organize our schedule?

These are only some of the questions that need answers, and many more will arise as the process unfolds.

In order for your company to get an initial understanding

of the best approach to a trade show program, you should first find out which shows are relevant to your industry and attend them. This will give you a general outlook on how other companies are handling their trade show marketing. Booth sizes, product displays, the effectiveness of different graphic approaches and demonstration techniques, as well as the general atmosphere of each show should present a picture of the shows and types of booth that will be suitable.

This is an important step. Nowadays there are a number of trade shows available for any given industry and, considering the expense of participating, you need to be very choosy in those you select. "You should do your homework," says Derek Retter of ExpoSystems, a full-service system exhibit company. "Phone some of the people who have gone into the shows, and don't always rely on what you get from the show managers."

Once you have a general feel for the shows you're interested in, the next step is to select an exhibit company to fulfill the mandate. This raises questions about the type of booth, the size of the company that should handle these needs and the objective of the exhibit program.

Selecting an exhibit company is a very important process and you can make an intelligent choice if you know what to look for. Ron Gooch, vice-president and general manager of J&O Exhibits and vice-president of the Exhibit & Display Association of Canada (EDAC), emphasizes the importance of visiting the premises of the exhibit company and asking a lot of questions. "Ask about the personnel," he says, "and look for qualities like stability and experience. And get references."

Sam Kohn, president of Exhibits International, another full-service exhibit company, agrees. "It's important, as with any major purchase, to know who you're buying from."

The buying process is a delicate one; you need to understand the process of utilizing the exhibit company as a marketing consultancy. One of the greatest impediments to developing an effective marketing solution is the prospective exhibitor's belief that "the prettiest picture wins." The rendering of the proposed exhibit, presented by the exhibit company, can hold far too much weight in the decision-making process.

This comes as a result of the speculative process of exhibit design. A client who wants an exhibit will invite three to five (sometimes more) companies to submit proposed designs. The companies, eager for business, will make presentations often consisting of colour renderings of the exhibit. But the quality of the drawing and the personal taste of the client can impair the decision.

Sam Kohn likens this to "wallpapering the wall with renderings and throwing a dart."

This also raises questions about who pays for the creative.

"There's nothing for free," says Ron Gooch. "We support the competition for creative concept, but we have an unwritten policy that if there are more than three bidders on a major project, one of the first questions we'll ask is what the budget is for creative."

This has been the subject of much debate among members of EDAC. The association recently ratified an agreement stating that every member will encourage compensation for creative. "Who pays?" Gooch asks. "If it's not the prospective client, it's my existing client who is paying for my right to compete in the market, and that's not fair."

Kohn agrees. "Design is one of our most valuable commodities, and yet, because competition is so fierce, we've been giving it away."

How do you select an exhibit design? Successful exhibits begin with planning. Depending on your requirements, four to six months ahead of the first show is a good time to begin. This gives you an opportunity to explain the objectives of the trade show program, the criteria the booth must satisfy, and other details of the program and your company to the exhibit designer.

It is best to involve the exhibit company from the very beginning. Bob Lingley of J&O Exhibits recalls one client, Delta Faucet, that was very organized when they approached the exhibit company. Delta presented J&O with a binder of information listing shows with dates and booth sizes so the designers would immediately understand the flexibility needed. The client also described in general terms the look they were after — something upscale that would set them apart from the competition.

EXHIBIT

BRAD BLACK + FRINGE LIMITED

E-5

"They didn't tell us what to do," Lingley observes. "They were giving us a good feel for the kind of exhibit they needed."

Delta's budget was realistic and Lingley's team won the contract over two other bidders. This was not a client that was hung up on aesthetics; the exhibit design was created to satisfy their trade show marketing objectives, and it succeeded on that basis.

One dilemma that might present itself to a new exhibitor is the choice between system and custom exhibits. System exhibits consist of modular components that fit together to form many different configurations, while custom exhibits are constructed for one particular design. While some companies specialize in one type, others supply both, depending on the client's needs.

David Sharp of Octanorm Canada says that systems have become as versatile as custom exhibits. Comparing his company's product to a big kids' Mecchano set, he asserts that it is "only restricted by the imagination."

Octanorm is a system that consists primarily of lightweight interlocking posts

and beams from which many different styles of exhibit can be designed and created. With the use of various laminates, formicas, cloth materials and wall coverings, system exhibits can be made to look unique and reflect a tailored design that specifically expresses the individual exhibitor's message.

"We supply the hardware and know-how to the client," says Jack Wisswell, Octanorm's sales manager. "We work closely with the exhibit companies, and show them how to design with the modular material."

Another feature of this particular system is that it is part of an international network. Sharp explains that, for example, a local exhibit company can design an Octanorm booth for the client for a show in the Orient. The design is shipped to an affiliated company in Hong Kong, which assembles the booth at the show. "There's no shipping cost, no damage in transit. You arrive at the show with your product samples and your exhibit is set up."

Custom exhibits, by their very name, suggest a more personalized approach. These are designed and constructed from more conventional structural building materials

and can be built from scratch to suit the exhibitor's needs. Custom is, of course, the older concept in exhibit construction. And systems have been on the market for at least as long as ExpoSystems, an exclusively system exhibit company that recently marked its 25th anniversary.

The debate over system versus custom exhibits is levelling off. "The custom exhibit people truly believe in custom exhibits," says Derek Retter. "But systems came in as an alternative to help buffer the increasing costs, and now the custom people can't deny our existence."

Today, both custom and system exhibits can be created to fit various configurations and booth sizes. "People want modular custom exhibits," Retter says, "and they want systems that look custom," and both effects can be achieved by a good exhibit designer. The general consensus in the industry is that there is room for both types and, as the cost differential between the two decreases, whichever is best for the customer should be recommended by the exhibit specialist.

System or custom, the exhibit company's most important objective is to create an accurate and

effective visual marketing medium. "The exhibit has to make a statement," says David Sharp. "A trade show can create the best contacts sales people can generate."

Charles Godbout of Polystand Concepts in Montreal feels that the exhibit ought to be "an extension of the corporate image. Obviously, it needs to attract attention, but it should also communicate a clear message."

Trying to show too much is a common fault among exhibitors. "It's not about emptying the company warehouse," Godbout explains. "The exhibitor should select and develop a principal theme, occasionally with some satellite themes that are adapted to the context of a particular trade show."

"Simplicity is in the best taste" is Godbout's golden rule.

Sam Kohn agrees. "Most exhibitors try to say too much. They're taking away their selling message from their own reps and products by trying to put it in the copy. Too much copy does not work."

What does work is a strong and appropriate visual impact. But the success of the exhibit involves much more than the booth. It takes planning, a setting out of objectives and an effective strategy for fulfilling those objectives to make a trade show work for you. This begins with the pre-show publicity.

The first step is to get the right people — prospective clients — into the booth. Mailing invitations and brochure packages to the clients you want to reach is a good way to notify qualified prospects that you will be exhibiting at the show. Offering samples and gifts or presenting invitations for cocktails will entice the people you want into your booth.

The objective of trade show participation is usually to generate leads. Qualifying those leads is equally important. A good way to do this with someone who has entered the booth is to carefully establish who the person is, their company and position in the initial conversation. This information can be recorded quickly on a tick sheet to which the prospect's business card is attached.

At the end of the show, when the exhibitor has generated a number of qualified leads, the job is far from over. These leads will be wasted unless there is a planned follow-up procedure aimed at turning them into sales. Sam Kohn advises an immediate direct-mail follow-up and a telemarketing program.

The people who work the booth are as important as the booth itself. Exhibit company specialists have seen the best and the worst of exhibit personnel, and will advise you on how to get the best results from the people working the exhibit. A good rule is for the person in the booth to act as if he or she is in the prospective client's office. That means no eating, drinking, smoking or chatting with other salespeople.

Too often, the person in the booth is underqualified to handle the opportunity that a prospect entering the booth can present. If the customer doesn't receive the answers or information he needs, he'll get a negative impression of the company and go somewhere else. The booth must be tended by trained salespeople who are not tired from setting up the booth themselves or working shifts of more than four hours. They must be alert and receptive and they should look happy to be there.

The ingredients of a trade show exhibit can produce successful results for the exhibitor. But if any step in the process is neglected, the opportunity can be squandered. What are the basic steps to trade show success?

Nobody can guarantee success, but a well planned trade show program is the best way to ensure that the money invested will pay off in sales. Organized effectively, it can out-perform other advertising media. According to Sam Kohn, it costs about $250 to cold call and work a lead versus $110 to develop one at a trade show.

But these results don't come by themselves. It takes co-operation between exhibit company and exhibitor to create an effective exhibit. And it takes a concerted, strategic effort to turn qualified leads into sales. Handled with professionalism and organization, a trade show program is a great vehicle for achieving excellent sales goals. ◁

1. Plan early. Six months to a year ahead of time for a new program; six months for a new exhibit.

2. Select an exhibit company that can handle your requirements and is interested in giving you the best marketing results — not the best looking rendering.

3. Be receptive to the exhibit company's design proposal based on rationale rather than personal taste.

4. Plan the program with a co-ordinated pre-show effort to get the prospects you want into your booth.

5. Put qualified, trained salespeople in the booth.

6. Qualify the leads you generate at the show.

7. Be prepared to follow up on those leads.

CREATING A GREAT EXHIBIT
FORMICA
CASE HISTORY

➤ How does a truly successful

exhibit come about? Formica

Canada Inc.'s booth at the 1989

International Interior Designers

Exhibition — IIDEX — was

unquestionably a winner.

◆ ◆ ◆

Created by Terrelonge Design Inc. of Toronto, it drew acclaim from the interior design community (Formica's target audience), the show's judging committee and the media alike.

A great many components contributed to the Formica success story. But underlying all of them was one vital factor. "Open communication," says Linda Zuber-Chislett, Formica's advertising manager. "That's the key. Open communication was essential from the beginning right through to the very end."

The "beginning" in fact was a catalogue that Terrelonge designed for Formica. After extensive research, the client had determined that its perceived position in the marketplace was quite different from its actual position — as a producer of high-end design materials for interior, furniture and industrial designers. So Terrelonge's first assignment with Formica, explains Del Terrelonge, was "to design an upscale catalogue that would reposition Formica in the market. The catalogue would feature a distinctive look that would separate them from the crowd and communicate to interior designers what Formica actually is."

Zuber-Chislett approached Terrelonge with the attitude that it was essential to be completely open and honest. "You have to be," she explains, "if you want the designer to be able to respond to your concerns and work with you. I said to Del, 'I'm going to spell it out like it is, because to achieve what I'm going to ask you to achieve, you've got to know everything.'"

This approach paid off. Terrelonge was able to zero in on Formica's requirements and translate them imaginatively into a highly successful piece; within days of the catalogue's release, positive responses began coming in.

Following the success of the catalogue, Zuber-Chislett enlisted Terrelonge's assistance in a project at the Royal Ontario Museum (ROM). Formica was launching a new countertop surfacing material, called "Surell." The upcoming IIDEX was an obvious place to introduce the product. "But I felt Surell required a very special niche," says Zuber-Chislett. "I wanted to approach the design community in a different way. What I did was create the event at the ROM, which we called Prolific Impressions."

Zuber-Chislett asked eight of Canada's premier architectural, graphic, interior and furniture designers each to create an object using Surell. These she would unveil at Prolific Impressions — to which more than 400 design professionals were invited — the evening before IIDEX opened. Following the event, these innovative works of art would be moved down to IIDEX and placed on display as the focal point of Formica's booth. As well as being one of the contributors, Terrelonge was asked to develop a poster and invitations for for Prolific Impressions.

But Zuber-Chislett still only knew of Terrelonge as a graphic designer who worked in two dimensions. And she had some concerns about the Iidex exhibit. In the past, the company had used a system (modular components) for exhibits, which had worked quite well. But this show was different. Zuber-Chislett wanted the new image of Formica — the one that Terrelonge had created on paper — interpreted in the booth.

There was an additional challenge too: within the 600 square feet of floor space the company would have at the show, two purposes had to be served. Along with a miniature gallery displaying the art objects that would introduce Surell, Formica would be showing a collection of new laminate designs from Europe. Neither message could override the other.

Del Terrelonge

Del Terrelonge Design

"I don't think we really take risks. It's just the way we design and think."

Linda Zuber Chislett

Formica Canada

"Open communication was essential from the beginning right through to the very end."

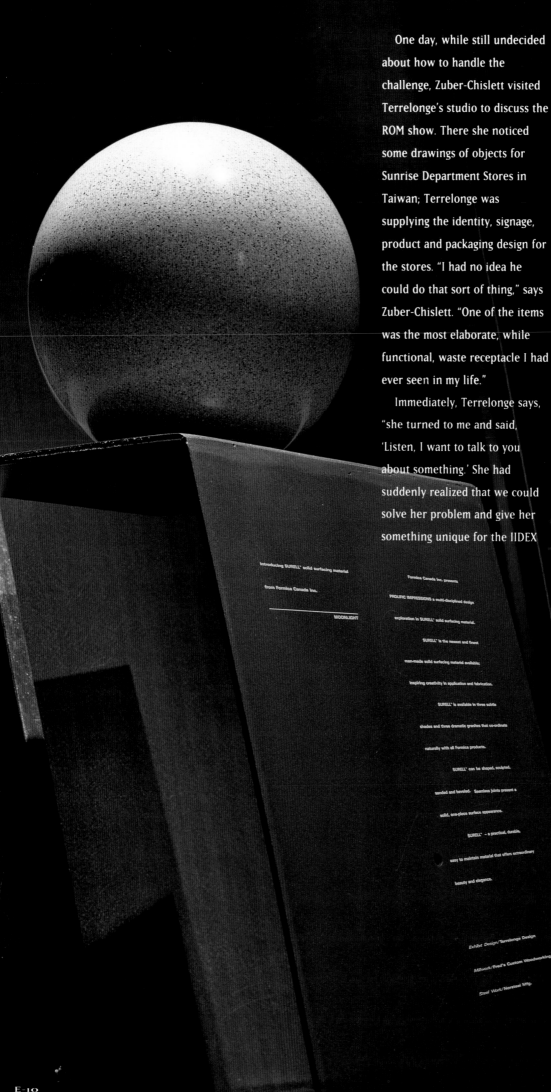

Introducing SURELL® solid surfacing material
from Formica Canada Inc.

MOONLIGHT

Formica Canada Inc. presents

PROLIFIC IMPRESSIONS a multi-disciplined design

exploration in SURELL® solid surfacing material.

SURELL® is the newest and finest

man-made solid surfacing material available;

inspiring creativity in application and fabrication.

SURELL® is available in three subtle

shades and three dramatic graphics that co-ordinate

naturally with all Formica products.

SURELL® can be shaped, sculpted,

sanded and beveled. Seamless joints present a

solid, one-piece surface appearance.

SURELL® — a practical, durable,

easy to maintain material that offers extraordinary

beauty and elegance.

Exhibit Design/Terrelonge Design

Millwork/Fred's Custom Woodworking

Steel Work/Norsteel Mfg.

One day, while still undecided about how to handle the challenge, Zuber-Chislett visited Terrelonge's studio to discuss the ROM show. There she noticed some drawings of objects for Sunrise Department Stores in Taiwan; Terrelonge was supplying the identity, signage, product and packaging design for the stores. "I had no idea he could do that sort of thing," says Zuber-Chislett. "One of the items was the most elaborate, while functional, waste receptacle I had ever seen in my life."

Immediately, Terrelonge says, "she turned to me and said, 'Listen, I want to talk to you about something.' She had suddenly realized that we could solve her problem and give her something unique for the IIDEX show — something that would communicate Formica's image as effectively as the catalogue had."

The deadline was tight. "We had maybe five weeks from beginning to end," Terrelonge points out. But the intense briefing he'd already gone through for the previous projects had prepared him well for this complex challenge. Added to that was the trust the client had in his ability. "We were given almost complete freedom. Linda just said, 'I want you to design something that in your opinion is going to work.' That's a very rare situation."

Once Terrelonge had developed a design, it went back to Formica for approval by Zuber-Chislett and senior staff. "The whole process was very smooth," Terrelonge emphasizes. "The senior staff believed in Linda's direction and she believed in us."

Terrelonge's design did away with a traditional sign displaying the company's name. Instead, he created one that incorporated Formica's products; combined with carefully planned lighting, the result was a dramatic exterior to draw people in. Once inside, they would have an unobstructed view of the Surell gallery without distractions from other booths.

So the construction wheels were set in motion. Not wanting to go with the discipline of a conventional system booth, Terrelonge chose to have everything custom built, monitoring each stage of the work. "We had carefully figured out every detail beforehand," he says, explaining that they worked hand in hand with a talented craftsman who had been involved in projects for Formica in the past.

IIDEX opened — and Formica became the star of the show. "We received the largest number of hard sales leads and enquiries about our products that we've ever had at any show," says Zuber-Chislett. By the end of the first day more than 3,000 catalogs had been handed out,

and interviews of Formica staff had been conducted by representatives from periodicals, trade publications, newspapers and television.

As Zuber-Chislett points out, "That wonderful publicity is very important for Formica. I've never had the pleasure of working on an exhibit before that drew so much acclaim. Everyone at Formica felt very proud to be exhibiting from the booth. And we felt that we were very clearly expressing the right image about Formica." In the end, that's what a successful exhibit is all about.

Del Terrelonge
♦ ♦ ♦

Koen de Winter
♦ ♦ ♦

George Yabu
Glenn Pushelberg
♦ ♦ ♦

Thomas Lamb
♦ ♦ ♦

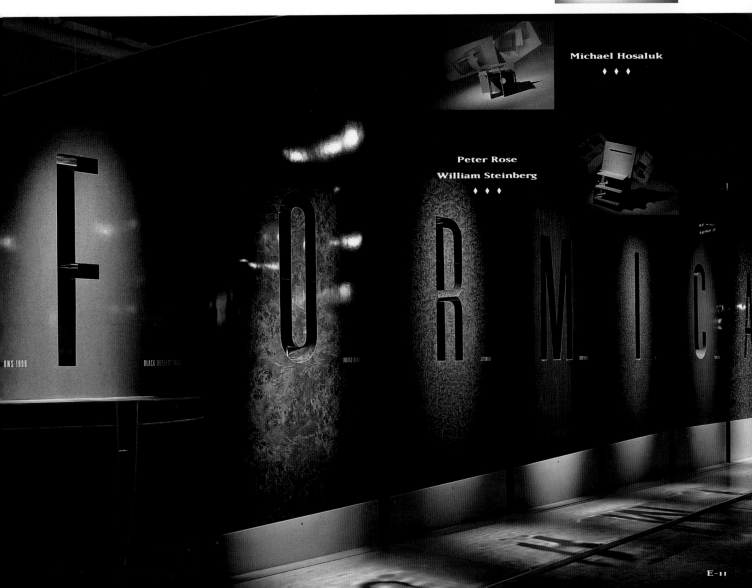

Michael Hosaluk
♦ ♦ ♦

Peter Rose
William Steinberg
♦ ♦ ♦

ALPHAFORM
EXHIBITS + DESIGN INC.

Design: Taylor Browning

Design: The Spencer Francey Group

ALPHAFORM EXHIBITS
+ DESIGN INC.
833 Oxford Street
Toronto, Ontario, Canada
M8Z 5X4
Telephone: (416) 253-9403
FAX: (416) 253-5164

The ALPHAFORM group offers designers and planners a comprehensive exhibit service that includes implementing concept and design through production, shipping, installation and exhibit storage.

Octa-Node

MODULAR PANEL SYSTEM

Design: Tudhope Associates

Unique in North America, Octa-Node meets the designer's need for a high-profile appearance while still allowing for those special 'customizing' touches that create the special environment. Infinitely flexible, ultimately stylish and priced for a broad range of budgets, Octa-Node has provided the answer for hundreds of display and exhibit applications across North America. Available with a vast colour and finish selection, Octa-Node can be modified with a broad range of accessories which combine function with form in complete harmony. When personalizing Octa-Node for your specific display needs, visual flexibility is ensured as all graphics can be silkscreened onto the panels or attached with Velcro.

For the client, time and money savings are realized thanks to Octa-Node's lightweight, rigid, modular construction. Octa-Node is easy-to-install (following our simple step-by-step instructions), compact for shipping and efficient to store when not in use. Gone is the necessity of hiring professional installers. Today, Octa-Node means maximum efficiency for impact and minimum effort for installation.

Whether you are seeking the ideal solution for a Commercial office environment; a product-enhancing retail display; a flexible, travelling Trade and consumer shows display or; a Large scale exhibition booth, Octa-Node can become the central essence of your designed environment.

Moboform

GEODETIC SPACE FRAME SYSTEM

For those pursuing an economical solution to exhibits, lighting grids, office or commercial ceiling applications or retail applicators, Moboform offers an open airy appearance while still providing focus on a special area. Made from a wide colour selection of plastic and aluminum, Moboform is easy to assemble and disassemble making it ideal for those environments that change or for retailers who move from time to time. Moboform is inexpensive compared to other spaceframe grids and shipping is very economical due to its light weight and compactness when disassembled. Moboform is the ideal tool for those seeking the definitive, yet economical finishing touch for an environment.

Design: Taylor Browning

Design: Don Wolf + Associates

ALPHAFORM
EXHIBITS + DESIGN INC.

Design: Taylor Browning

Design: Taylor/Sprules Corporation

Design: Abbott Jenkins Group

Through innovation, an uncompromising commitment to detail and a resourceful, service-oriented project team, ALPHAFORM has defined its role as one soley dedicated to communicating your client's objectives in a manner that creates clear and lasting impressions.

Sophisticated modular systems, combined with total custom fabrication facilities, allow ALPHAFORM to produce p.o.p. displays, small exhibits and elaborate trade show booths to your specifications.

ALPHAFORM's portfolio includes exhibit work for corporations throughout North America.

OCTANORM®

OCTANORM® SERVICE PARTNERS

The OCTANORM® exhibition system is only supplied to highly qualified exhibit-builders.

Each of these selected companies distinguish themselves through their service, creativity, technical know-how and experience.

Here is the proof.

OCTANORM ®

Let us introduce you to our
OCTANORM® SERVICE PARTNER
in your area.
For further information please contact:

OCTANORM® CANADA LTD.
15 Lockport Avenue
Toronto, Ontario M8Z 2R6
Canada
Telephone (416) 233-2108
Telefax   (416) 233-3773

• CREATIVE DESIGN
• QUALITY PRODUCTION
• DEPENDABLE INSTALLATION

• Creative Exhibits
• Creative Display

A DIVISION OF CDA INDUSTRIES INC.

At CDA, our winning team of professionals, will provide you with creative solutions that fit your budget.

Creative Exhibits is Canada's largest designer and producer of custom-built exhibits. Our 130,000 sq. foot plant in Toronto has full in-house production facilities, be it wood, wire, metal, plastic, vacuum forming or silk screen. As well, we install and service all trade and consumer shows right across Canada.

Creative display, by having access to a full range of in-house facilities, has produced many award-winning point-of-purchase displays, be it floor stands, counter units or mobils.

Let CDA provide innovative solutions to all your specific marketing problems, and help you take your show on the road!

Phone or write for your FREE exhibit evaluation

cda industries inc.
1430 Birchmount Road, Scarb.
Toronto, Canada M1P 2E8
Telephone (416) 752-2301
Fax (416) 752-9653

Creative Wire
a division of CDA Industries, Inc.
2370 South Sheridan Way
Mississauga, Ontario L5J 2M4
Telephone (416) 823- 8851
Fax (416) 823- 0161

SERVICE OCTANORM PARTNER

Design

EXHIBIT & DISPLAY

MASTERING THE CHALLENGES OF THE 90's

Rubbermaid

Tel: (416) 252•0442
Fax: (416) 252•0953

60 NEWCASTLE STREET
ETOBICOKE • ONTARIO

OCTANORM PARTNER
SERVICE

E-22

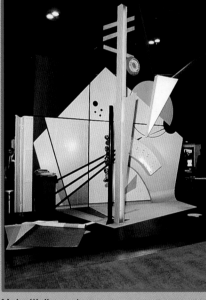

GUIBERT *graphik*

171 JEAN PROULX, HULL
QUÉBEC, CANADA J8Z 1W5
(819) 771-9180 FAX (819) 771-4017

IN HOUSE SERVICES
SERVICES INTERNES

Exhibits / Displays	Exposition / Stand
Project Management	Gestion de projets
Graphic / Design	Design / Graphiques
Custom Fabrication	Fabrication sur mesure
Screen Printing	Sérigraphie
Computerized Storage	Entreposage informatisé
Transportation	Transport
Installation / Dismantle	Montage / Démontage

Giltspur

Giltspur is recognized for creativity and leadership in all facets of trade show activity. We are the singular source capable of meeting any client need, anywhere in the world.

■ Our goal is to maximize your trade show results both in and beyond the confines of the convention hall. To that end we bring a wealth of talents and experience unmatched in the industry.

■ Great care and a meticulous eye for detail are the hallmarks of Giltspur construction. The skill of our craftsmen is clearly visible in every aspect of an exhibit. An exhibit that lends credence to the intrinsic excellence of your company's products and services, enhancing your reputation in the marketplace.

■ Marketing and selling at a trade show is different than in any other environment. The number of high potential prospects is large, the time available to spend with them is limited, and the competition is right next door. To assist clients in overcoming these obstacles, Giltspur has a complete line of marketing, promotional, sales training and follow-up services exclusively for trade shows.

120 Carrier Drive   Toronto, Ontario M9W 5R1   Canada   Telephone: (416) 674-0845   Fax (416) 674-1228

Atlanta ■ Boston ■ Buffalo ■ Chicago ■ Cincinnati ■ Dallas ■ Las Vegas ■ Los Angeles ■ New Orleans
New York ■ Orlando ■ Phoenix ■ Pittsburgh ■ Rochester ■ San Francisco ■ Tampa ■ Toronto ■ Washington, D.C.

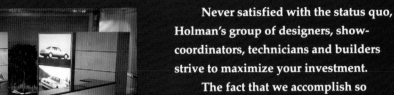

At Holman Design, we pride ourselves in effectively communicating our clients' corporate images, products, and services through dynamic visual marketing.

As specialists in exhibits, displays and showroom interiors, we are a completely versatile three-dimensional design firm.

Never satisfied with the status quo, Holman's group of designers, show-coordinators, technicians and builders strive to maximize your investment.

The fact that we accomplish so many successful exhibits is testimony to the "team" approach, where the aim is to achieve our clients' objectives though excellence.

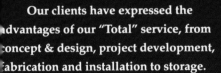

Our clients have expressed the advantages of our "Total" service, from concept & design, project development, fabrication and installation to storage.

Through creative integration of quality custom work in wood, metal, plastic, and graphics, we have produced powerful show-stoppers for outstanding value.

"Results by Design" is more than just our motto, it is the focus of our energies.

Holman Design, 160 Lesmill Road, Don Mills, Ontario, Canada, M3B 2T5
Tel:(416) 441-1877   Fax:(416) 441-3556

J&O exhibits

QUALITY
INTEGRITY
SERVICE
SINCE 1955

Anne Murray Centre Springhill, N.S

Air Canada

E-28

J&O EXHIBITS LTD.
1450 THE QUEENSWAY
TORONTO, ONTARIO
M8Z 1S4

FACSIMILE (416) 231-3053
TELEPHONE (416) 252-9575

STEVEN's

SIGNS AND DISPLAYS LIMITED

Display your product or service effectively. Careful design and production in our full-service facility will save you time and money. Stevens offers sales and rentals ranging from tabletop to large custom-designed exhibits. Call Stevens. We'll help you make a good impression.

Stevens Signs & Displays Ltd.
23 Heather Crescent
London, Ontario N5W 4L6
Tel. (519) 453-2040
Fax (519) 453-6760

O.S.P. OCTANORM® SERVICE PARTNERS

A select group of exhibit builders specializing in all aspects of design, service and fabrication.
Their expertise can benefit your trade show marketing.

ABLE EXHIBITS
Mississauga, Ont.

ALL SEASONS
DISPLAY INC.
Langley, B.C.

ALL SET DESIGN LTD.
Vancouver, B.C.

CDA INDUSTRIES
INC.
Scarborough, Ont.

C.E.S. EXHIBITS INC.
Toronto, Ont.

CHAIRMAN MILLS
LTD.
Willowdale, Ont.

CONVENTIONS
UNLIMITED
Burnaby, B.C.

DERRICK EXHIBIT &
TRADE SHOW
SERVICES LTD.
Edmonton, Alta.

DERRICK EXHIBIT &
TRADE SHOW
SERVICES LTD.
Port Coquitlam, B.C.

DESIGNAMATION
LIMITED
Etobicoke, Ont.

ED MANNING
AGENCIES LTD.
St. John's, Nfld.

EXCEL EXPO INC.
Ville Lasalle, Qué.

EXHIBITS
INTERNATIONAL
Etobicoke, Ont.

THE EXHIBITORS
INC.
Toronto, Ont.

EXHIBITS PLUS
Toronto, Ont.

EXPO 4 INC.
Lachine, Qué.

EXPO GRAPHICS
Hull, Qué.

GERON
ASSOCIATES
Markham, Ont.

GILTSPUR TORONTO
Rexdale, Ont.

HOLMAN DESIGN
LTD.
Don Mills, Ont.

IDEACON DISPLAY
PRODUCTS INC.
Calgary, Alta.

IMAGE 1ST DISPLAY
SERVICE INC.
Regina, Sask.

J & O EXHIBITS LTD.
Toronto, Ont.

KADOKE DISPLAY
LTD.
Mississauga, Ont.

LEVY SHOW
SERVICES LTD.
Richmond, B.C.

MEGATEK INC.
Ancienne-Lorette,
Qué.

NEAT
WOODWORKING
& DISPLAY LTD.
Downsview, Ont.

PIERRE GUIBERT
GRAPHIK INC.
Hull, Qué.

P.W. EXHIBIT GROUP
Burnaby, B.C.

PIDDI DESIGN LTD.
Toronto, Ont.

QUALITY EXHIBITS
INC.
Mississauga, Ont.

SMYTH FISHER LTD.
Mississauga, Ont.

STEVENS SIGNS &
DISPLAYS LTD.
London, Ont.

THOMPSON
DESIGN AND
DISPLAY SERVICES
INC.
Brantford, Ont.

JACQUES VAAST
ENR.
Montréal, Qué.

O.S.P.I. OCTANORM® SERVICE PARTNERS INTERNATIONAL

OCTANORM® SERVICE PARTNERS INTERNATIONAL guarantee your success at exhibitions abroad with 250 OSPI in 35 countries. Your company can plan an exhibition booth together with an OCTANORM® SERVICE PARTNER INTERNATIONAL anywhere in the world.

ALL SEASONS
DISPLAY INC.
Langley, B.C.

C.E.S. EXHIBITS INC.
Toronto, Ont.

CONVENTIONS
UNLIMITED
Burnaby, B.C.

DERRICK EXHIBIT &
TRADE SHOW
SERVICES LTD.
Edmonton, Alta.

EXHIBITS
INTERNATIONAL
Etobicoke, Ont.

EXPO 4 INC.
Lachine, Qué.

KADOKE DISPLAY
LTD.
Mississauga, Ont.

PIERRE GUIBERT
GRAPHIK INC.
Hull, Qué.

MEGATEK INC.
Ancienne-Lorette,
Qué.

CANADIAN OCTANORM® SERVICE PARTNERS

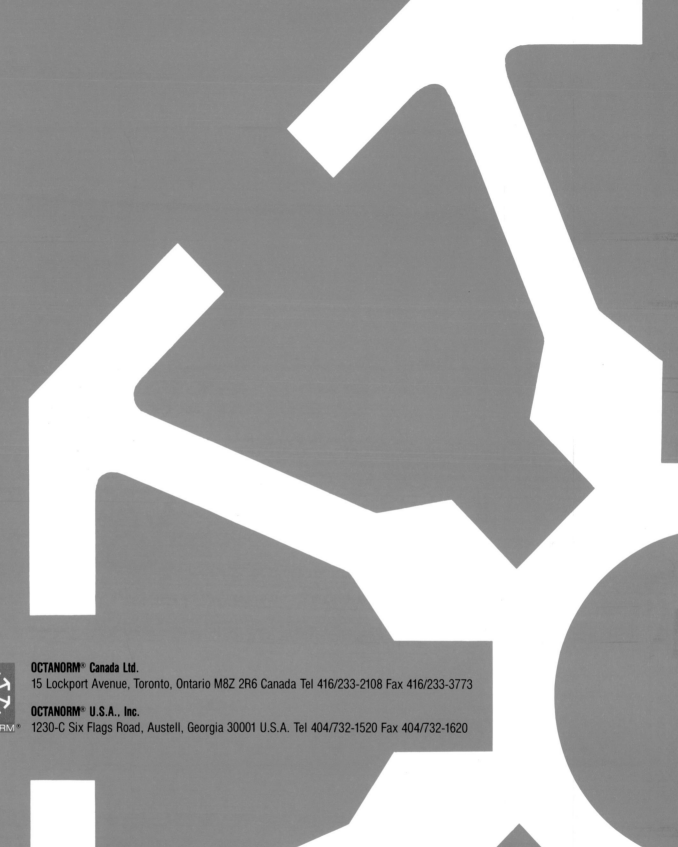

OCTANORM® Canada Ltd.
15 Lockport Avenue, Toronto, Ontario M8Z 2R6 Canada Tel 416/233-2108 Fax 416/233-3773

OCTANORM® U.S.A., Inc.
1230-C Six Flags Road, Austell, Georgia 30001 U.S.A. Tel 404/732-1520 Fax 404/732-1620

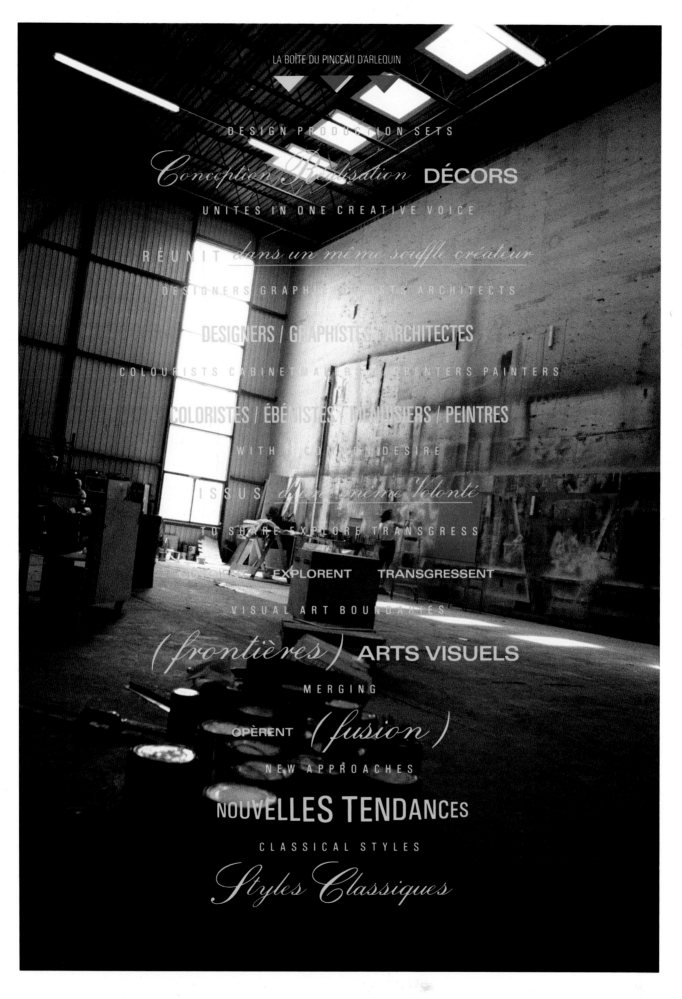

LA BOÎTE DU PINCEAU D'ARLEQUIN

DESIGN PRODUCTION SETS

Conception Réalisation DÉCORS

UNITES IN ONE CREATIVE VOICE

RÉUNIT *dans un même souffle créateur*

DESIGNERS GRAPHIC ARTISTS ARCHITECTS

DESIGNERS / GRAPHISTES / ARCHITECTES

COLOURISTS CABINETMAKERS CARPENTERS PAINTERS

COLORISTES / ÉBÉNISTES / MENUISIERS / PEINTRES

WITH A COMMON DESIRE

ISSUS *d'une même Volonté*

TO SHARE EXPLORE TRANSGRESS

PARTAGENT EXPLORENT TRANSGRESSENT

VISUAL ART BOUNDARIES

(frontières) ARTS VISUELS

MERGING

OPÈRENT *(fusion)*

NEW APPROACHES

NOUVELLES TENDANCES

CLASSICAL STYLES

Styles Classiques

 LA BOÎTE
DU PINCEAU D'ARLEQUIN

1919, RUE WILLIAM
MONTRÉAL (QUÉBEC) H3J 1R7

TÉLÉPHONE: (514) 939-1919
TÉLÉCOPIEUR: (514) 939-1991

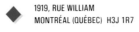

Conception
DESIGN

LA BOÎTE DU PINCEAU D'ARLEQUIN

Fabrication

PRODUCTION

LA BOÎTE DU PINCEAU D'ARLEQUIN

Peinture

PAINTING

LA BOÎTE DU PINCEAU D'ARLEQUIN

JEFFREY COWLING & ASSOCIATES

CORPORATE & EXHIBIT DESIGN

Noma Corporation

Commercial Telecom Group Inc.

From the most elaborate custom exhibits to small trade show booths, we offer innovative, cost effective, timely solutions to your display and exhibit needs.

Our comprehensive services cover all aspects of concept and design, artwork and graphics, construction and installation, shipping and storage.

So breathe a sigh of relief, and relax, we'll even complete those nasty forms in your exhibitors package, no sweat!

Satisfied clients include:
City of Toronto – Festival of Fashion
Noma Corporation
Commercial Telecom Group Inc.
Brewers of Canada
Para Paint
McConnell & Associates
Ministry of Skills Development

Jeffrey Cowling & Associates
61 Huntley Street
Toronto Ontario
M4Y 2L2

(416) 962-8188

City of Toronto – Festival of Fashion

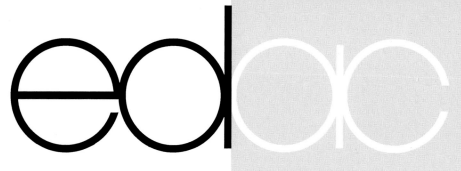

the exhibit

2200 lakeshore blvd. west, suite 108
toronto, ontario m8v 1a4
telephone: (416) 503-0842
fax#: (416) 259-7272

EDAC 1990 Regular Members

Mr. Neil Fardy
CHAIR-MAN MILLS LTD.
300 Consumers Road
Toronto, Ontario M2H 1P8
(416)492-0400 Fax (416)492-0669

Mr. Campbell Whyte
CONVEX SYSTEMS
38 Riviera Drive
Markham, Ontario L3R 5M1
(416)479-1493 Fax (416)479-1785

Mr. Heinze Meuller
CREATIVE SIDPLAY (CDA)
1430 Birchmount Road
Scarborough, Ontario M1P 1N1
(416)752-2301 Fax (416)752-9653

Mr. Roland Michie
DESIGN CRAFT LTD.
20 Butterick Road
Toronto, Ontario M8W 3Z8
(416)252-3361 Fax (416)252-2365

Mr. Vic Moore
DESIGNAGE INDUSTRIES LTD.
3600 Danforth Ave., Bldg. 1, Unit 101
Scarborough, Ontario M1N 4C5
(416)690-4006 Fax (416)690-9409

Mr. Ed Staines
EAS EXHIBITION SERVICES
41 Leeswood Crescent
Toronto, Ontario M1S 2P4
(416)292-2784 Fax (416)292-1651

Mr. Sam Kohn
EXHIBITS INTERNATIONAL
431 Horner Avenue
Toronto, Ontario M8W 4W3
(416)252-2818 Fax (416)252-3708

Mr. Sol Tolkin
EXPOSERVICE STANDARD INC.
4480 Cote de Liesse
Montreal, Quebec H4N 2R3
(514)395-2450 Fax (514)395-8999

Mr. Ross Perkins
EXPOSYSTEMS CANADA
2161 Midland Avenue
Scarborough, Ontario M1P 4T3
(416)291-2931 Fax (416)291-0383

Mr. Alan Fattori
GERON ASSOCIATES
231 Bentley Street
Markham, Ontario L3R 3L1
(416)470-0205 Fax (416)470-1789

Mr. Kent Allen
GILTSPUR/TORONTO
120 Carrier Drive
Rexdale, Ontario M9W 5R1
(416)674-0845 Fax (416)674-1228

Mr. Ivan Goring
GORING ASSOCIATES
77 Mowat Street #210
Toronto, Ontario M6K 3E3
(416)536-3509 Fax (416)536-5357

Mr. Pierre Guibert
GUIBERT GRAPHIK INC.
171 Jean-Proulx
Hull, Quebec J8Z 1W5
(819)771-9180 Fax (819)771-4017

Mr. Al Yolles
HOLMAN DESIGN LTD.
160 Lesmill Road
Don Mills, Ontario M3B 2T7
(416)441-1877 Fax (416)441-3556

Mr. Brian Ormerod
HORIZON EXHIBITS INC.
5438 - 176 Street #104
Surrey, British Columbia V3S 4C3
(604)576-2841 Fax (604)574-4084

Mr. Ron Gooch
J & O EXHIBITS LTD.
1450 The Queensway
Toronto, Ontario M8Z 1S4
(416)252-9575 Fax (416)231-3053

and display association of canada

Mr. Peter McAllister
McALLISTER & COMPANY
16 Ramblewood Drive
West Hill, Ontario M1C 3E1
(416)284-8230 Fax (416)284-0189

Mr. John Zubic
ONTARIO PROMOTIONAL SERVICES
45A Wilmot Street #5
Richmond Hill, Ontario L4B 1K1
(416)886-3244 Fax (416)886-6679

Mr. Henry Mazur
PANEX SHOW SERVICES
66 Akron Road
Toronto, Ontario M8W 1T2
(416)252-7806 Fax (416)252-6067

Mr. Fred Piddington
PIDDI DESIGN ASSOCIATES LTD.
1 Beaverdale Road
Toronto, Ontario M8Y 1H5
(416)259-3768 Fax (416)259-1192

Mr. Robert Jenner
QUALITY EXHIBITS INC.
6355 Danville Rd., Unit 14
Mississauga, Ontario L5T 2L4
(416)564-3472 Fax (416)564-3473

Mr. Frank Loves
QUALITY EXHIBITS INC.
6355 Danville Rd., Unit 14
Mississauga, Ontario L5T 2L4
(416)564-3472 Fax (416)564-3473

Mr. Robert Wands
TAYLOR MANUFACTURING INDUSTRIES
55 Vansco Road
Toronto, Ontario M8Z 5Z8
(416)251-3155 Fax (416)251-9908

Mr. Robert George
WESTERN DISPLAY SERVICE LTD.
511 76th Avenue S.E.
Calgary, Alberta T2E 1W5
(403)243-2477 Fax (403)287-0504

Mr. Glenn Worden
WORDEN-WATSON LTD.
12 Progress Avenue
Scarborough, Ontario M1P 2Y4
(416)291-3432 Fax (416)299-4117

Mr. Red Hobson
AINSWORTH ELECTRIC CO. LTD.
131 Bermondsey Road
Toronto, Ontario M4A 1X4
(416)751-4420 Fax (416)751-9402

Mr. Joe Munch
AMHERST GREENHOUSES INC.
General Delivery
Claremont, Ontario L0H 1E0
(416)427-3240 Fax (416)427-3241

Mr. Robert Williams
BLACK & McDONALD
101 Parliament Street
Toronto, Ontario M5A 2Y7
(416)366-2541 Fax (416)361-3170

Mr. Kevin Gallagher
COLOUR PRINTS
119 Vanderhoof Avenue
Toronto, Ontario M4G 4B4
(416)421-4136 Fax (416)721-4716

Mr. Hal Cryderman
CP EXPRESS & TRANSPORT
30 Newbridge Road
Toronto, Ontario M8Z 2L7
(416)252-4481 Fax (416)253-3573

Mr. David Hill
D.A. HILL PHOTOGRAPHY
62 Fraser Avenue
Toronto, Ontario M6K 1Y6
(416)534-2060

Mr. Richard Krangle
DOMINION FURNITURE RENTAL
240 Logan Avenue
Toronto, Ontario M4M 2N3
(416)469-5175 Fax (416)469-5197

Mr. Garry Moore
HENDRIE TRANSPORT INC.
27 Automatic Road
Brampton, Ontario L6S 4K6
(416)458-5555 Fax (416)458-9899

Mr. Paul Urben
MENDELSSOHN COMMERCIAL LTD.
8 Colborne Street 6th Floor
Toronto, Ontario M5E 1K4
(416)863-9339 Fax (416)868-1947

Mr. David Sharp
OCTANORM NORTH AMERICA LTD.
15 Lockport Avenue
Etobicoke, Ontario M8Z 2R6
(416)233-2108 Fax (416)233-3773

Mr. Vito Froio
SCARBORO COLOUR LAB
190 Milner Avenue
Scarborough, Ontario M1S 5B6
(416)293-9943 Fax (416)293-1064

Mr. Ralph Strachan
SOUTHAM AUDIO VISUAL
189 Dufferin Street
Toronto, Ontario M6K 1Y9
(416)533-6511 Fax (416)534-8469

Mr. Harold Thiel
TEL AV AUDIO VISUAL SERVICES
124 The East Mall
Etobicoke, Ontario M8Z 5V5
(416)234-5444 Fax (416)234-1974

Mr. George Vago
VAGO LIGHTING INDUSTRIES INC.
57 Rutherford Avenue
Toronto, Ontario M6M 2C5
(416)243-2356 Fax (416)243-2356

Choose a pro! For expert assistance in planning your exhibit requirements call on any member listed above. These are the professionals.

PHOTOGRAPHY

"The heart and the mind are the true lens of the camera."

Yousuf Karsh

LIGHT IMPRESSIONS

PHOTOGRAPHY IN CORPORATE COMMUNICATIONS

> The power of a good photograph is often underestimated in the corporate marketplace. An effective photograph can bring excitement to a static product, introduce drama to an ordinary situation and instill thoughts and emotions in the viewer. Photography presents

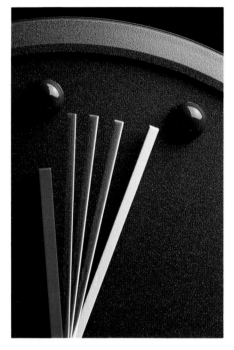

**Tom Malone for
Xerox Canada**
♦ ♦ ♦

the opportunity to demonstrate a product, activity or service under completely controlled conditions.

**Tom Malone for
Wardair**
♦ ♦ ♦

The mundane becomes dynamic; the inanimate comes alive; the commonplace becomes perfect.

To some corporate buyers, photography is viewed as an expense. But as part of the overall corporate strategy, the photographs that illustrate a brochure, an annual report or any other visual corporate communications medium are carriers of the corporate message. A photograph can be a direct reflection of a company's professionalism, vision or philosophy. Almost regardless of its content, a photographic style can evoke a sense of tradition, innovation, adventure or trust. When used effectively, photography is a versatile tool of communication and a powerful component of the corporate strategy.

Why then do some corporate communications buyers tend to undervalue this resource, allocating little time and limited budgets for photography? There is still some confusion concerning the power of good

photography, the cost of producing it and the time required to set up and execute an effective shot.

Tom Malone is a Toronto photographer who works for both advertising and corporate clients. "Advertising people generally seem to be more realistic about budgets," he says. "Some corporations don't seem to realize what it takes to create good quality work." Malone has seen some major corporations with blue chip names claim they don't have the budget available to finance the most effective photography. "They aren't really making the financial commitment that it would take to create high-calibre work."

It certainly isn't a matter of these major corporations being short of money. They simply don't understand the amount of effort and expertise it takes to produce an excellent photograph.

But Malone continues to apply

Yuri Dojc for Learning Disabilities Association of Ontario
♦ ♦ ♦

his skills to corporate assignments, partly because the restrictions inherent in this kind of work make it particularly challenging. With severe time and budget limitations, "you really have to meet the challenge by making the shot look exciting without having ideal conditions."

Also, Malone has learned that corporate work often puts him directly in touch with the client, a situation nearly unheard of in advertising. "You almost have to become a mini-agency when you're dealing with the corporation because there's no buffer between you and the client. The photographer has to be prepared to explain pre- and post-production processes to the client, who is often not a professional buyer."

Since corporate photography is a strategic communication tool, it is important that the photographer be selected very carefully. Malone suggests that, when buying photography services directly, you first find out if the photographer has experience in the type of work being assigned. If not, look at the portfolio and decide if you like the work and feel that the photographs are appropriate to their respective objectives. Also talk to the photographer to determine if you will be able to work with that individual.

"You want the style of the photographer to match your job," photographer Pat LaCroix advises. "Don't look for the exact product in the portfolio; look for the type of lighting, the mood and the photographer's approach."

LaCroix has observed some fundamental differences between corporate work and advertising assignments. He finds that the corporate projects are less rigid and rely more on the photographer's own ability to come up with a solution. If the problem is to bring an otherwise mundane object or situation to life, effective lighting can introduce drama and excitement. Also, adding a human element is an effective way of bringing things into perspective.

As a photographer, LaCroix prefers to become involved in the whole communication process. "I always like to find out the objective of the project, the target group, how the clients view their own product. This information gives me an insight into what we're trying to accomplish. The important thing is to communicate clearly, share information and ask the photographer for his or her solution."

Toronto photographer Yuri Dojc is well known for his witty, creative approach to photography. He suggests "going with the photographer whose work has the style and feeling that may add to your project and uniquely reflect your corporate personality." Dojc is always searching for and finding unusual visual solutions, but he believes photography is a serious business, not art. "If you want to make art, do it on your own leisure time. Good corporate photography brings results to the client, not recognition to the photographer from art directors' awards."

He enjoys bringing life to an ordinary situation or product. "To me every assignment creates a new, interesting challenge. There's no such thing as a boring corporate project. It's the responsibility of the photographer to translate the client's corporate objectives into strong visual language for the target audience or end user."

"You have to get your hands dirty," says Frank Grant, a successful corporate photographer, on the importance of communicating with all levels of the client corporation. He notes that everyone "from the top people down to engineers and supervisors is very important to the overall success of the project."

On a recent project for Denison Mines, Grant suggested to the corporate manager shooting all the mining equipment together in one photograph. Executing the shot was an involved process that required temporarily shutting down part of the mining operation. The shot took 28 hours to light and just five minutes to shoot. "This took trust and courage from the client, but in the next few months they received more than 2,000 requests from the industry all over the world for copies of this photograph."

According to Toronto photographer Steve Behal, clients should "look further into the portfolio and see exactly what it is that they like in the photographs, and ask themselves if that's the feeling they want to have in their finished product."

Behal is sensitive to the differences between being hired by a design firm and working directly for the corporation. "The client is under pressure. It's their

Bernard Bohn for
Provigo
annual report
♦ ♦ ♦

Bernard Bohn for
C.D.C. Life Sciences
annual report
♦ ♦ ♦

baby, and their money."

But designers are under a different kind of pressure. "They have a sense of detachment, where their job is to objectively see what the client's needs are and solve problems."

Designers tend to approach the problem-solving process through "creative exploration," something corporate executives, by the nature of their professions, are not expected to have experience with. Yet Behal is quick to point out the value of the client's direct involvement in any project, noting that, whether he is hired by a design firm or a corporation, the flow of information between photographer and client is crucial to the project.

"My job, before I even pick up the camera, is to stimulate the client with ideas, educate the client," he says. "And the client has to educate me. It's their responsibility to tell the photographer what their corporation is all about. I need to know where the corporation is going. Reading the existing literature on the company is important, but this only shows the past. Their vision for the future is still unclear from this information. They must educate me on who they want to become tomorrow.

"My goal as a photographer is to capture the imagination of the reader, inspire the reader and get

the juices flowing."

Michael Kohn is a photographer who agrees that corporate work offers more freedom for the photographer, but warns, "Too much freedom can lead to anarchy." The best way to avoid anarchy is for the client to communicate the objectives of the project to the photographer.

"If the client wants Irving Penn, that's not possible. No one wants to be known for imitations of some else's style. Astute clients can see what the photographer is good at and let him do his own style."

According to Kohn, the best way for the client to communicate the company's needs for the project at hand is to give the photographer a full presentation of visual references: what has been done in the past — good or bad — samples of the competition's work, or any other photography samples the client feels are effective.

Kohn sums up his advice to corporate clients this way: "Try to be visually literate; if you can't describe things accurately, communicate through samples. Tell the photographer what you expect, but allow some leeway and trust the photographer to solve your problem."

Very often, however, the corporate photographer is hired by the client's design firm. But it is still helpful for the client to

understand the photographic process and the value the photographer brings to the overall project.

Karen Perlmutter is a Toronto photographer who specializes in annual reports, corporate brochures and editorial work for business publications. Perlmutter believes that, since the client makes the final decision, a more educated client would be better qualified to make an effective selection.

After the designer has short-listed two or three photographers and presented samples with price quotes, the client's decision is "often based on the quote itself," according to Perlmutter. But shopping by price is not a good way to select anything as important as corporate photography.

John Harquail is a corporate location photographer who generally deals directly with the client. "They usually give me more freedom. I do my best work when I don't have to work to rigid layouts and have the option to find the best visual solution to fit the client's needs."

Harquail also warns of the pitfalls of shopping for photographers by price alone. "It's a false economy to expect someone to do a $5,000 project for $1,000. Buyers of photography should shop carefully and compare quotes. A photographer

Steve Behal for
Government of
Ontario insert in
Small Business
magazine
♦ ♦ ♦

Michael Kohn for
The Corporate Book
by The Saturday
Night Group
♦ ♦ ♦

submitting a much lower quote most probably lacks experience, the proper equipment or both."

Paul Orenstein, also of Toronto, shoots photographs for a number of corporate clients. "The enlightened client is still a rarity," he contends, citing the process of decision-making by committee as a still-prevalent problem among the corporations that hire photographers.

This can lead to what Orenstein calls the "overloaded" image. Some of today's budget-conscious corporate buyers try to get too much out of a single shot as a way of fighting the high cost of photography. "Some people try to make one photo do too much. They crowd so many things into one shot that the message is cluttered and nothing at all is being clearly communicated."

If the project has a good idea behind it to begin with, Orenstein continues, it is off to a good start. While they are still few, the corporate buyers who do understand the power of clarity and simplicity get the best results. "If the client already has a strong concept, they are bringing in the photographer's taste and good judgement. The most effective corporate photographs come as a result of teamwork and support."

Orenstein believes in having a good rapport with his clients, and holds that the best photographs communicate through strong, simple images. "You have to make every shot count, make every shot great."

Julie Kovacs, general manager of The Image Bank Canada — part of a worldwide stock photography and illustration agency — has insight into the photographer's perspective. "Professional photographers have experience, knowledge and skill. Many of them deserve to be making more money. But there are clients who feel they could just as easily pick up a camera and take a picture as the photographer because they know how to push the button."

Jean-Pierre Lacroix, president of Boulevard Communications, also regards photography as a tool in the same way as the design firm is a tool for the client. Part of the designer's responsibility is to help the client choose the right photographer for the job and work with that person to create the images that will ultimately achieve the communication objectives.

"We give the photographer linears and layouts of how we want it shot and we art direct the shot," says Lacroix. "There's a lot of interpretation between the client presentation of the idea and its actual execution." The only person who can understand that vision, he explains, is its creator. It's crucial that the designer and photographer work closely together to produce the preconceived image that has been communicated to the client.

This might sound as if the photographer is merely a technical extension of the designer. But Lacroix insists that, even with strict instructions and specific layouts, "a photographer brings a different dimension, a creative aspect, and can add a whole new attitude to the concept."

Leslie Sam Smart, head of Leslie Smart and Associates, a Toronto graphic design firm, has found a way to strictly direct a shot without impeding the photographer's style. "I do this all the time," he confides. "I type specific instructions and give the photographer the layout, telling him, 'Do what's on there and don't waver. After you've done that, take some shots the way you would handle it.' Almost invariably we'll use some of the shots they shoot their own way."

There is a creative value that every photographer brings to a project, and many photographers feel they are often too tightly restricted to fully contribute to a project.

"The business world is very suspicious of conceptual photographs, and therefore very often settles for photos that show people and give visual information," says Mario Doucet, agent for Montreal photographer Jean Blais. "We try to propose

Paul Orenstein
photograph of Dr.
Walter Hannah for
Toronto Life
magazine
♦ ♦ ♦

Honeywell **Amplitrol** made strong gains in revenue and profit over the previous year, and return on investment was over plan.

The Honeywell Protection Services Division, as Amplitrol will be known in 1990 for marketing purposes, capitalized on its long standing customer relationships to access new bank security areas. As a result, the division achieved a 30 per cent growth in revenues from financial institution business.

A major security contract was awarded the division by the Department of External Affairs, Ottawa, for its Chancery Alarms Response System (CARS). The first 12 systems were delivered at year-end. This was a team effort with our Aerospace and Defence Group.

A new joint venture selling agreement was reached with Sears Canada. Honeywell Protection Services' residential security systems will be sold in various Canadian locations under the "Sears/Honeywell Home Security System" label.

In research and development, the division completed development of three new bank security products, to better meet new customer needs. The division also advanced its monitoring station automation significantly. It can now cost-effectively provide much more security information to customers on a fast turnaround basis.

Industrial **Automation and Control Group** performed ahead of last year in revenue and profit in each of its divisions.

The Industrial Automation Systems Division, Canada's leading supplier of process control systems to the country's petrochemical refining, pulp and paper and steel-making industries, achieved significant gains in revenues and profits.

Major projects in petroleum refining and pulp and paper, which were successfully completed during the year, contributed to the strong performance.

The division won major new systems contracts from Fletcher Challenge's mill in Elk Falls, British Columbia, and from MacMillan Bloedel's Powell River mill to expand its share of the British Columbia pulp and paper market.

The division also strengthened its leadership position in petroleum refining by winning major orders from Shell Canada for gasoline blending systems at its Montreal, Quebec, and Scotford, Alberta, refineries. The systems will use the Oil Movement and Storage software application

Eric Farquharson (foreground) of Honeywell, and Csaba Becsy, of Dofasco, review details associated with Honeywell's TDC 3000 computerized process control system. The system controls the continuous casting process at this state-of-the-art steelmaking facility where, at extremely high temperatures, steel is formed into slabs of uniform quality and consistency.

Significant productivity gains and quality control in Canada's steel-making industries are made possible with Honeywell's computerized process control systems. Here, a TDC 3000 ensures quality and consistency in production – from raw steel to hot rolled coils.

Paul Orenstein for
the Honeywell
Limited Annual
Review 1989
♦ ♦ ♦

8

something other than the inevitable photo of the president behind his desk, to create atmosphere, and that isn't always easy."

Doucet doesn't think the potential impact of a good photograph is fully appreciated in the corporate market. He notes that enormous amounts of money are invested in annual reports, yet the photographer is rarely given more than 15 minutes to take the picture.

Not all photographers are satisfied to work as executors of a preconceived image. Julie Kovacs feels that they are forced into a position where they do become technicians. "A lot of art directors and clients will hire a photographer to produce what they've wrought on a piece of paper and the photographer's latitude is being suppressed," she observes. In these situations, the client could be missing out on the added value a creative photographer could be contributing. Kovacs adds that this results in "giving the client what he wants rather than making full use of the photographer's skill and style."

Karen Perlmutter agrees. In order to bring her creativity as well as her technical ability into a project, she prefers to work very closely with the designer at the conceptual stages, offering concepts of her own that might be presented to the client. "These are based on my own personal style and will work very well with what's at hand. The ideal situation is when you're given almost complete freedom. It shows a lot of respect for me as a photographer when somebody will trust me that closely."

Peter Baumgartner, a Montreal photographer, has found that direct contact with the corporate client makes for a relatively unrestrained creative process. "The photographer is commissioned to create the look most appropriate to the history and aims of his customer. The challenge is to suggest a different visual interpretation of otherwise very ordinary activities and commonplace things by showing them in a new light."

Another Montreal-based photographer, Bernard Bohn, believes in dynamic collaboration with the client. "The first step is to listen; to hear the client's message and read all the texts with care. Then the exciting process of creation begins as we communicate that message visually in innovative ways. The result should be so striking and at the same time so appropriate that the reader automatically turns to the text in order to find out more."

The question of how far to let the photographer go in creative style is a difficult one, and the debate will continue for years to come. On the one hand, someone who has developed a strong reputation has usually done so by creating a distinctive style. If the photographer has been selected on that basis, it could be a waste of talent to place excessive restrictions on the application of the style. An experienced photographer brings to every assignment more than the ability to operate a camera and apply visual creativity; there is also the skill to create images that communicate the message to be conveyed by the piece.

The art director/designer and client bring the photographer into the process to execute the concept they have developed and approved, making the photographer a part of the creative team, who can contribute valuable insights and perspectives that should be considered. Photography is a creative profession, but corporate photographers, like designers, are also visual communicators, entrusted with the crucial role of creating an important component of a communication program.

The best way to fully utilize a tool is to know it well. Photography, as a tool of communication, is most successfully used when its potential is appreciated, understood and respected. ◁

**Frank Grant for
Denison Mines**
◆ ◆ ◆

**Jean-Pierre Lacroix
for Curragh
Resources annual
report**
◆ ◆ ◆

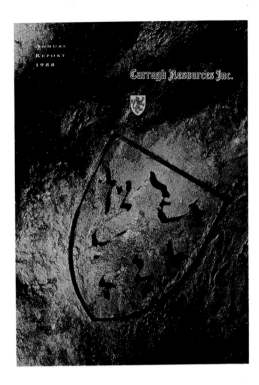

**Pat LaCroix for
Sound Ideas**
◆ ◆ ◆

PHOTOGRAPHY INDEX

			Aerial	Annual Reports	Architectural	AV Presentation	Brochures/Catalogues/Print	Editorial	Executive Portraits	Fashion	Food	Industrial/Commercial	Legal	People	Photo-Journalism	Product	Publicity	Sports	Trade Shows
			1	2	3	4	5	6	7	8	9	10	11	12	13	14	15	16	17

Photo Laboratories/Laboratoires Photo

Scarborough Colour Laboratories	(416)293-9943	P-15

Stock Photography/Phototheque

Canada Wide Feature/Div. of Toronto Sun	(416)947-2067	P-16
Image Bank, The	(416)322-8840	P-17-44

Photography/Photographie

Name	Phone	Page	1	2	3	4	5	6	7	8	9	10	11	12	13	14	15	16	17
Bart, Casimir Photographics	(416)469-0056	P-48		◆	◆		◆	◆	◆	◆	◆					◆			
Benard, Joel	(416)340-6366	P-47		◆					◆			◆		◆		◆			
Bohn, Bernard Photographe	(514)287-1589	P-72,73		◆	◆		◆	◆	◆	◆		◆		◆		◆	◆		
Brooks, Roger and Associates	(604)872-2717	P-68,69		◆	◆			◆				◆							
Brown, Richard Photography	(416)862-0861	P-46		◆			◆	◆	◆					◆	◆	◆			
Brunelle, François	(514)288-6612	P-74,75		◆					◆					◆		◆	◆		
Carruthers, Allan	(514)288-4333	P-90		◆	◆	◆	◆					◆		◆		◆	◆		
Courtney, Michael Photography	(416)564-3694	P-49		◆	◆		◆	◆				◆	◆	◆	◆	◆			
Dubé, Yvan	(514)646-3946	P-71		◆	◆		◆	◆				◆		◆			◆		◆
Edgar, Robin	(514)762-0785	P-76	◆	◆	◆		◆	◆		◆		◆		◆	◆		◆	◆	
Gagnon, Sylvain Photographe	(514)768-9792	P-77	◆	◆	◆	◆		◆	◆									◆	
Gray, David Photography	(604)877-1550	P-70		◆			◆	◆	◆	◆		◆		◆	◆	◆			
Harquail, John Photography Inc	(416)535-1620	P-52,53	◆	◆	◆	◆	◆		◆			◆			◆		◆		
Holman, Greg Photography	(416)362-8285	P-54		◆	◆	◆	◆	◆						◆	◆	◆		◆	
Johnson, Bryon Photography	(416)449-9102	P-55						◆				◆		◆	◆		◆		
Labelle, Paul Photographe Inc	(514)845-5523	P-78,79		◆	◆		◆	◆				◆		◆	◆				

	1	2	3	4	5	6	7	8	9	10	11	12	13	14	15	16	17
	Aérienne	Rapports Annuels	Architecturale	Présentation Audio-Visuelle	Brochures/Catalogues/Imprimé	Éditoriale	Portraits Corporatifs	Mode	Nourriture	Industrielle/Commerciale	Légale	Personnage	Photo Journalisme	Produit	Publicité	Sports	Salons et Exhibits

INDEX DES PHOTOGRAPHES

Nobody knows you
when you're down and out.

CANADA
nabs
A Friend in Deed

Patricia Crosbie
Executive Director

National Advertising Benevolent Society of Canada
2 Bloor Street West, Suite 1200, Toronto, Ontario M4W 3R3   (416) 962-0446

One of the greatest misconceptions about advertising is that people in the business never need help.

The fact is, advertising people often do need help. Because they work in one of the most stressful and insecure industries in the world.

A business where mergers, politics, failed brands, client moves, re-organizations and personal problems like burn-out and breakdowns are often the rule rather than the exception.

Nabs is for everybody in advertising or advertising related businesses.

The National Advertising Benevolent Society (NABS) is the non-profit organization that helps people in the industry who encounter illness, injury, unemployment, addictions, financial difficulties or other misfortunes.

Anyone from a filing clerk to a creative person to a marketing executive who earns all or most of their income from advertising or an advertising related business is eligible for benefits from NABS. And families are included because trouble affects everyone.

For some, it might be as simple as a friendly face and a sympathetic ear. While for others, professional

counselling, retraining or financial assistance could be the answer.

Nabs wants to help advertising people get back on top.

Sometimes advertising people who are in trouble are embarrassed to ask for help.

And that really is a shame.

Because at NABS, each and every person's situation is treated with care and complete confidentiality. No matter how menial or insurmountable the problem might seem.

So if you work in advertising and need help or know someone who does, call NABS today. Before the situation gets out of hand.

Right now Nabs needs your help to help others.

NABS is not a huge company with lots of money.

They have a very small staff and are supported by cash donations and various fund raising events organized by NABS volunteers. And frankly, they need your help to keep up the good work.

So if you would like to make a donation or become a volunteer, please call NABS today.

CANADA
nabs
A Friend in Deed

(416) 962-0446

With thanks to: Tyler-Clarke for art and production, Tri-ad Graphics for film, Ann Holland and Cathy Bennett for creative.

Can't find the right picture? That's news to us!

We go to the ends of the earth for a good picture.

CANADA WIDE's photo library includes more than one million color and B & W images.

We provide a broad range of material only available from an upbeat newspaper like the Toronto Sun and satellite publications.

Our ever expanding stock also includes the Toronto Telegram archives dating back to the late 1800's — for when you need a blast from the past.

From a moon shot to a snap shot, images captured by our award winning photographers will enhance your publications and presentations.

For more information or for a research appointment, call Wanda Goodwin, *Photo Editor* (416) 947-3123 Fax: (416) 947-2450

Or write to Canada Wide Feature Service 333 King St. E., Toronto, Ontario M5A 3X5

A division of

Shuttle photo by: Sun photographer, Greig Reekie

THE **IMAGE** BANK®

IMAGE

A SAMPLER OF
CANADIAN IMAGES

The Image Bank is an international creative source for stock photography and illustration representing over 300 internationally acclaimed photographers and illustrators. This special catalogue edition highlights a sample of our Canadian material.

Our images are consistently chosen for many of the most creative and successful advertising, editorial, travel and corporate projects produced across Canada and throughout the world.

All material reproduced in this catalogue is fully released and available in transparency form. Images from this catalogue or from our file of 350,000 images in Toronto can be delivered to your office within 48 hours or less anywhere across Canada. Or, if you prefer, you are welcome to visit our image library and make a selection yourself.

A sample of images from our library is reproduced in our catalogues. For your complete set of Image Bank catalogues, just call us toll free across Canada at: 1-800-387-9837 or in Toronto (416)322-8840 Fax: (416)322-8855.

NORTH AMERICA

CANADA
The Image Bank Canada
40 Eglington Avenue East
Suite 307
Toronto, Ontario
Canada M4P 3A8
Tel. (416) 322-8840
   or 1-800-387-9837
   (toll-free in Canada)
Fax. (416) 322-8855

MEXICO
The Image Bank Mexico
Oso. No. 41
Col. del Valle
Deleg. B. Juarez
03100 Mexico, D.F.
Tel. (905) 524-4644/660-1528
Tlx. 1760718
Fax. (52) (5) 524-5125

UNITED STATES
Atlanta
The Image Bank South
3490 Piedmont Road, N.E.
Suite 1106
Atlanta, GA 30305
Tel. (404) 233-9920
Fax. (404) 231-9389

Boston
The Image Bank Boston
500 Boylston Street
Suite 260
Boston, MA 02116
Tel. (617) 267-8866
Fax. (617) 267-4682

California
The Image Bank West
4526 Wilshire Boulevard
Los Angeles, CA 90010
Tel. (213) 930-0797
Fax. (213) 930-1089

The Image Bank San Francisco
22 Battery Street
Suite 202
San Francisco, CA 94111
Tel. (415) 788-2208
Fax. (415) 392-6637

Chicago
The Image Bank Chicago
510 N. Dearborn Street
Suite 930
Chicago, IL 60610
Tel. (312) 329-1817
Fax. (312) 329-1029

Detroit
The Image Bank Detroit
3150 Livernois
Suite 150
Troy, MI 48083
Tel. (313) 524-1850
Fax. (313) 524-3243

Florida
The Image Bank Florida
5811 Pelican Bay Boulevard
Suite 302
Naples, FL 33963
Tel. (813) 566-3444
Fax. (813) 566-1346

Minneapolis
The Image Bank Minneapolis
822 Marquette Avenue
Minneapolis, MN 55402
Tel. (612) 332-8935
Fax. (612) 344-1717

New York
The Image Bank
111 Fifth Avenue
New York, NY 10003
Tel. (212) 529-6700
Tlx. 7607921 IMAGE
Fax. (212) 529-7024

Texas
The Image Bank Texas
Reverchon Plaza
3500 Maple Avenue
Suite 1150
Dallas, TX 75219
Tel. (214) 528-3888
Fax. (214) 528-3878

Texas (Continued)
The Image Bank Houston
10351 Stella Link Road
Houston, TX 77025
Tel. (713) 668-0066
Fax. (713) 664-4441

SOUTH AMERICA

ARGENTINA
The Image Bank Argentina
Alsina 943-3er Piso Of 3
1088 Buenos Aires
Argentina
Tel. (54) (1) 334-8121
Tlx. 17199 TIB AR
Fax. (54) (1) 334-4099

BRASIL
Porto Alegre
The Image Bank Brasil
Rua Coronel Bordini, 249
90420 Porto Alegre, RS
Brasil
Tel. (55) (512) 43-30-23
Tlx. 520304 FBPF BR

Rio de Janeiro
The Image Bank Brasil
Rua Visconde de Piraja, 433/5
22410 Rio de Janeiro, RJ
Brasil
Tel. (55) (21) 267-1643
Tlx. 2130577 TRAV BR
Fax. (55) (21) 267-1890

São Paulo
The Image Bank Brasil
Rua Augusta 2529/21
01413 São Paulo, SP
Brasil
Tel. (55) (11) 852-3466
Tlx. 1132439 TRAV BR
Fax. (55) (11) 853-9064

CHILE
The Image Bank Chile
Santa Beatriz 125
Providencia-Santiago
Chile
Tel. (56) (2) 251-2296
Tlx. 645129 CMTX CT
Fax. (56) (2) 429-49

COLOMBIA
The Image Bank Colombia
Carrera 14, Nr. 85-24
Bogota, Colombia
Tel. (57) (1) 257-9674
Tlx. 44970 CXBOICO
Fax. (57) (1) 211-4598*
* Attn: Maria Victoria
   de Mazuera

VENEZUELA
The Image Bank Venezuela
CCCT
Primera Etapa
Piso Nr. 2/Oficina 222
Caracas, Venezuela
Tel. (58) (2) 959-2210

AFRICA

SOUTH AFRICA
Capetown
The Image Bank South Africa
Alianz Building
52 St. George Street
Capetown
South Africa
Tel. (27) (21) 24-4830

Johannesburg
The Image Bank South Africa
P.O. Box 783227
Sandton 2146
South Africa
Tel. (27) (11) 883-7825/6
Fax. (27) (11) 884-1581
Office Address:
79-12th Street
Parkmore, Sandton 2196
South Africa

EUROPE

AUSTRIA
The Image Bank Austria
Brahmsplatz 2/2
A-1040 Vienna
Austria
Tel. (43) (222) 505-3724
Fax. (43) (222) 505-3726

BELGIUM
The Image Bank Benelux
60, Avenue de Mars
1200 Brussels
Belgium
Tel. (32) (2) 735-6762
Fax. (32) (2) 734-7171

DENMARK
The Image Bank Denmark
Nyhavn, 31C
DK-1051 Copenhagen
Denmark
Tel. (45) 33-15-15-24
Fax. (45) 33-15-72-15

ENGLAND
The Image Bank London
7 Langley Street
Covent Garden
London WC2H 9JA England
Tel. (44) (71) 240-9621
Tlx. 894839 TIB G
Fax. (44) (71) 831-1489

FINLAND
The Image Bank Finland
Keskuskatu 1
00100 Helsinki 10
Finland
Tel. (358) (0) 17-40-66
Tlx. 124910 ULLA SF
Fax. (358) (0) 65-60-92

FRANCE
The Image Bank France
126, Rue Reaumur
75002 Paris
France
Tel. (33) (1) 45-08-86-98
Tlx. 212687 TIB F
Fax. (33) (1) 40-13-02-54

GERMANY
Frankfurt
The Image Bank Frankfurt
Hanauer Landstr. 186-198
D-6000 Frankfurt/Main 1
West Germany
Tel. (49) (69) 430-171
Fax. (49) (69) 432-756

Hamburg
The Image Bank Hamburg
Danziger Strasse 35A
2000 Hamburg 1
West Germany
Tel. (49) (40) 280-12-28
Fax. (49) (40) 280-31-17

Munich
The Image Bank Munich
Prinzregentenstrasse 89
8000 Munich 80
West Germany
Tel. (49) (89) 418-6930
Tlx. 5214832 TIB D
Fax. (49) (89) 470-67-66

GREECE
The Image Bank Greece
103 Kefallinias Street
Athens 11251
Greece
Tel. (30) (1) 867-5386/6611
Tlx. 214925 HPSE GR
Fax. (30) (1) 865-5989

HOLLAND
The Image Bank Nederland
World Trade Center
Strawinskylaan 1129
1077 XX Amsterdam
Holland
Tel. (31) (20) 575-33-24

ITALY
Milan
The Image Bank Italia
Via Terraggio 17
20123 Milano
Italy
Tel. (39) (2) 86-93-964
Tlx. 315149 ACPRES 1
Fax. (39) (2) 879-109

Modena
The Image Bank Italia
Via della Tecnica, 2
41018 S. Cesario Sul Panaro
Modena, Italy
Tel. (39) (59) 920263/927998
Fax. (39) (59) 927993

Rome
The Image Bank Italia
Via dei Cappuccini, 6
00100 Rome
Italy
Tel. (39) (06) 4824904

NORWAY
The Image Bank Norway
Radhusgatan 9 D
0151 Oslo 1
Norway
Tel. (47) (2) 33-06-50
Fax. (47) (2) 33-25-81

PORTUGAL
The Image Bank Portugal
Rua Eca De Queiroz, 42
Aldeia De Juso
2750 Cascais, Portugal
Tel. (351) (1) 285-1505
Fax. (351) (1) 285-1620

SPAIN
Barcelona
The Image Bank Espana
Muntaner 244-5-1
08021 Barcelona
Spain
Tel. (34) (3) 209-3544
Fax. (34) (3) 209-3611

Madrid
The Image Bank Espana
Manuel Silvela, 7
28010 Madrid
Spain
Tel. (34) (1) 446-9061/9362
Fax. (34) (1) 593-4582

SWEDEN
The Image Bank Sweden
Kungsgatan 62
S-111 22 Stockholm
Sweden
Tel. (46) (8) 10-17-70
Fax. (46) (8) 11-04-25

SWITZERLAND
The Image Bank Switzerland
Dufourstrasse 56
P.O. Box 156
CH-8034 Zurich
Switzerland
Tel. (41) (1) 262-11-60
Tlx. 816300 WKR CH
Fax. (41) (1) 262-19-40

AUSTRALIA
Melbourne
The Image Bank Australia
256 Albert Road
South Melbourne 3205
Australia
Tel. (61) (3) 699-7833
Fax. (61) (3) 699-6777

Sydney
The Image Bank Australia
131 Blues Point Road
McMahons Point, Sydney 2060
NSW Australia
Tel. (61) (2) 954-4255
Fax. (61) (2) 922-6373

MIDDLE EAST

ISRAEL
The Image Bank Israel
Image Mar'ot Ltd.
2 Koifman Street
Tel-Aviv 68012
Israel
Tel. (972) (3) 662-588
Fax. (972) (3) 660-896

TURKEY
The Image Bank Turkey
Neyir/Yildiz Posta Cad.
Dedeman Ishani No. 48/2
Gayrettepa, Istanbul
Turkey
Tel. (90) (1) 174-6875/7/8
Fax. (90) (1) 174-6876

ASIA

HONG KONG
The Image Bank Hong Kong
Suite A, 2nd Floor
Miami Mansion
13-15 Cleveland Street
Causeway Bay
Hong Kong
Tel. (852) 576-2022
Fax. (852) 576-5990

JAPAN
Osaka
The Image Bank Japan
Kouyou Building, 5th Floor
5-62 Minamikyuhougi-Cho
Higashi-Ku, Osaka 541
Japan
Tel. (81) (6) 243-0300
Fax. (81) (6) 243-3200

Tokyo
The Image Bank Japan
Sekiguchi Building 2F
1-2-6 Shiba-daimon
Minato-ku, Tokyo 105
Japan
Tel. (81) (3) 435-8360
Tlx. 2523193 IMAGE J
Fax. (81) (3) 435-8370

KOREA
The Image Bank Korea
Room 401, Kum-Poong Bldg.
48-27, Jeo-Dong 2KA, Chung-ku
Seoul, Korea
Tel. (82) (2) 273-27-92
Tlx. 32644 IMAGE
Fax. (82) (2) 277-70-64

MALAYSIA
Image Bank Malaysia
55-2, Plaza Damansara
Medan Setia, 1
Damansara Heights
50490 Kuala Lumpur, Malaysia
Tel. (60) (3) 254-7118
Fax. (60) (3) 256-1812

SINGAPORE
The Image Bank Singapore
#02-10 Beach Centre
15 Beach Road
Singapore 0718
Tel. (65) (2) 338-3052
Fax. (65) (2) 338-0349

TAIWAN
Taipei
Harvard Management Services, Inc.
9th Floor
118 Nanking East Road, Sec. 5
Taipei, Taiwan
Republic of China
Tel. (886) (2) 765-7364/769-1752
Fax. (886) (2) 767-1661

Taichung
The Image Bank Taichung
12-3, 185 Minchuan Road
Taichung, Taiwan, R.O.C.
Tel. (886) (4) 227-4113
Fax. (886) (4) 222-0835

THE IMAGE BANK, INC.
CORPORATE HEADQUARTERS, 111 FIFTH AVENUE, NEW YORK, NY 10003

601188   ANDRÉ GALLANT

601189   ANDRÉ GALLANT

601740   LINDA MONTGOMERY

601190   ANDRÉ GALLANT

601191   ANDRÉ GALLANT

601192   GRANT V. FAINT

601193   ANDRÉ GALLANT

601194   JOHN STRADIOTTO

601195   MARGARET W. PETERSON

601196   ANDRÉ GALLANT

601197   ANDRÉ GALLANT

601198   STUART DEE

601199   ANDRÉ GALLANT

601741 LINDA MONTGOMERY

601200 STUART DEE

601201 STUART DEE

601202 PAT LACROIX

601203 ANDRÉ GALLANT

601204 STUART DEE

601205 STUART DEE

601206 GRANT V. FAINT

601207 ANDRÉ GALLANT

601208 STUART DEE

601742 LINDA MONTGOMERY

601209 STUART DEE

601210 BOB BROOKS

601211   BOB BROOKS

601743   PAUL MORIN

601212   GARY CRALLÉ

601744   ROCCO BAVIERA

601213   GRANT V. FAINT

601214   GRANT V. FAINT

601215   JÜRGEN VOGT

601216   GRANT V. FAINT

601217   D.S. HENDERSON

601218   BOB BROOKS

601219   JOHN STRADIOTTO

601220   GRANT V. FAINT

601745   JAN SOVAK

601221   GRANT V. FAINT

601222   STUART DEE

601746   JOHN ORESNICK

601223   STUART DEE

601224   JÜRGEN VOGT

601747   GARY MCLAUGHLIN

601225   GARY FABER

601226   GRANT V. FAINT

601227   GRANT V. FAINT

601748   TOM BJARNASON

601228   GRANT V. FAINT

601229   GRANT V. FAINT

601230   GRAFTON MARSHALL SMITH

601231   GRANT V. FAINT
CASTLE ROCK,
CANADIAN ROCKIES

601232   GARY CRALLÉ

601233   STEVE SATUSHEK
MORAINE LAKE,
BANFF NATIONAL PARK

601234   GRANT V. FAINT

601235   HARALD SUND
MT. GARIBALDI, BRITISH COLUMBIA

601236   JÜRGEN VOGT

601237   GUIDO ALBERTO ROSSI
NIAGARA FALLS

601238   D.S. HENDERSON

601239   DAVID JEFFREY
BAFFIN ISLAND

601749   TOM MCNEELY
BIRCH TREES

601240   D.S. HENDERSON

601241   D.S. HENDERSON

601750   PAUL MORIN

601242   GRANT V. FAINT
CAPE SPEAR, NEWFOUNDLAND

601243   STEVE SATUSHEK

601244   JÜRGEN VOGT
CAMPOBELLO ISLAND

601245   GRANT V. FAINT
NIAGARA FALLS

601246   ANDRÉ GALLANT
GASPE PENINSULA, QUEBEC

601247   D.S. HENDERSON
HOODOOS, BADLAND HILLS, ALBERTA

601248   GRANT V. FAINT

601249   GRANT V. FAINT

601250   GRANT V. FAINT
CANADIAN ROCKIES

601251   GARY CRALLÉ
NIAGARA FALLS

601751   CARL CHAPLIN
BEAR GLACIER, BRITISH COLUMBIA

601252   JÜRGEN VOGT
NIAGARA FALLS

601253   GRANT V. FAINT

601254   JOSEPH DEVENNEY

601255   GRANT V. FAINT
MORAINE LAKE,
BANFF NATIONAL PARK

601256   GARY CRALLÉ

601257   PAT LACROIX

601258   GRANT V. FAINT
MT. RUNDLE, CANADIAN ROCKIES

601259   GRANT V. FAINT

601260   GUIDO ALBERTO ROSSI
CORTEZ ISLAND, BRITISH COLUMBIA

601261   ANDRÉ GALLANT

601262   DAVID HISER

601263   GARY CRALLÉ

601264   GUIDO ALBERTO ROSSI
CORTEZ ISLAND, BRITISH COLUMBIA

601265   GARY V. FAINT

601266   DON LANDWEHRLE
BANFF NATIONAL PARK

601267 STUART DEE
FEMALE RACCOON

601752 ROCCO BAVIERA
DEER

601268 JOHN STRADIOTTO
SPARROW HAWK

601269 ANDRÉ GALLANT
GANNET

601270 ANDRÉ GALLANT
CHIPMUNK

601271 JAKE RAJS
WHALES

601272 ANDRÉ GALLANT
GANNETS

601273 JÜRGEN VOGT
MOUNTAIN GOATS, MT. HUBER

601274 GRAFTON MARSHALL SMITH
DEER

601275 D.S. HENDERSON
DEER

601753 ROCCO BAVIERA
WOLVES

601276 ANDRÉ GALLANT
PUFFINS

601277 LYNN M. STONE
MALLARD DUCKS & CANADIAN GEESE

601278   ANDRÉ GALLANT
NOVA SCOTIA

601279   ANDRÉ GALLANT
NOVA SCOTIA

601280   ANDRÉ GALLANT
BLUE ROCKS, NOVA SCOTIA

601281   JÜRGEN VOGT
REED LAKE, MANITOBA

601282   JOSEPH DEVENNEY

601283   ANDRÉ GALLANT
BLUE ROCKS, NOVA SCOTIA

601284   GRANT V. FAINT

601285   GRANT V. FAINT
UCLUELET, BRITISH COLUMBIA

601286   GRANT V. FAINT
PEGGY'S COVE, NOVA SCOTIA

601287   ANDRÉ GALLANT
BLUE ROCKS, NOVA SCOTIA

601288   ANDRÉ GALLANT
PEGGY'S COVE, NOVA SCOTIA

601289   GARY CRALLÉ
BLUE ROCKS, NOVA SCOTIA

601290   ANDRÉ GALLANT
NOVA SCOTIA

601291   GRANT V. FAINT
NOTRE DAME CATHEDRAL

601292   GUIDO ALBERTO ROSSI
FRENCH QUARTER, MONTREAL

601293   BRETT FROOMER
GASTOWN, VANCOUVER

601294   BRETT FROOMER
PARLIAMENT, VICTORIA

601295   PETER MILLER
GEODESIC DOME, MONTREAL

601296   MARC ROMANELLI
RUE ST. DENIS, MONTREAL

601297   WALTER BIBIKOW
ESSO TOWER, MONTREAL

601298   WALTER BIBIKOW
HOTEL DE VILLE, MONTREAL

601299   GRANT V. FAINT
VANCOUVER

601300   EDDIE HIRONAKA
HOTEL VANCOUVER

601301   GRANT V. FAINT
VANCOUVER

601302   GRANT V. FAINT
CANADA PLACE, VANCOUVER

601303   GUIDO ALBERTO ROSSI
VANCOUVER

601304 GRANT V. FAINT
QUEBEC CITY

601305 GRANT V. FAINT
MONTREAL

601306 GRANT V. FAINT
QUEBEC CITY

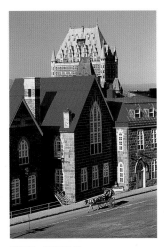

601307 JAKE RAJS
QUEBEC CITY

601308 MARC ROMANELLI
PARLIAMENT, QUEBEC CITY

601309 MARC ROMANELLI
QUEBEC

601310 MARC ROMANELLI
QUEBEC

601311 GRANT V. FAINT
NATIONAL GALLERY, OTTAWA

601312 GRANT V. FAINT
PARLIAMENT HILL, OTTAWA

601313 D.S. HENDERSON
RIDEAU CANAL, OTTAWA

601314 WALTER BIBIKOW
OTTAWA

601315 GUIDO ALBERTO ROSSI
PARLIAMENT, OTTAWA

601316 BRETT FROOMER
BANFF SPRINGS HOTEL, ALBERTA

© THE IMAGE BANK, INC. 1990

P-31

601317 BRETT FROOMER
SADDLE DOME, CALGARY

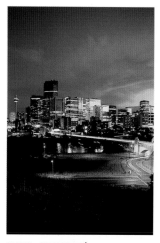

601318 GARY CRALLÉ
CALGARY

601319 GRANT V. FAINT
TORONTO

601320 ANTHONY BOCCACCIO
TORONTO

601321 GRAFTON MARSHALL SMITH
CALGARY

601322 GRANT V. FAINT
CALGARY

601323 GRANT V. FAINT
SKYDOME & CN TOWER, TORONTO

601324 GUIDO ALBERTO ROSSI
TORONTO

601325 ANDRÉ GALLANT
TORONTO

601326 GRANT V. FAINT
SKYDOME & CN TOWER, TORONTO

601327 ANDRÉ GALLANT
SKYDOME, TORONTO

601328 BRETT FROOMER
TRACT HOUSES, TORONTO

601329 ANDRÉ GALLANT
SKYDOME & CN TOWER, TORONTO

601330 JÜRGEN VOGT
CANADIAN MINT, WINNIPEG

601331 GARY CRALLÉ
CITY HALL, TORONTO

601332 GRANT V. FAINT
LEGISLATIVE BUILDING,
SASKATCHEWAN

601333 GARY CRALLÉ
VICTORIA HARBOR,
BRITISH COLUMBIA

601334 DC PRODUCTIONS
ST. JOHN'S, SIGNAL HILL, NEWFOUNDLAND

601335 ALVIS UPITIS
EDMONTON

601336 GUIDO ALBERTO ROSSI
QUEBEC FORTRESS

601337 GARY CRALLÉ
CONVENTION CENTER, MONTREAL

601338 GRANT V. FAINT
BAMFIELD, BRITISH COLUMBIA

601339 GARY CRALLÉ
ONTARIO

601340 GUIDO ALBERTO ROSSI
VANCOUVER

601341 MARC ROMANELLI
RUE NOTRE DAME, MONTREAL

601342 ALBERT NORMANDIN
VANCOUVER

601343   GARY CRALLÉ   601344   GRANT V. FAINT   601345   JÜRGEN VOGT   601346   GRANT V. FAINT

601347   JÜRGEN VOGT
GRAIN ELEVATOR, MANITOBA

601348   GRANT V. FAINT

601349   JÜRGEN VOGT
GRAIN SILOS, MANITOBA

601350   GRANT V. FAINT

601351   JÜRGEN VOGT

601352   GRANT V. FAINT
GRAIN ELEVATOR, CALGARY

601353   GRANT V. FAINT

601354   WILLIAM LOGAN
ALBERTA

601355   WEINBERG/CLARK

601356   GRANT V. FAINT
GRAIN FIELD

601357   HANS WENDLER
POTATO FIELD

601358   WALTER BIBIKOW
GRAIN FIELD, ONTARIO

601359   JÜRGEN VOGT
GRAIN ELEVATOR, ALBERTA

601360   GRANT V. FAINT

601361   WALTER BIBIKOW
GRAIN FIELD, ONTARIO

601362   GARY CRALLE
CORN

601363   GRANT V. FAINT
GRAIN ELEVATOR, ALBERTA

601364   GARY CRALLE

601365   GRANT V. FAINT
RAPESEED FIELD, MANITOBA

601366   JÜRGEN VOGT

601367   JÜRGEN VOGT
ALBERTA, CANADA

601368   D.S. HENDERSON

THE IMAGE BANK®

601369 GARY CRALLÉ
        DAIRY FARM,
        PRINCE EDWARD ISLAND

601370 GARY CRALLÉ

601371 GRANT V. FAINT
        WHEAT

601372 JÜRGEN VOGT
        GRAIN HARVESTING,
        SASKATCHEWAN

601373 GRANT V. FAINT
        WHEAT

601374 GRANT V. FAINT
        PRINCE EDWARD ISLAND

601375 GRANT V. FAINT
        WHEAT HARVESTING

601376 D.S. HENDERSON
        BARLEY HARVESTING

601377 YURI DOJC

601378 D.S. HENDERSON
        PRINCE EDWARD ISLAND

601379 JÜRGEN VOGT
        GRAIN ELEVATOR, ALBERTA

601380 GARY CRALLÉ
        MUSTARD FIELD, ONTARIO

601381 GRANT V. FAINT
        GRAIN HARVESTING, MANITOBA

601382 GRANT V FAINT

601383 GARY CRALLÉ
TORONTO STOCK EXCHANGE

601754 JOHN FRASER

601384 GARY CRALLÉ

601385 GARY CRALLÉ
UNION STATION, TORONTO

601386 STUART DEE

601387 JAY FREIS
BELL CANADA CONTROL ROOM

601388 STUART DEE

601389 WALTER BIBIKOW
COUR MONT ROYAL, MONTREAL

601390 STUART DEE

601391 YURI DOJC
TORONTO STOCK EXCHANGE

601755 JOHN MARTIN

601392 GARY CRALLÉ
TORONTO STOCK EXCHANGE

601393   GARY CRALLÉ

601394   GRANT V. FAINT
BOEING 737

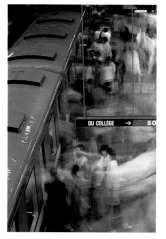

601395   MARC ROMANELLI
MONTREAL

601396   WALTER BIBIKOW

601397   GARY CRALLÉ

601398   GUIDO ALBERTO ROSSI
NIAGARA FALLS

601399   ALBERT NORMANDIN
BRITISH COLUMBIA

601400   GRANT V. FAINT
SKYTRAIN, VANCOUVER

601401   GUIDO ALBERTO ROSSI
VANCOUVER

601402   ALBERT NORMANDIN
LIONS GATE BRIDGE, BRITISH COLUMBIA

601403   GRANT V. FAINT

601404   YURI DOJC

601405   EDDIE HIRONAKA
VANCOUVER

THE IMAGE BANK®

601406 JÜRGEN VOGT
PAN PACIFIC HOTEL,
VANCOUVER

601407 JÜRGEN VOGT

601408 GRANT V. FAINT
BRITISH COLUMBIA

601409 GRANT V. FAINT

601410 GRANT V. FAINT
WHITE ROCK, BRITISH COLUMBIA

601411 ALBERT NORMANDIN
LIONS GATE BRIDGE, BRITISH COLUMBIA

601412 GRANT V. FAINT

601413 BRETT FROOMER
CALGARY

601414 GRANT V. FAINT

601415 GARY CRALLÉ

601416 GRANT V. FAINT
FERRY, QUEEN CHARLOTTE ISLAND

601417 GRANT V. FAINT
CONTAINER SHIP, VANCOUVER

601418 GARY CRALLÉ
CESSNA & GRUMMAN TIGER

601419   GRANT V. FAINT
         CONTAINER SHIP, VANCOUVER

601420   BRETT FROOMER
         OIL REFINERY, EDMONTON

601421   GRANT V. FAINT

601422   GRANT V. FAINT
         REFINERY, VANCOUVER

601423   GARY CRALLÉ
         STEEL MILL, ONTARIO

601424   GRANT V. FAINT
         TRANSFORMERS

601756   LINDA MONTGOMERY

601425   GRANT V. FAINT

601426   GRANT V. FAINT
         REFINERY, VANCOUVER

601427   STUART DEE

601428   YURI DOJC

601429   GRANT V. FAINT
         TRANSFORMER

601430   BOB BROOKS
         STEEL MILL

601757   PAUL MORIN
OFFSHORE OIL PLATFORM

601431   STUART DEE

601432   STUART DEE

601433   GRANT V. FAINT

601434   GRANT V. FAINT

601435   STUART DEE

601436   GRANT V. FAINT
GRAIN ELEVATORS, THUNDER BAY

601437   D.S. HENDERSON
GEOLOGIST, ELLESMERE ISLAND

601758   ROCCO BAVIERA
OIL RIG

601438   GRANT V. FAINT
ALUMINUM

601439   ARTHUR D'ARAZIEN
ZINC FLOTATION

601440   ALBERT NORMANDIN
VANCOUVER

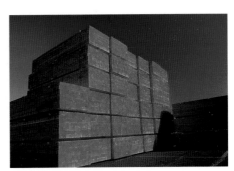

601441   GRANT V. FAINT

601759 GARY MCLAUGHLIN
ROYAL CANADIAN
MOUNTED POLICE

601760 JOHN FRASER

601442 JAY FREIS

601443 ADRIEN DUEY
GOLD BARS

601444 JÜRGEN VOGT
ROYAL CANADIAN MOUNTED POLICE

601445 BRETT FROOMER
ATHABASCA GLACIER, ALBERTA

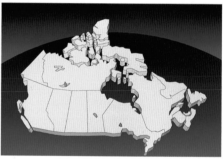

601446 GRANT V. FAINT

601447 ROB ATKINS
TOTEM POLES, BRITISH COLUMBIA

601448 PAT LACROIX
CANADIAN CURRENCY

601449 GRANT V. FAINT
ROYAL CANADIAN MOUNTED POLICE

601450 GRANT V. FIANT

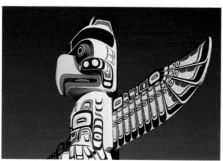

601451 STUART DEE
TOTEM POLE

601452 MURRAY ALCOSSER
CANADIAN CURRENCY

THE IMAGE BANK®

MARKETING

ART DIRECTION

DEDICATION

TYPOGRAPHY

PHOTOSTATS

ASSEMBLY

EXPERIENCE

RETOUCHING

HAND LETTERING

AIRBRUSHING

DESIGN

SALES

TALENT

TRANSIT

CONCEPTS

LIGHTING

DISPLAY

LOCATION

RESEARCH

LINE FILM

TRANSLITES

PHOTOGRAPHY

COPY WRITING

ILLUSTRATION

DIRECT MAIL

CORPORATE

MECHANICAL

*C*reative and effective advertising
just happens to be our cup-of-tea.

SCL VISUAL MARKETING GROUP

190 MILNER AVENUE
SCARBOROUGH, ONTARIO M1S·5B6
PHONE (416) 298·0955 FAX (416) 293·7694
A DIVISION OF SCARBORO COLOUR LABS LTD.

COMPUTER

PACKAGING

Bénard

JOËL BÉNARD

372 Richmond Street West, Suite 120

Toronto, Ontario M5V 1X6 Telephone 340-7435

Fax 340-6366

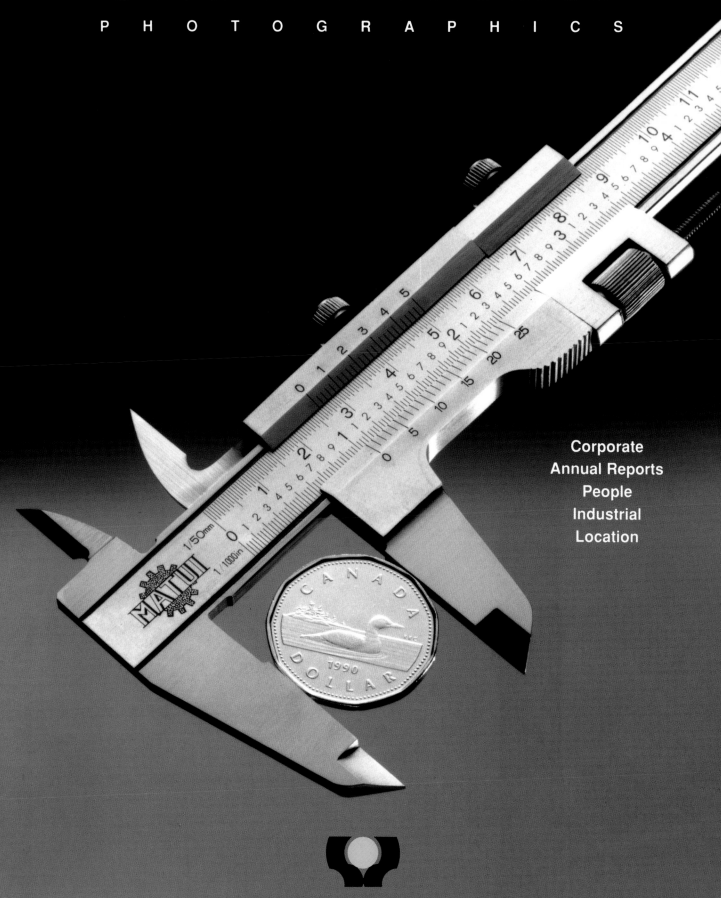

MICHAEL COURTNEY

PHOTOGRAPHY

Corporate

Industrial

Commercial

Editorial

416•565•7144

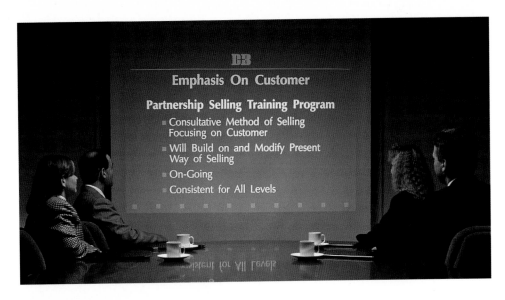

L'Association Canadienne de
Photographes et Illustrateurs de
Publicité

The Canadian Association of
Photographers & Illustrators in
Communications

Toronto   (416) 462-3677   Montréal   (514) 933-6299
Ottawa   (613) 594-5955   Calgary   (403) 266-4094
Edmonton (403) 486-3966   Vancouver (604) 683-2257

SANDOR

PHOTOGRAPHY

252 Glengrove Avenue West, Suite 3, Toronto, Ontario M5N IWI   416-480-0918

Dynamic
photographs of
people,
places
and things –
everywhere!

John Harquail
Photography Inc.

67 Mowat Avenue
Suite 340
Toronto, Ontario, Canada
M6K 3E3
416. 535.1620 Studio
416. 535.1543 FAX

Harquail

G R E G   H O L M A N

4 1 6   3 6 2   8 2 8 5

P-55

J. Michael LaFond

Photographer

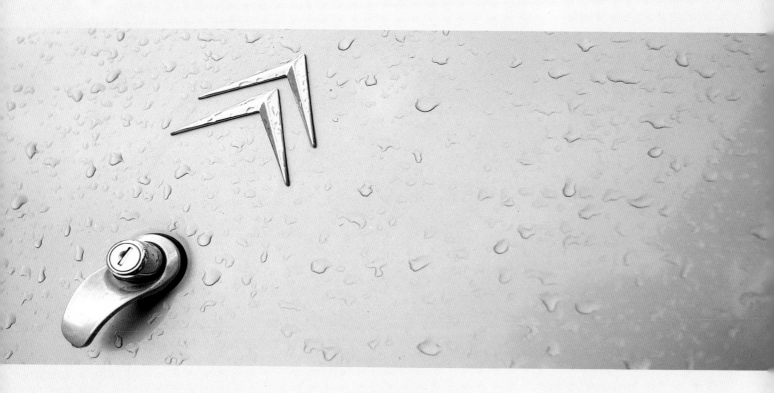

272 Avenue Road, Toronto

Ontario, Canada M4V 2G7

(416) 927-8383 (416) 927-8972

Avon Canada Inc.

Coca-Cola Foods Canada Inc.

Holt Renfrew Company

Royal Bank of Canada

Royal Doulton Canada Inc.

Sony of Canada Ltd.

Telemedia Publishing Inc.

The Toronto-Dominion Bank

Trinadad & Tobago Tourist Board

Vickers & Benson Advertising Ltd.

DESIGN MARC STEWART PRODUCTIONS COLOUR SEPARATIONS STUDIO COLOUR GROUP INC

PAT LACROIX

ラックローイ
ハット

THE BRANT GROUP, 25 BRANT STREET, TORONTO, CANADA (416) 864-1858

Jim Merrithew

613-259-3331

R.R. #2 (Middleville), Lanark, Ontario, Canada K0G 1K0
Located a short distance from Ottawa

Sun up to sun down
men working in the dark, underground.
Below the surface
a seemingly barren landscape to explore.
Hard fissures of rock
creating an uncompromising image;
the miners,
craggy faces and blackened clothes,
painful muscles cradled by the earth,
seem more aware of their mortality . . .
lives hewn in stone.
These elements are composed
with such symmetry and humility
that we go seeking
capture
and with a lens
show light to darkness
and life to shadow.

John
Narvali photography

5
Soho st. TORONTO
ONTARIO M5T 1Z6
416 / 593-0813

CORPORATE • ANNUAL REPORTS • COMMERCIAL • INDUSTRIAL

MATTHEW
PLEXMAN
PHOTOGRAPHY LTD.

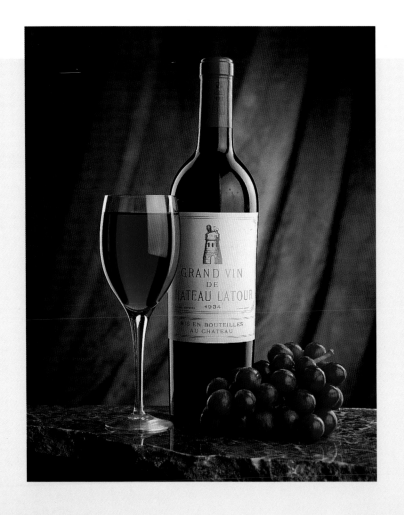

146 FIRST AVENUE TORONTO M4M1X1 416•463•3914

The Product Studio

Specializing in product photography

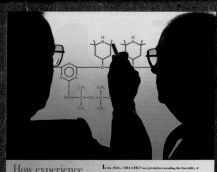

THE ORIGINAL TRIPLE R PROMISE IS STILL TRUE.

How experience can extend the life of your polymer

DÉCOR 1990

Libbey ST CLAIR

GLASSWARE FOR THE RETAIL TRADE
VERRERIE POUR LE COMMERCE DE DÉTAIL

NUMBER 2 *Injectioneering*
The Hot Runner Technology Newsletter From Mold-Masters

RACK & PINION:
RELIABILITY IN
SINGLE CAVITY
VALVE GATING

307 Bering Ave. Toronto Ont. M8Z 3A5 Telephone: 239-4417 Fax: 234-9799

RICHARD SANDERS

SKS PHOTOGRAPHY LIMITED

200 STEELCASE ROAD EAST, UNIT 3, MARKHAM, ONTARIO L3R 1G2   PHONE (416) 474-0712

SANDOR

PHOTOGRAPHY

252 Glengrove Avenue West, Suite 3, Toronto, Ontario M5N IWI   416-480-0918

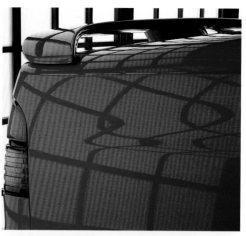

punch

1463, Préfontaine
Montréal
(Québec)
H1W 2N6
(514) 598-5100
fax: (514) 523-2312

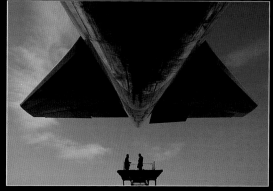

Steve Stober

Photography

416/ 370-5828

DAVID TREVOR
& ASSOCIATES INC.
PHOTOGRAPHY

*Specialists in
the photography and production
of catalogues, sales promotion/marketing material
and flyers*

276 CARLAW AVE. STE. 308 TORONTO ONTARIO M4M 3L1 (416) 466-2650

Roger
Brooks

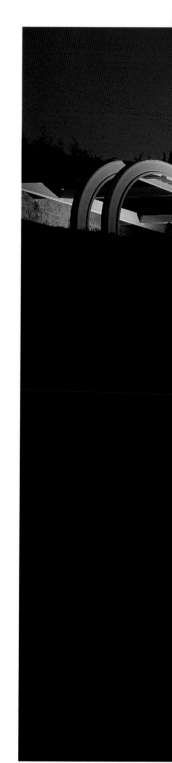

Roger Brooks has a simple philosophy: take care of the details and the rest will take care of itself. This attitude is evident in the quality of the photographs presented here. Attention to lighting and styling produce pictures that appear three dimensional in their detail. The result of this detailed photography: instant impact.

An early architectural career in England has given Brooks a trained eye that understands that the building of the perfect shoot is only as good as the creative interpretation he and a design team bring to it.

With 10 years of creating and building images for such diverse clients as Cadillac Fairview, the Hudson's Bay Company, and the Bank of Montreal, Roger Brooks brings professionalism and detail to the whole business of photography.

- ❧ Architecture
- ❧ Interiors
- ❧ Portraits
- ❧ Products
- ❧ Corporate

200 – East First Avenue

Vancouver, British Columbia

Canada   V5T 1A9

Tel (604) 872-2717

Fax (604) 879-1009

Represented in Toronto by:

Pierre Guevremont

First Light Associated Photographers

Tel (416) 532-6108

Fax (416) 532-7499

Stock Photography:

Julia Day

Image Finders Photo Agency Inc.

Tel (604) 688-9818

Fax (604) 684-2452

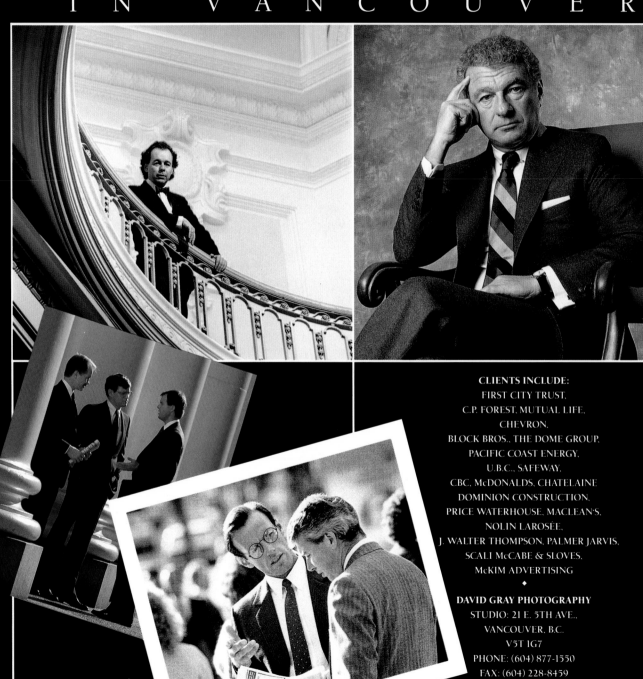

GRAY
IN VANCOUVER

YVAN DUBÉ
P H O T O G R A P H E

MONTRÉAL, QUÉBEC
(514) 646-3946
ACPIP/CAPIC

**PHOTOGRAPHIE
INDUSTRIELLE,
TOURISTIQUE,
PUBLICITAIRE,
D'ARCHITECTURE
ET DE PORTRAIT**

**INDUSTRY,
ARCHITECTURE,
ADVERTISING,
TOURISM AND
PORTRAIT
PHOTOGRAPHY**

Phyllis Lambert, Centre Canadien d'Architecture

Bernard Bohn

4060, boul. St-Laurent, 4e étage
Montréal, Québec
H2W 1Y9
514.287.1589

Jean Campeau, Caisse de dépôt et de placement du Québec

Bernard Bohn

4060, boul. St-Laurent, 4e étage
Montréal, Québec
H1W 1Y9
514.287.1589

ROBIN
EDGAR

899, rue De l'Église, Verdun (Québec) Canada H4G 2N4   514.762.0785

Sylvain Gagnon

PHOTOGRAPHE

390 rielle, suite 105, Montréal, Québec, Canada, H4G 2S8, téléphone: 768-9792

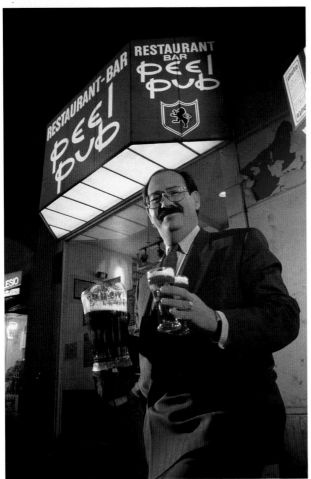

Satisfaction garantie ou vous ne payez pas!
Satisfaction guaranteed or you don't pay!

Jean-Claude Delorme
Président du conseil et de chef de la direction
de la Caisse de dépôt et de placement du Québec.

André J. Boutin
Vice-président
Groupe des câbles Northern Telecom

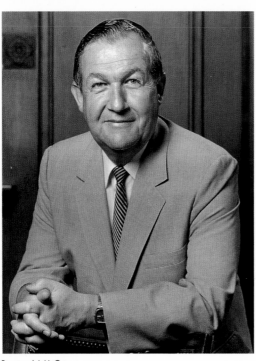

Raymond J. V. Cyr
Président du conseil et chef de la direction
de B.C.E. inc.

Raffi Arménian
Directeur musical
de l'Orchestre de Kitchener-Waterloo

PAUL LABELLE
PHOTOGRAPHE INC.

PAUL LABELLE
PHOTOGRAPHE INC.

(514) 845-5523

CLIENTS:

Bell Canada

Téléglobe Canada

Northern Telecom

Banque Royale du Canada

Le Groupe SNC

Ultramar Canada

Price Waterhouse

Burson and Marsteller

Claude-Simon Langlois

CORPORATIF

COMMERCIAL

INDUSTRIEL

PUBLICITÉ

CORPORATE

COMMERCIAL

INDUSTRIAL

ADVERTISING

milnox INC.

PRODUCTIONS PHOTO

822 DE L'ÉPÉE, MONTRÉAL, QC H2V 3V3 TÉL. (514) 279-1352

P-80

PHOTO PRODUCTIONS

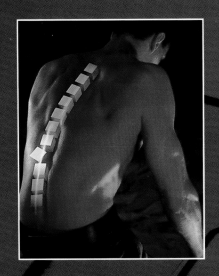

Dany Eigenmann
Michel Mayer
1583 boul. St-Laurent
Montréal (Québec)
H2X 2S9
Tél.: 288-4823
Fax.: 288-4039

- Publicité
  Brochures
  Rapports annuels
  Emballages
  (en studio ou location
  du 35mm au 8x10)
- Effets spéciaux optiques
  35mm et 4x5
- Effets spéciaux ordinateur
  35mm
- Production diaporamas
- Production films et vidéo

Toutes ces images ont été
réalisées à la caméra
sans retouche, airbrush
ou procédé "Scitex".

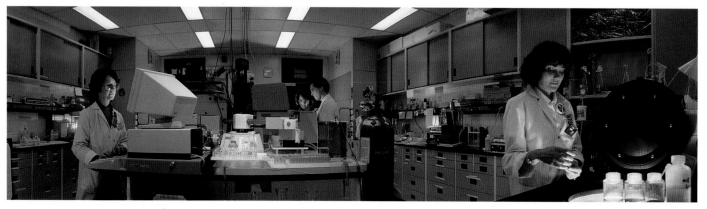

▲ MERCK FROSST

▲ MERCK FROSST

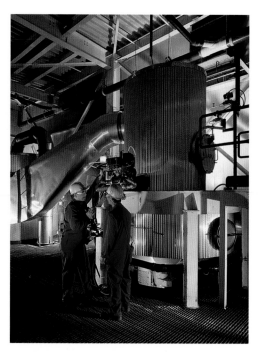

▲ REPAP PAPER

▶ McGILL UNIVERSITY

▶ KOHN, PEDERSON, FOX, ARCHITECTS

YVES LEFEBVRE

PHOTOGRAPHE

Spécialiste
en
photographie
d'intérieur,
d'architecture
et
industrielle

6001, Jeanne-Mance
Montréal, (Québec)
H2V 4K9
Tél.: (514) **270-4372**

GUY TESSIER
PHOTOGRAPHE

1061 Saint-Alexandre
Studio 404
Montréal (Québec)
H2Z 1P5
(514) 866-0998

1061 Saint-Alexandre
Studio 404
Montréal (Québec)
H2Z 1P5
(514) 866-0998

SOCANAV — STEINBERG

514 • 395 • 2227
95 RUE PRINCE, MONTRÉAL, H3C 2M7
FAX • 875 • 9017

Jean Vachon Photographe

MARCONI

514 • 395 • 2227
95 RUE PRINCE, MONTRÉAL, H3C 2M7
FAX • 875 • 9017

P-89

ALAN CARRUTHERS

FASHION • BEAUTY • ADVERTISING • EDITORIAL • ILLUSTRATION • CELEBRITY & CORPORATE PORTRAITURE • ANNUAL REPORTS • TRAVEL

Partial client list: Air Canada • Bell • Nabisco • Domtar • AT & T • Royal Bank • Imasco • Marconi • Yellow Pages • Steinberg • Prudential • Wawanesa • Northern Telecom • Power Corp • Canada Steamship Lines • Diners Club • Union Bank of Switzerland • Canada Tourism (C.G.O.T.) • Ayerst • Canadair • Royal Ontario Museum • Banque Laurentienne • Union Carbide • Compact Computers • Queens University, Kingston • Texaco • Pratt & Whitney • Michelin / Time • Newsweek • Forbes • People • Actualité • MacLeans • National Geographic • International Wildlife • Harvard Business Review • Equinox • Harrowsmith • Photo (Paris) • Canadian Business • Financial Post • Globe & Mail • Destination • Geo (German) • New-York Times

Annual Report – Ultramar

Senate, Ottawa – Equinox

Stock available: Gold refining • Shipbuilding • Brain surgery • Theatre • Architecture • Rodeo • Industrial • Hi-tech • Etc...

5 1 4 • 2 8 8 • 4 3 3 3

Jonathan Wenk 42, avenue des Pins ouest, Montréal, Québec H2W 1R1 **(514) 842-4589**

ILLUSTRATION

"What is the use of a book without pictures or conversations?"

Lewis Carroll

THE ART OF COMMUNICATION

It is somewhat ironic that the oldest form of visual communication — illustration — is still regarded as a cutting-edge innovation in corporate communication. Now that photography has practically become a foregone conclusion in annual reports and company brochures, more and more corporations are turning to illustration to give their communications stylistic and conceptual qualities that can't be achieved with photography. Why the shift back to illustration at a time when technology has brought photography to the brink of perfection?

As an alternative to, rather than a replacement for photography, the illustration is still capable of expressing ideas that elude the camera. According to Bill Grigsby, founding partner of Reactor Art and Design and a representative of some 36 Reactor artists, "Photography is a selection process, where illustration is a constructive process. With photography you go out and edit; the world is all there. With illustration, you start with nothing and then you build."

Grigsby goes on to explain that corporate people are thinking retail, citing the example of banks that now target the "retail investor." This is all part of the move toward a service-based economy, where intangibles like quality and productivity must be communicated. "These are concepts that can be illustrated, but they can't be photographed," Grigsby says. "The core thing about illustration is that aspect of what it can talk about, conceptual information, its ability to work in metaphors, to be surreal, and therefore be able to talk about very abstract or very paradoxical kinds of things. Illustration is really at its best when it is dealing with communication as opposed to sales vehicles like catalogues."

Alain Massicotte, a Montreal illustrator, feels that illustration "encourages a different level of reading and lets the customer express a particular audacity and imagination more easily." But this quality can only come through, Massicotte cautions, "if a photographic approach is not imposed on the illustrator." Massicotte created a series of illustrations for a recent Canadian Pacific annual report that evoked different themes "in a uniform, metaphorical and perhaps more harmonious manner" than photography would have done.

Julie Kovacs, general manager of the Image Bank Canada, an international stock photography agency that now includes stock illustrations in its library, acknowledges the importance of illustration as a corporate communications tool. "Illustration has a lot of power because of the interpretation of the illustrator, the ability to extend reality into something that can be very symbolic and incorporate a style that is far more difficult to obtain when you're shooting photography."

Hamilton illustrator Rocco Baviera is well known for his imaginative, mystical illustrations. "The main difference in using illustration versus photography," he says, "is the possibility of creating excitement, evoking a special mood or adding unique textures to the subject."

Some corporate or industrial assignments are not very appealing visually or are almost impossible to photograph well. This was the case recently when Baviera was commissioned to work on an annual report for LAC Minerals Limited. The company wanted to show their operations in South America, the United States and various sites

Olco annual report cover by Carlo Constentino

♦ ♦ ♦

LE GROUPE PÉTROLIER OLCO PETROLEUM GROUP INC.

in Canada. Although they had a large supply of photographs to choose from, these were taken by a number of photographers during different seasons and lighting conditions. Even the best design or retouching could not present these well together to create a quality image for the corporation.

Baviera harmonized the many components, carefully edited out unwanted details and created a visually interesting illustration at a small fraction of the cost it would have taken to send a photographer on location in an attempt to achieve similar results.

John W. Stewart, an illustrator based in Montreal, says, "Illustration can be very useful when you want to go beyond the facts, when you seek to challenge the people you are addressing and convey the philosophy and vision of the company to them. The work of the illustrator aims to shed light on the message with an image. It's an exacting process." Stewart's recent work on the National Bank annual report metaphorically presented four symbolically detailed themes. "Photography has the technical means to do this as well," Stewart concedes, "but most of the time it is required only to depict reality."

Carlo Cosentino's illustrations for the Olco Oil Company's

**LAC Minerals
annual report
illustrations by
Rocco Baviera**
♦ ♦ ♦

annual report solved problems in presenting "the order of importance of the various elements as well as the arrangement of colours that only illustration could solve," the illustrator explains.

Illustration can come with its own unique problems, however. Baviera suggests that clients are often conditioned to more readily accept flaws in a photograph, because it is real. They tend to request more changes from an illustrator, just because such changes are possible, without realizing the effort necessary to make them.

The decision to employ illustration is a relatively easy one compared to the perplexing process of deciding on the type of illustration or which illustrator to use. By its very nature, illustration presents limitless possibilities of style and medium. And the many visual and conceptual effects that can be achieved through the skills of an illustrator must be chosen to reflect the message that needs to be communicated.

There is further irony in the fact that the use of illustration in a corporate piece is regarded by many clients as a bold move into new territory, especially when the illustration is conceptual rather than realistic. Although novel illustrative approaches appear in corporate communications every year, Bill Grigsby says it is the market's acceptance of illustration that is changing rather than the artistic styles themselves. "All the art styles that have developed over the centuries are now being made commercial. When you look at an overview of all Picasso's styles, and add a little Dada and some tight realism and all the historical styles before that, what you get is a style book for illustration."

That style book is highly visible in the form of editorial illustration. But according to Grigsby, many corporate people and infrequent buyers tend to shy away from using the kinds of illustrations they see in the same magazines they advertise in. "There seems to be a general principle that if something is in the editorial, it's too radical."

It is the versatility of illustration that makes it an excellent editorial medium. And this editorializing capability is another factor in its increasing appearance in corporate communications. As environmental and social concerns become important components of the message, corporate communications are moving into a more editorial point of view. As Grigsby says, "There is a need to move closer to the editorial side because it will force communicators to come to grips with the fact that people are not as inarticulate or visually illiterate as some think they are."

But how does one find the appropriate mode of communicating to this articulate, visually literate audience?

When selecting a style of illustration, the buyer should understand that the style itself is part of the message, acting as a frame for the information being conveyed in the illustration. A tendency still exists, in believing that a powerful illustrated image might be too extreme for the audience, to dilute it to what Grigsby calls "a sort of pleasant reality." This only weakens the impact of the image and defeats its purpose.

Although illustration continues to contribute to many ground-breaking annual reports, corporate brochures and other corporate communications projects every year, it should be remembered that in visual art, nothing is new. Corporate illustration is the commercial application of a tool that has been with us since the dawn of civilization. Amid the technology of the 1990s, illustration is a hand-hewn art that is part of an ancient continuum — one whose beauty is that it can be whatever you want it to be, say whatever you want it to say.

STYLE

A. Abstract	G. Editorial	M. Period/Historical
B. Advertising	H. Fashion	N. Realist
C. Architectural	I. Murals	O. Surrealist
D. Cartoon	J. Nature	P. Technical
E. Caricatures	K. Portrait	
F. Children's Books	L. Product	

Acrylics	Airbrush	Appliqué	Collage	Computer	Dyes	Fimo/Plasticine	Gouache	Hand Tinting	Marker Rendering	Medical	Mixed Media	Oils	Paper Sculpture	Pastels	Pen & Ink	Pencil	Scratch Board	Soft Sculpture	Storyboards	Water Colour	Page	Phone	Name (Style)
1	2	3	4	5	6	7	8	9	10	11	12	13	14	15	16	17	18	19	20	21			
◆			◆	◆		◆	◆		◆		◆	◆		◆	◆	◆			◆	◆	I-22,23	(416)778-0805	Adquest — B,D,E,G,H,J
			◆								◆				◆	◆				◆	I-18	(514)843-3219	Béha, Philippe — B,E,F,G,O
◆														◆							I-7	(416)485-8555	Berger, Robert — B,G,N
◆	◆						◆		◆		◆									◆	I-20,21	(416)294-9205	Chen, Paul Illustration — B,C,I,J,L,N,O
◆									◆			◆		◆	◆	◆			◆	◆	I-6	(514)876-1442	Cosentino, Carlo — B,H,K,N
	◆						◆				◆				◆	◆				◆	I-12	(416)278-1401	Dovaston, Terry & Associates — B,C,G,L,N,P
				◆																	I-8,9	(416)535-1931	Frampton, Bill — B,D,I,K,L,P
	◆		◆				◆		◆		◆	◆			◆	◆					I-10,11	(519)672-9090	Kearns, Cliff Inc — B,I,K,L,N
														◆						◆	I-13	(416)782-0947	Leopold, Susan — A,B,F,G
◆	◆						◆				◆	◆	◆								I-14,15	(416)898-4968	Ormond, Richard — B,D,E,G,J,K,L,M,N
◆			◆												◆					◆	I-19	(514)849-1001	Roberts, Bruce — A,C,D,G,I,J,L,O
◆							◆		◆		◆	◆		◆	◆	◆			◆	◆	I-16	(416)251-5938	Sisco, Sam Illustration — B,D,E,G,H,J,K,L,M,N
												◆		◆							I-17	(514)761-0669	Trudel, France — B,F,G,H,J,K,N

Acrylique	Aérographe	Appliqué	Collage	Infographie	Teintures	Fimo/Plasticine	Gouache	Teinté à la main	Maquette de crayon feutre	Médicale	Médiums Multiples	Huile	Sculpture de papier	Pastel	Encre de chine	Crayon	Carton à gratter	Sculpture de Tissu	Maquettes de Scénario	Aquarelle
1	2	3	4	5	6	7	8	9	10	11	12	13	14	15	16	17	18	19	20	21

STYLE

A. Abstrait	G. Éditoriale	M. De période/Historique
B. Publicitaire	H. Mode	N. Realist
C. Architecturale	I. Murales	O. Surrealist
D. Bande Dessinée	J. Nature	P. Technical
E. Caricaturale	K. Portrait	
F. Livre pour enfant	L. Produit	

INDEX DES ILLUSTRATEURS

A PASSION FOR COLOUR... A SEARCH FOR PURE LIGHT

Carlo

MORE SAMPLES
AVAILABLE IN
CREATIVE SOURCE
7 · 8 · 9 · 10 · 11 · 12

514 · 876 · 1442

BERGER

BOB BERGER · ILLUSTRATION
52 McNAIRN AVENUE
TORONTO ONTARIO CANADA
M5M 2H5

416 · 485-8555   FAX · 322-4852

· HOMEMAKER'S
MAGAZINE
ART DIRECTOR ·
GEORGES HAROUTIUN

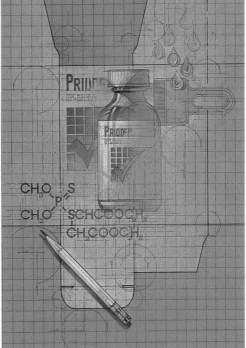

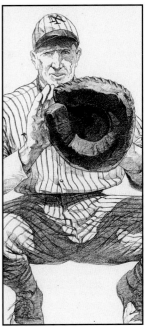

· McDADE + MONTY (ONTARIO) INC
ART DIRECTOR · SCOTT PARKS

VISCOM LIMITED: AN INTEGRATED MARKETING COMMUNICATIONS COMPANY
99 SUMACH STREET, TORONTO, ONTARIO M5A 3J8   TEL (416) 366-6400 FAX (416) 366-3139

CLIFF KEARNS

519-672-9090
FAX 519-672-6080

392
MURRAY ST.
LONDON
ONTARIO
CANADA
N6C 4X4

◄ 75th
Anniversary
Poster
H.B. Beal
Secondary
School.

One of four
paintings
for 60th
Anniversary
Ontario
Separate
School
Trustees
Assoc.

◄ 1990
London
International
Air Show
Poster.

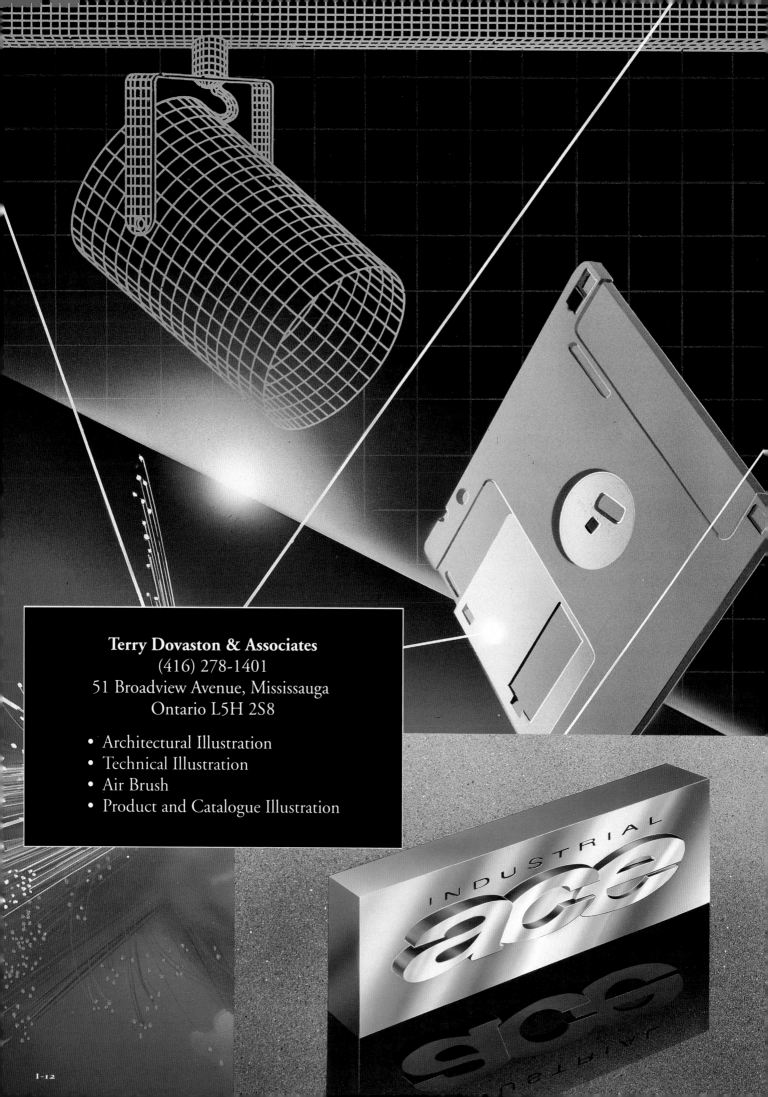

Terry Dovaston & Associates
(416) 278-1401
51 Broadview Avenue, Mississauga
Ontario L5H 2S8

- Architectural Illustration
- Technical Illustration
- Air Brush
- Product and Catalogue Illustration

Bell Canada

Telemedia

135 MARLEE SUITE 804 TORONTO M6B 4C6 FAX 487-3981

John Sibbald, President, Briar's Inn & Country Club, Jackson's Point, Ontario. Oil on Canvas, 44" x 33"

Richard Ormond
Portrait Artist
42 Portland Crescent, Newmarket, Ontario L3Y 6A5 Telephone: 416-898-4968

Ms Lynn Garber, New York. Oil on Canvas, 24" x 20"

Richard Ormond
Portrait Artist

42 Portland Crescent, Newmarket, Ontario L3Y 6A5   Telephone: 416-898-4968

SISCO

1-16

France Trudel

(514) 761-0669

(514) 271-7935

BEHA

TÉL. : (514) 843-3219

FAX : (514) 843-3219

BRUCE ROBERTS MTL 514·849·10 01 TOR 416·367·24 46

I-19

PAUL CHEN

Fax/Phone (416) 294-9205

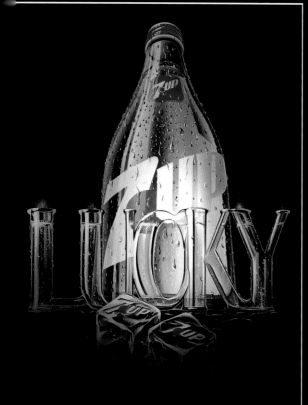

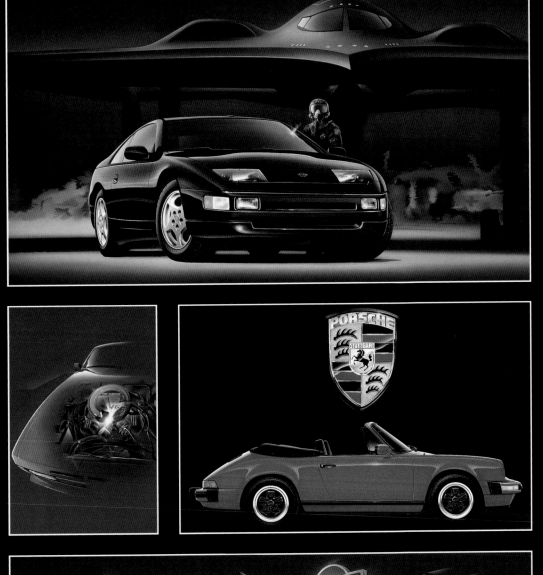

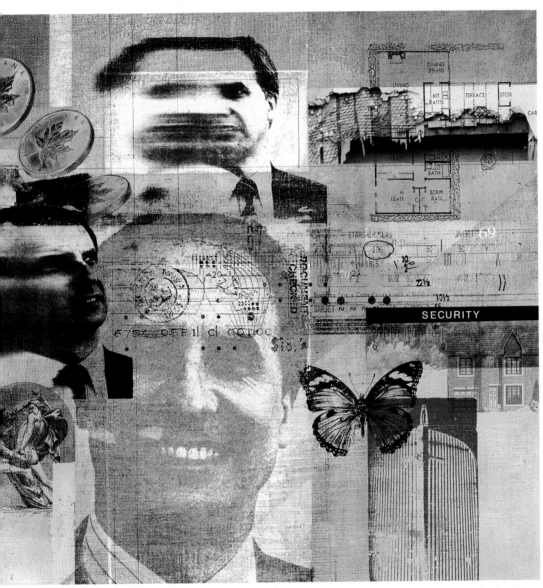

CIBC Corporate Publication

Paul Garbett .... (416) 778-0805 .... Fax (416) 778-0867

100 Broadview Ave., Ste. 322, Toronto, Ontario, M4M 2E8 ....

.... Represented by Adquest Inc.

DIRECTORY

<(5)>

DESIGNERS — TORONTO

212 Graphics Limited
212 Church St Oakville Ontario .... TEL (416)842-8090

A.L. Graphics
465 Milner #10 Scarborough Ontario .... TEL (416)298-4427

Abbott Jenkins Associates
326 Richmond St W Toronto Ontario .... TEL (416)598-1830

Ad Productions Ltd
240 Duncan Mill Rd #101 Toronto Ontario .... TEL (416)391-4257

Adability Inc
1345 Hurontario St Mississauga Ontario .... TEL (416)274-4912

Adorjan Thomsen Graphic Design Artist
222 Bedford Rd Toronto Ontario .... TEL (416)928-0813

Adquest
100 Broadview Ave #322 Toronto Ontario .... TEL (416)778-0805

AES Company
120 Carlton St #301 Toronto Ontario .... TEL (416)924-1818

Alter Design Group
77 Mowat Ave #205 Toronto Ontario .... TEL (416)588-1811

AM Studios
20 Eglinton Ave E #200 Toronto Ontario .... TEL (416)486-6279

Amazing Graphics
1519 Dupont St Toronto Ontario .... TEL (416)533-8723

Ames, Ann Design Associates Inc
1110 Yonge St 3rd Fl Toronto Ontario .... TEL (416)928-3282

Angeloff, Laurel Designs
377 Milverton Blvd Toronto Ontario .... TEL (416)466-9785

Anno Domini Inc
197 Church St 2nd Fl Toronto Ontario .... TEL (416)364-2144

Appletree Creative Services
30 Wertheim Court #19 Richmond Hill Ontario .... TEL (416)881-0137

Arshavsky and Smith Design
600 King St W #402 Toronto Ontario .... TEL (416)360-0303

Art Works, The
2a Gibson Ave Toronto Ontario .... TEL (416)929-9950

Assembly Communications Design Inc
67 Mowat Ave #239 Toronto Ontario .... TEL (416)537-6886

Associated Advertising Ltd
160 Rivalda Rd #398 Weston Ontario .... TEL (416)742-6921

Atlanta Art & Design Inc
511 King St W #400 Toronto Ontario .... TEL (416)581-1531

Avatar Communications Inc
2740 Matheson Bl E #3 Mississauga Ontario .... TEL (416)629-8900

B & B/Mystique Creative Services
1200 Eglinton Ave E #302 Don Mills Ontario .... TEL (416)441-2666

B.P.A. Design Consultants Ltd
219 Carlton St Toronto Ontario .... TEL (416)961-7664

Baker Communications Group
261 Glen Oak Dr Oakville Ontario .... TEL (416)842-3027

Bakersmith Design Associates Inc
65 Heward Ave #109 Toronto Ontario .... TEL (416)469-8109

Bamford, Robert & Associates
24 Mercer St Toronto Ontario .... TEL (416)597-2646

Barike Graphics
16 Florence Ave Willowdale Ontario .... TEL (416)250-9444

Barr Associates
100 Richmond St E #525 Toronto Ontario .... TEL (416)365-1977

Baum Marketing
260 Richmond St W #207 Toronto Ontario .... TEL (416)596-1209

Beakbane Marketing Inc
130 Bridgeland Ave #314 Toronto Ontario .... TEL (416)787-4901

Beard, Mike & Associates Inc
366 Adelaide St E Toronto Ontario .... TEL (416)362-9290

Belair Creative Concepts
PO Box 174, Stn L Toronto Ontario .... TEL (416)654-2160

Bender, Cam Designer
151 Bloor St W #370 Toronto Ontario .... TEL (416)968-9105

Bentwater Creative Services Inc
400 Eastern Ave #270 Toronto Ontario .... TEL (416)778-4600

Berkeley Studios Ltd
155 Withrow Ave Toronto Ontario .... TEL (416)465-6825

Berta, Paul & Associates Ltd
222 Bedford Rd Toronto Ontario .... TEL (416)926-0888

Bist Designers Ltd
2025 Sheppard Ave E #2219 Willowdale Ontario .... TEL (416)495-1441

Black, Brad + Fringe Ltd
99 Glendale Ave Toronto Ontario .... TEL (416)588-9162

Blackbird Design
394 Euclid Ave #301 Toronto Ontario .... TEL (416)972-6293

Bloss & Moore Design
4387 Spruce Ave Burlington Ontario .... TEL (416)681-7041

Boudreau, Dean & Associates
391 Berkeley St #2 Toronto Ontario .... TEL (416)929-2146

Boulevard Communications
260 King St E 3rd Fl Toronto Ontario .... TEL (416)860-0605

Bowen Designs
1200 Bay St #204 Toronto Ontario .... TEL (416)928-1215

Bowman, Cliff Boulevard
260 King St E Toronto Ontario .... TEL (416)860-1111

Bridgeford Dunn Associates
3281 Yonge St #200 Toronto Ontario .... TEL (416)481-1747

Brygier Graphic & Design
24 James St #5 St Catharines Ontario .... TEL (416)688-4937

Bulzan, Alex Designs
30 Draper St Toronto Ontario .... TEL (416)599-5984

ByGRAPHICS
1252 Lawrence Ave E #203 Don Mills Ontario .... TEL (416)391-3636

Bytown Design Group, The
64 Jefferson Ave #1 Toronto Ontario .... TEL (416)588-8616

Canmark Communications
3075 14th Ave #222 Markham Ontario .... TEL (416)477-4470

Caplan, Kenneth & Associates
200 Town Centre Blvd #200 Markham Ontario .... TEL (416)940-6911

Capon & Austin Associates Ltd
9240 Woodbine Ave Button Forge Gormley Mark. Ontario . TEL (416)477-5357

Carpenter & Company Design Inc
734 Huron St Toronto Ontario .... TEL (416)923-7150

Carter, Lynn & Associates
199 Spadina Ave #505 Toronto Ontario .... TEL (416)360-8276

Caswell & Armstrong Design
25 Aintree Cres Brampton Ontario .... TEL (416)793-9318

Cheeseman, Karen Inc
RR #2 Holstein Ontario .... TEL (416)334-3195

Chik-Lau, Florence Graphic Design
42 Wellington St E 3rd Fl Toronto Ontario .... TEL (416)363-5206

Ciaraldi and Rosen Ltd, Design Consultants
745 Queen St E Toronto Ontario .... TEL (416)469-5599

Cimeron Design
469 Queen St E Toronto Ontario .... TEL (416)359-0644

Clearlight Inc
186 Bessborough Dr Toronto Ontario .... TEL (416)486-1350

Clemmer Advertising Images Limited
128 Parliament St Toronto Ontario .... TEL (416)364-4054

Clientelle Graphics Ltd
296 Richmond St W Toronto Ontario .... TEL (416)977-3890

Coldiron Graphics Ltd
162 Norfinch Dr Downsview Ontario .... TEL (416)663-9048

Communique Limited
106 Front St E #301 Toronto Ontario .... TEL (416)365-7200

Comp-Tec Graphics Inc
797 Don Mills Rd #1301 Don Mills Ontario .... TEL (416)696-7251

Compact Business Systems Limited
93 Dunn Ave Toronto Ontario .... TEL (416)537-4777

Compal Communications
357 Bloor St E 5th Fl Toronto Ontario .... TEL (416)920-0161

Competitive Edge Merchandising Group
5090 Explorer Dr #502 Mississauga Ontario .... TEL (416)238-8309

Concepts Inc
277 Richmond St W Toronto Ontario .... TEL (416)340-1000

Concrete Design & Marketing Consultants
2 Berkeley St #206 Toronto Ontario .... TEL (416)366-9908

Continental Studios
415 Yonge St 10th Toronto Ontario .... TEL (416)598-8988

Cooper & Williamson Inc
1 Eva Rd #302 Etobicoke Ontario .... TEL (416)622-1005

Cooper Bell Ltd
440 Gerard St E Toronto Ontario .... TEL (416)598-2555

Corporate Vision Communications Inc
Box 575 Stn R Toronto Ontario .... TEL (416)488-8580

Corporate Visuals
49 Spadina Ave #506 Toronto Ontario .... TEL (416)593-6764

Corrado Designs
22 Marilyn Pl Woodbridge Ontario .... TEL (416)851-0585

Cote Graphics Inc
400 Esna Park Dr #6 Markham Ontario .... TEL (416)940-4578

Craan, Tania Design
26 Lennox St 3rd Fl Toronto Ontario .... TEL (416)535-0803

Craib Corporate Graphics Inc
42 Wellington St E 3rd Fl Toronto Ontario .... TEL (416)363-5206

Cranwell Pietrasiak Design Associates
9 Hazelton Ave 3rd Fl Toronto Ontario .... TEL (416)975-1699

Crawford, Darryl & Associates
15 Gervais Dr #602 Don Mills Ontario .... TEL (416)443-0819

Creative Direction
145 Front St E #301 Toronto Ontario .... TEL (416)863-6523

Creative Edge Design Associates
2240 Midland Ave #205C Scarborough Ontario ...... TEL (416)293-8418

Creative Empire Inc
80 Nashdene Rd #107 Scarborough Ontario .... TEL (416)297-8036

Creative Impulse Ltd
517 Wellington St W # 305 Toronto Ontario .... TEL (416)977-6777

Creative Insight Inc
195 Roe Ave Toronto Ontario .... TEL (416)781-6657

Creative Pages
312 Dolomite Dr #207 Downview Ontario .... TEL (416)665-7405

Creative Publishers
1500 Don Mills Rd #205 Don Mills Ontario .... TEL (416)445-5667

Creative Resources Co. Ltd
30 Hillsboro Ave #1506 Toronto Ontario .... TEL (416)960-5400

Creative Works Inc
489 Queen St E #201 Toronto Ontario .... TEL (416)368-6728

Cruise, Ted & Associates Ltd
504 King St E Toronto Ontario .... TEL (416)863-0838

Cumberland Press, The
612 Mt Pleasant Rd Toronto Ontario .... TEL (416)487-3496

Cumis Creative Services
3310 South Service Rd Burlington Ontario .... TEL (416)632-5390

Cundari Group, The
160 Vanderhoof Ave #201 Toronto Ontario .... TEL (416)421-9900

D.M. Kulig Design Inc
366 Adelaide St E #431 Toronto Ontario .... TEL (416)367-8933

Dagma Studio Inc
5 Soho St Toronto Ontario .... TEL (416)977-4742

David Martin Group Ltd
10 Gateway Blvd #560 Don Mills Ontario .... TEL (416)429-7133

Dawkins, Jack Creative Limited
25 Prince Arthur Ave Toronto Ontario .... TEL (416)925-7004

Design Attitude Inc
40 Main St E Stouffville Ontario .... TEL (416)642-1721

Design Communications
486A Red River Dr Waterloo Ontario .... TEL (519)357-9765

Design Consultancy
35 Booth Ave #200 Toronto Ontario .... TEL (416)461-8351

Design Force
187 King St E Toronto Ontario .... TEL (416)367-0077

Design Innovations Inc
75 Berkeley St Toronto Ontario .... TEL (416)362-8470

Design Media Ltd
67 Mowat Ave #133 Toronto Ontario .... TEL (416)537-1170

Design Partners Ltd
282 Richmond St East #200 Toronto Ontario .... TEL (416)368-3800

Design Plus
1262 Apier Cres Oakville Ontario .... TEL (416)844-3917

Design Profile
216 Glenwood Cres Toronto Ontario .... TEL (416)757-1041

Design Workshop
30 St Patrick #700 Toronto Ontario .... TEL (416)971-9970

Designcore Group
109 Vanderhoof Ave Toronto Ontario .... TEL (416)425-2067

Designers Inc
43 Eglinton Ave E #903 Toronto Ontario .... TEL (416)483-7888

DesignPrint Communications
30 Duncan St 2nd Fl Toronto Ontario .... TEL (416)977-6377

Designs On You
67 Mowat Ave #243 Toronto Ontario .... TEL (416)532-7352

DesignSource
77 Mowat Ave #304 Toronto Ontario .... TEL (416)537-7616

Diamant Gassyt Design & Communications
142 Woburn Ave #3 Toronto Ontario .... TEL (416)488-2147

Dicasa Design Group Inc
7015 Tranmere Dr #3 Mississauga Ontario .... TEL (416)672-0130

DiCresce & Associates
415 Yonge St 10th Fl Toronto Ontario .... TEL (416)971-6923

Dima Communications Inc
276 Carlaw Ave #311 Toronto Ontario .... TEL (416)462-9601

Dimson, Theo Design Inc
96 Avenue Rd Toronto Ontario .... TEL (416)923-2427

Dollery Rudman Design Associates Inc
600 King St W 3rd Fl Toronto Ontario .... TEL (416)362-0065

Dominick Design Associates
Box 277 Jordan Ontario .... TEL (416)562-7100

Donaghue, Ritchie & Associates
1179A King St W #310 Toronto Ontario .... TEL (416)588-1980

Douglas, Cameron & Associates Inc
34 Park Rd Toronto Ontario .... TEL (416)920-0953

Dreadnaught Design
46 Harbord St Toronto Ontario .... TEL (416)977-0769

Dunjko, Carmen Associates Limited
66 Gerrard St E #300 Toronto Ontario .... TEL (416)977-0767

Duo Strategy and Design Inc
1179A King St W #208 Toronto Ontario .... TEL (416)534-2575

Durand Design Associates Inc
44 Charles St Oshawa Ontario .... TEL (416)686-6281

Dussault, Diane & Associates Ltd
100 Adelaide St W #1500 Toronto Ontario .... TEL (416)366-5052

Earthmark Inc/Green Marketing
77 Mowat Ave #504 Toronto Ontario .... TEL (416)588-6488

Eklipse Art & Design Inc
99 Queen St E #500 Toronto Ontario .... TEL (416)864-0811

Emerson Group Inc, The
72 Fraser Ave #212 Toronto Ontario .... TEL (416)588-0009

Environmental Graphics
36 Robb Blvd Orangeville Ontario .... TEL (519)941-7131

Eskind Waddell
260 Richmond St W #201 Toronto Ontario .... TEL (416)593-1626

Estrada, Jorge Design
102 Fortrose Cres Don Mills Ontario .... TEL (416)444-9538

Exokraf Limited
71 Glenmount Park Rd Toronto Ontario .... TEL (416)699-6088

Falcom Design & Communications Inc
73 Laird Dr #305 Toronto Ontario .... TEL (416)467-0090

Fiala, Paul & Associates Ltd
151 Bloor St W #370 Toronto Ontario .... TEL (416)968-9105

Firstcom Marketing Inc
105 Valleybrook Dr Don Mills Ontario .... TEL (416)449-3322

Fisher Design Associates Inc
77 Mowat Ave #504 Toronto Ontario .... TEL (416)535-3889

Five Seven Nine Design
366 Adelaide St E #434 Toronto Ontario .... TEL (416)361-6336

Flight Path Design & Communications Inc
5710 Timberlea Blvd #201 Mississauga Ontario .... TEL (416)624-9199

Forbes, Tim Design Inc
263 Adelaide St W #502 Toronto Ontario .... TEL (416)593-5040

Foster, Richard S. & Associates
1 St Clair Ave E #500 Toronto Ontario .... TEL (416)960-0888

Fraiman Design Inc
110 Bond St Toronto Ontario .... TEL (416)591-1444

Freelancers Unlimited Inc
1491 Yonge St #203 Toronto Ontario .... TEL (416)969-9088

Freeman Communications
11 Gloucester St Toronto Ontario .... TEL (416)967-6970

Galer & MacMillan Communcations Inc
106 Berkeley St Toronto Ontario .... TEL (416)364-2960

Geist & Associates Inc
327 Renfrew Dr #301 Markham Ontario .... TEL (416)475-1022

Giambrone Design Limited
352 Rusholm Rd Toronto Ontario .... TEL (416)531-9988

Gillette & Associates
RR #1 Bognar Ontraio .... TEL (519)371-7460

Gilmour Marketing
255 Bamburgh Circle #808 Scarborough Ontario .... TEL (416)497-7505

Gingko Design & Communications
4950 Yonge St #600 North York Ontario .... TEL (416)221-2244

Glyphics Inc
406 Keewatin Ave Toronto Ontario .... TEL (416)481-1714

Goldline Graphics Inc
PO Box 24 Toronto Ontario .... TEL (416)857-2638

Gottschalk + Ash International
11 Bishop St Toronto Ontario .... TEL (416)963-9717

Grafika Art Studios
366 Adelaide St E #345 Toronto Ontario .... TEL (416)368-0356

Grafiks
320 Talfourd St Box 2251 Sarnia Ontario .... TEL (519)336-5230

Graham & Associates Ltd
65 St Clair Ave E 8th Fl Toronto Ontario .... TEL (416)975-9750

Grainge, Ian Designer/Illustrator
280 Southcrest Dr London Ontario .... TEL (519)471-6852

GraphCom Creative Art
20 Railside Rd Don Mills Ontario .... TEL (416)447-4121

Graphcomm Group Inc
305 Arlington Ave Toronto Ontario .... TEL (416)656-4297

Graphic Art
40 Rathburn Rd Etobicoke Ontario .... TEL (416)231-6877

Graphic Assistants
391 Berkeley St #2 Toronto Ontario .... TEL (416)929-6333

Graphic Design Systems
47 Forestbrook Cres Scarborough Ontario .... TEL (416)499-7723

Graphic Directions Ltd
663 Carlaw Ave Toronto Ontario .... TEL (416)465-3403

Graphic Zone Inc
117 Parkview Hill Cres Toronto Ontario .... TEL (416)288-5440

Graphline Graphics
1170 Sheppard Ave W #35 North York Ontario .... TEL (416)631-9400

Greaves & Allen Studios Limited, The
151 Esna Park Dr #30 Markham Ontario .... TEL (416)474-1666

GreenOaks Communications
84 Oaks Ave Richmond Hill Ontario .... TEL (416)889-1987

Griffin & Laphen Marketing
885 Don Mills Rd #121 Toronto Ontario .... TEL (416)444-8852

Hallcrown Group
50 Hallcrown Pl Willowdale Ontario .... TEL (416)756-3986

Hambly & Woolley Inc
152 King St E. Toronto Ontario .... TEL (416)867-1622

Hamilton, Palmer Design Associates Inc
477A Dupont St 2nd Fl Toronto Ontario .... TEL (416)533-1739

Harris/Bhandari Design Associates
67 Mowat Ave #544 Toronto Ontario .... TEL (416)588-9788

Harrison Inc, Adv & Promotion
512 King St E #104 Toronto Ontario .... TEL (416)947-9311

Haughton Brazeau Design Associates
2200 Lakeshore Blvd W #211 Toronto Ontario .... TEL (416)252-7363

Hayden Group, The
48 Hayden St Toronto Ontario .... TEL (416)923-3372

Heather Brown Designs
201 Madison Ave #2 Toronto Ontario .... TEL (416)967-9131

Hefkey, Bruce Associates Ltd
2145 Avenue Rd 2nd Fl Toronto Ontario .... TEL (416)486-0888

Henderson & Company
615 Yonge St #601 Toronto Ontario .... TEL (416)921-6925

Here's How Graphic
181 Carlaw Ave #216 Toronto Ontario .... TEL (416)469-8320

Hillary, Lauran & Charles Commun Inc
9011 Leslie St #210 Richmond Hill Ontario .... TEL (416)886-9432

Holman Communications Inc
The Keep, 250 The Esplanade Toronto Ontario .... TEL (416)362-7633

Hothouse
40 Wynford Dr #208 Don Mills Ontario .... TEL (416)447-6343

Howard Promotional & Mktg Group Ltd, The
703 Evans Ave #104 Toronto Ontario .... TEL (416)622-8900

Hughes, Grieve & Associates
366 Adelaide St E #414 Toronto Ontario .... TEL (416)362-7793

Hyland, Robert Design & Associates
945 Mt Pleasant Rd Toronto Ontario .... TEL (416)483-2097

Hynes, Haslip & Partners Inc
151 John St #303 Toronto Ontario .... TEL (416)971-9706

Ideacom
120 Front St E #201 Toronto Ontario .... TEL (416)941-9224

Images 'N Type Ltd
3575 14th Ave #14 Markham Ontario .... TEL (416)477-7660

Images Art Direction & Design Inc
52 Shaftesbury Ave Toronto Ontario .... TEL (416)964-2262

Index Communications Limited
512 King St E #102 Toronto Ontario .... TEL (416)862-0101

Infinity Graphics Ltd
744 Dundas St E Toronto Ontario .... TEL (416)363-3251

Information Graphics
29 High Park Gardens Toronto Ontario .... TEL (416)762-1055

Ink
555 Richmond St W #504 Toronto Ontario .... TEL (416)360-3894

Intergroup Graphics Inc
980 Yonge St 6th Fl Toronto Ontario .... TEL (416)968-2400

Intermark Design
119 Spadina Ave #600 Toronto Ontario .... TEL (416)599-0600

Introspec Designs
14 Allanford Rd Agincourt Ontario .... TEL (416)839-9887

Ireland, James Design
56 The Esplanade #400 Toronto Ontario .... TEL (416)360-5459

Jack Roberts Marketing Services Limited
40 Wynford Dr #204 Don Mills Ontario .... TEL (416)445-3720

Jaymor Designs
66 Gerrard St E #300 Toronto Ontario .... TEL (416)599-7981

Kalligrafika
2237 Mount Albert Rd Mount Albert Ontario .... TEL (416)473-5014

Kamnatnik, Robert Design Ltd
119 Yorkville Ave 2nd Fl Toronto Ontario .... TEL (416)961-2723

Karn & Garber
25 Curity Ave Toronto Ontario .... TEL (416)288-0500

Kinetics Design
23 Hepworth Dr Weston Ontario .... TEL (416)247-5379

King West Communications
511 King St W #100 Toronto Ontario .... TEL (416)591-8822

Kramer Design Associates Ltd
103 Dupont St Toronto Ontario .... TEL (416)921-1078

Krohnert Graphics Ltd
595 Middlefield Rd #7 Scarborough Ontario .... TEL (416)292-0560

Kuster, Martin A. Associates Limited
890 Queen St W Toronto Ontario .... TEL (416)537-1786

L&C Design Ltd
401 Richmond St W #208 Toronto Ontario .... TEL (416)340-9440

L. Lee Studio
105 Parkview Ave Willowdale Ontario .... TEL (416)221-7395

Laing, Wes & Associates Inc
4800 Dundas St W #203 Etobicoke Ontario .... TEL (416)236-3737

Landgraff Design Associates Ltd
5945 Airport Rd, Airway Centre Mississauga Ontario .... TEL (416)678-0398

Lashbrook Advertising Design
378 Queen St E Toronto Ontario .... TEL (416)366-9490

Laws, Sherman Studio
31 Progress Crt #5 Scarborough Ontario .... TEL (416)289-4477

Lennox Group Communications Inc
Royal Coliseum Exhibition Place Toronto Ontario .... TEL (416)698-0282

Leppik Graphics
37 Hanna Ave Toronto Ontario .... TEL (416)535-2210

Lettuce Design
76 Scollard St Toronto Ontario .... TEL (416)929-9579

Light Illusion
40 Carobob Crt #209 Agincourt Ontario .... TEL (416)754-8748

Lilly Desktop Design
8 First St Etobicoke Ontario .... TEL (416)259-9597

Lithart Associates Ltd
43 Lesmill Rd Toronto Ontario .... TEL (416)391-4036

Lockwood Design Associates
2028 Avenue Rd #201 Toronto Ontario .... TEL (416)481-1163

Lunaria Graphic Design Services
3107 Bloor St W #204 Toronto Ontario .... TEL (416)762-2690

M B I
511 King St W #100 Toronto Ontario .... TEL (416)340-1332

M.H. Orr and Associates
33 City Centre Dr #543 Mississauga Ontario .... TEL (416)566-7517

M.S. Art Services Ltd
23 Fraser Avenue Toronto Ontario .... TEL (416)537-8108

Maclennan, Joss Design & Illustration
182 Deleware Ave Toronto Ontario .... TEL (416)534-6062

MacNaughton, Neil Design Associates Inc
170 Donway W North York Ontario .... TEL (416)449-6001

Male, Richard Design Associates Limited
430 King St W #210 Toronto Ontario .... TEL (416)591-7921

Maleda Limited
135 West Beaver Creek Rd Richmond Hill Ontario ... TEL (416)889-2000

Mandala Communications Inc
2 Melanie Dr #5 Bramalea Ontario .... TEL (416)792-7606

Many Pens Design
543 Timothy St 2nd Fl Newmarket Ontario .... TEL (416)836-9800

Mariposa Communications & Promotions Inc
147 Liberty St Toronto Ontario .... TEL (416)588-6699

Marketcom Inc
100 Lombard St #200 Toronto Ontario .... TEL (416)862-7733

Marketing F/X Limited
205 Church St #100 Toronto Ontario .... TEL (416)862-0861

Marko Creative Productions Inc
245 Yorkland Blvd #302 North York Ontario .... TEL (416)756-0171

Marovino & Associates
365 Evans Ave #205 Toronto Ontario .... TEL (416)259-5270

Marshall Cummings & Associates
43 Davies Ave Toronto Ontario .... TEL (416)461-3563

Match Art Inc
219 Dufferin St #200B Toronto Ontario .... TEL (416)534-4227

MCG Graphics
88 University Ave 9th Fl Toronto Ontario .... TEL (416)593-1375

McLean Bilz & Co.
331 Eglinton Ave E Toronto Ontario .... TEL (416)485-9391

McMahon, Teri Graphic Art Ltd
433 Roselawn Ave Toronto Ontario .... TEL (416)481-8554

McManus & Associates Limited
99 Crowns Lane 2nd Fl Toronto Ontario .... TEL (416)922-6661

MDC Design Group Inc
939 Eglinton Ave E #100 Toronto Ontario .... TEL (416)467-1343

Media Decisions Inc
62 Shaftesbury Ave Toronto Ontario .... TEL (416)964-7191

Media Three Marketing Services
431 Alden Rd #11 Markham Ontario .... TEL (416)763-5453

Melaine Communications Group Inc
33 Niagara St Toronto Ontario .... TEL (416)362-3900

Meloche Communications Group, The
236 Avenue Rd Toronto Ontario .... TEL (416)922-1361

MG Communications
1244A Yonge St Toronto Ontario .... TEL (416)920-9083

Michael Peters Group Canada Inc
250 The Esplanade #210 Toronto Ontario .... TEL (416)367-8424

Middleton, R. Marketing & Design Ltd
77 Bloor St W #1106 Toronto Ontario .... TEL (416)964-2217

Miller Design Group
77 Mowat Ave #503 Toronto Ontario .... TEL (416)519-0927

Moniz Design Group Inc
219 Dufferin St #306B Toronto Ontario .... TEL (416)516-0927

MW&S Design Associates
124 Parliament St Toronto Ontario .... TEL (416)869-1811

Nash & Nash Ltd
353 Harbord St Toronto Ontario .... TEL (416)536-2934

Nasmith & Company Inc
100 Richmond St E #220 Toronto Ontario .... TEL (416)362-2799

National Graphics
276 Carlaw Ave #212 Toronto Ontario .... TEL (416)466-6227

Navarra Art Directions
67 Mowat Ave #547 Toronto Ontario .... TEL (416)588-8872

Network Studios Inc
1030 Islington Ave Etobicoke Ontario .... TEL (416)233-3232

Networx Inc
163 Sterling Rd Toronto Ontario .... TEL (416)533-7744

Newton Frank Arthur Inc
115A Matheson Blve W #207 Mississauga Ontario .... TEL (416)568-2360

Newton/Donoahue Design Consultants
544 Richmond St W Toronto Ontario .... TEL (416)366-5587

Norman Cameron Associates Ltd
602 The Queensway Toronto Ontario .... TEL (416)255-7801

O'Connell Studio Inc
2 Bloor St W 9th Fl Toronto Ontario .... TEL (416)923-9500

Oasis Creative Group Inc
5 Polson St Toronto Ontario .... TEL (416)461-7518

Obern Design Ltd
815 Queen St E Toronto Ontario .... TEL (416)469-2689

Oliveira, Manuel Graphic Design
260 Richmond St W #605 Toronto Ontario .... TEL (416)598-0518

Oliver, Peter & Company
2005 Sheppard Ave East # 100 Willowdale Ontario .... TEL (416)490-9091

On Topic Communications
201 Tremont Rd London Ontario .... TEL (519)451-0652

On-Line Design
10 Brentcliffe Rd #212 Toronto Ontario .... TEL (416)425-5621

Original Electronic Art
40 Ronson Dr Rexdale Ontario .... TEL (416)241-9121

Ove Design Toronto Ltd
73 Laird Dr #302 Toronto Ontario .... TEL (416)423-6228

Overdrive Design Limited
680 Queens Quay West #727 Toronto Ontario .... TEL (416)593-1659

Overleaf Design
94 Wheeler Ave Toronto Ontario .... TEL (416)691-8347

Page/Cooper Design
318 St Germain Ave Toronto Ontario .... TEL (416)256-1301

Panache Design
361 King St E Toronto Ontario .... TEL (416)369-0084

Panagraphics Ltd
62 Alness St #1 Downsview Ontario .... TEL (416)665-6767

Paquette Designs
20 Sorauren Ave #4 Toronto Ontario .... TEL (416)538-4444

Parallax Design Consultants
77 Mowat Ave #115 Toronto Ontario .... TEL (416)536-3143

Partners in Design
111 Queen Street East # 370 Toronto Ontario .... TEL (416)362-2836

Perfect Match Design
92 Bleeker St 3rd Fl Toronto Ontario .... TEL (416)324-9773

Pickett & Mulholland Creative Communications Inc
411 Wedgewood Dr Oakville Ontario .... TEL (416)928-7728

Pinpoint Design Studio
430 King St W #107 Toronto Ontario .... TEL (416)979-5800

Pixel Graphics Inc
111 Queen St E #370 Toronto Ontario .... TEL (416)362-8666

Plewes, William Design
102 Atlantic Ave 2nd Fl Toronto Ontario .... TEL (416)538-3002

PM Creative Services Inc
169 Gerrard St E Lwr Level Toronto Ontario .... TEL (416)925-1806

Portfolio Studio
277 Eglinton E Toronto Ontario .... TEL (416)487-3275

Premise Communications & Mktg Inc
47 Colborne St #404 Toronto Ontario .... TEL (416)947-9347

Prime Directive
2145 Dunwin Dr #3 Mississauga Ontario .... TEL (416)828-1032

Pritchard Creative Communications Inc
9 Davies Avenue # 302 Toronto Ontario .... TEL (416)778-6691

Product Initiatives
2200 Yonge St #607 Toronto Ontario .... TEL (416)487-5757

Production Blitz
8 Price St Lwr Lvl Toronto Ontario .... TEL (416)922-6434

Program Design Group
579 Richmond St W #300 Toronto Ontario .... TEL (416)366-8464

Promanad Communications
2645 Matheson Blvd E Mississauga Ontario .... TEL (416)238-8080

Promotion & Event Marketing Group, The
67 Mowat Ave #433 Toronto Ontario .... TEL (416)588-7740

Pronk & Associates
42 Prince Andrew Pl Don Mills Ontario .... TEL (416)441-3760

Public Good Design & Communications Inc
41 Dovercourt Rd Toronto Ontario .... TEL (416)588-3075

Pyxilus Communications Ltd
151 Esna Park Dr #10 Markham Ontario .... TEL (416)940-1300

Quadra Graphics
40 Wynford Dr #210 Don Mills Ontario .... TEL (416)447-2409

R.K. Studio Limited
309 Wellesley St E Toronto Ontario .... TEL (416)964-6991

Radar, Inc
201 Madison Ave Toronto Ontario .... TEL (416)967-9131

Raleigh Associates Mktg Communications
4180 Dundas St W Toronto Ontario .... TEL (416)234-0614

Rapport Graphics Inc
920 Commissioners Rd E London Ontario .... TEL (519)471-6260

Reactor Art & Design
51 Camden St Toronto Ontario .... TEL (416)362-1913

Read, Robert Design
7 Kingswood Rd Toronto Ontario .... TEL (416)691-7293

Rebus Communications
17 St. Joseph St. # 207 Toronto Ontario .... TEL (416)960-1597

Reflex Marketing Communications
One Yonge St #1801 Toronto Ontario .... TEL (416)360-7507

Reid, Robert Graphics Ltd
40 Wynford Dr #204 Don Mills Ontario .... TEL (416)449-6616

Reilly, Rennie Campbell Ltd
100 Midwest Rd Scarborough Ontario .... TEL (416)759-5870

Renaissance, Emmanuel Design
419 Nairn Ave Toronto Ontario .... TEL (416)656-1283

Riordon Design Group Inc, The
5945 Airport Rd #195 Airway Centre Mississauga .... TEL (416)673-2416

Robert Keller & Associates
1087 Sawgrass Cres Mississauga Ontario .... TEL (416)276-5761

Robin Sharpe Associates Ltd
157 Princess St 3rd Fl Toronto Ontario .... TEL (416)360-5886

Robinson, John L.
567 Avenue Rd #705 Toronto Ontario .... TEL (416)920-8652

Roger Murray and Associates, Inc
124 Galaxy Blvd Toronto Ontario .... TEL (416)675-1997

Rogers, William M. & Associates Inc
146 Laird Dr #110 Toronto Ontario .... TEL (416)425-7551

Rood, R & Associates
2055 Dundas St E #105 Mississauga Ontario .... TEL (416)238-0150

Roseborough, Everett Ltd
4174 Dundas St W Toronto Ontario .... TEL (416)236-2811

Ross, Mah Design Associates
103 Lisgar St 2nd Fl Toronto Ontario .... TEL (416)535-9053

Roth, George
212 Willowdale Ave Waterloo Ontario .... TEL (519)885-4325

Rotstein, Joel & Associates
112 Merton St, Courtyard Toronto Ontario .... TEL (416)487-9973

RSB Communications Inc
474 Richmond St W Toronto Ontario .... TEL (416)868-6262

Rubin, Walter Communication Design
85 Langley Ave Toronto Ontario .... TEL (416)466-9953

Ruddan Corporate Sports
152 Sheppard Ave W #200 Toronto Ontario .... TEL (416)250-6066

Rushton, Green & Grossutti Inc
905 Broadview Ave Toronto Ontario .... TEL (416)469-4178

Russell Design Inc
720 King St W #821 Toronto Ontario .... TEL (416)594-3701

Ryan, Chong & Associates Inc
41 Thompson St Toronto Ontario .... TEL (416)461-2377

Ryan, G. Design
197 Eastern Ave 2nd Fl Toronto Ontario .... TEL (416)868-6500

S&E Graphics Ltd
4701 Steeles Ave W #202 Weston Ontario .... TEL (416)746-3985

Savage Sloan Limited
2 Pardee Ave #300 Toronto Ontario .... TEL (416)536-4050

SCF Limited
232 Parliament St Toronto Ontario .... TEL (416)368-4999

Schembri, David Design Associates Inc
4155 Sheppard Ave E #201 Scarborough Ontario .... TEL (416)297-9331

Schieber Design Associates Inc
135 Broadview Ave Toronto Ontario .... TEL (416)778-8866

SD Graphics Ltd
50 Tissield Rd #3 Scarborough Ontario .... TEL (416)291-9869

Semark Design
121 Brunel Road Mississauga Ontario .... TEL (416)890-1714

SG & Associates
1060 Britannia Rd E #12 Mississauga Ontario .... TEL (416)670-5814

Sibley, Gordon Design Inc
1179 King St W #324 Toronto Ontario .... TEL (416)534-0059

Sierra Corporate Production Inc
102 Atlantic Avenue, # 302 Toronto Ontario .... TEL (416)531-8757

Signacom Design Inc
250 The Esplanade #400 Toronto Ontario .... TEL (416)362-8787

Skymark Graphics Ltd
333 Denison St #14 Markham Ontario .... TEL (416)475-5118

Smarketics Inc
205 Church St #100 Toronto Ontario .... TEL (416)862-0861

Smart, Leslie & Associates
108 Parliament St Toronto Ontario .... TEL (416)363-0441

Smerdon, Richard & Associates
55 Eglinton Ave E #706 Toronto Ontario .... TEL (416)487-5589

Smith & Locke Associates Ltd
889 Broadview Ave Toronto Ontario .... TEL (416)461-0719

Smith Unlimited
68 Claremont St Toronto Ontario .... TEL (416)363-1934

Smith, Don & Associates
400 Mt Pleasant Rd #1 Toronto Ontario .... TEL (416)480-2759

Smith, Wycliffe Design
56 The Esplanade #301 Toronto Ontario .... TEL (416)360-1788

Socha, Michele Art Studio
220 Goulding Ave Willowdale Ontario .... TEL (416)225-6476

Solstice Communications Ltd
2 Sheppard Ave E #204 Willowdale Ontario .... TEL (416)733-2215

Square Six Design
411 Richmond St E #204 Toronto Ontario .... TEL (416)862-2748

St. John Group, The
230 Niagara St Toronto Ontario .... TEL (416)364-3884

Stahl, Jack & Associates Ltd
100 Adelaide St W #202 Toronto Ontario .... TEL (416)368-3081

Starta/Com Marketing Communications Inc
920 Yonge St #710 Toronto Ontario .... TEL (416)972-6140

Steiner, Jack Graphic Design
366 Adelaide E #442 Toronto Ontario .... TEL (416)368-8595

Stewart, Edward A. Ltd
37 Front St E 4th Fl Toronto Ontario .... TEL (416)863-6332

Strada Communications Inc
15 Delisle Ave Toronto Ontario .... TEL (416)921-5345

Strata/Com Marketing Communications Inc
920 Yonge St #710 Toronto Ontario .... TEL (416)972-6140

Strategies International
250 The Esplanade #100 Toronto Ontario .... TEL (416)366-8883

Studio K Art & Design Inc
30 St Clair Ave W #200 Toronto Ontario .... TEL (416)961-6200

Summa Promotions
13 Northmount Ave Downsview Ontario .... TEL (416)739-7207

Sun Controlled Ventures Inc
333 King St E Toronto Ontario .... TEL (416)947-2191

Sung, Philip Design
221 Richmond St W Toronto Ontario .... TEL (416)581-1620

Symbol Graphics
111 Peter St #504 Toronto Ontario .... TEL (416)596-7579

Synergex
124 Merton St 5th Fl Toronto Ontario .... TEL (416)484-6275

Synergy Design Ltd
67 Berkeley St Toronto Ontario .... TEL (416)363-3507

Ta-Ke Graphics Inc
6032b Yonge St Willowdale Ontario .... TEL (416)225-5263

Taylor & Browning Design Associates
10 Price St Toronto Ontario .... TEL (416)927-7094

Taylor/Levkoe Associates Ltd
11 Church St #307 Toronto Ontario .... TEL (416)366-8961

Taylor/Sprules Corporation
1 Polson St Unit 1 Toronto Ontario .... TEL (416)461-9214

TDF Artist Ltd
980 Yonge St 2nd Fl Toronto Ontario .... TEL (416)924-3371

Tech Plus Marketing Consultants
2133 Royal Windsor Dr #16 Mississauga Ontario .... TEL (416)822-3330

Telemedia Procom Inc
50 Holly St Toronto Ontario .... TEL (416)482-9399

Telmet Design Associates
553 Queen St W #300 Toronto Ontario .... TEL (416)366-5646

Terra Media Design Ltd
414 Moore Ave Toronto Ontario .... TEL (416)425-8391

Terrelonge Design Inc
11 Davies Ave Toronto Ontario .... TEL (416)462-1960

Thadaney, Witterman Design
366 Adelaide St E #544 Toronto Ontario .... TEL (416)922-0842

That Graphics Place Ltd
190 Wellington St London Ontario .... TEL (519)434-6524

The Creative Marketing Network
70 Jefferson Ave Toronto Ontario .... TEL (416)539-0694

The Entertainment Business Centre
387 Bloor St E 5th Fl Toronto Ontario .... TEL (416)925-5437

The Forefront Communications Group Inc
1781 Avenue Rd Toronto Ontario .... TEL (416)787-5603

The Incentive Design Co
18 Banigan Dr Toronto Ontario .... TEL (416)467-1211

The Long Group
1220 Yonge St 3rd Fl Toronto Ontario .... TEL (416)972-6306

The Merton Circle Ltd
250 Merton St Toronto Ontario .... TEL (416)483-8997

The Richmond Studio
508 Richmond St E Toronto Ontario .... TEL (416)366-0049

The Works Plus + Advertising
46 Brantwood Dr Toronto Ontario .... TEL (416)438-8148

Third Generation Graphics
134 Peter St #400 Toronto Ontario .... TEL (416)593-9424

Tibbles, William & Company Inc
239 McRae Drive Toronto Ontario .... TEL (416)422-0022

Tier One Communications Inc
140 Renfrew Dr #101 Markham Ontario .... TEL (416)470-0444

Timmerman Group
165 John St 2nd Fl Toronto Ontario .... TEL (416)977-5832

Tomcik, Andrew Graphic Design Consultant
48 Parkhurst Blvd Toronto Ontario .... TEL (416)482-7082

Tomlinson, Lynne Communications
76 Pearl South Hamilton Ontario .... TEL (416)528-4936

Torpedo! Design
18 Delroy Dr Toronto Ontario .... TEL (416)252-4259

Torsney Barnett Roberts Advertising
20 Dundas St W #1030 Toronto Ontario .... TEL (416)977-2125

Total Creative Alliance Inc
75 Lesmill Road, Unit 3 Don Mills Ontario .... TEL (416)633-1502

Tri-Alpha Publications
10 Falconer Dr #12 Mississauga Ontario .... TEL (416)858-7933

Tribco Communications Group
134 Peter St Toronto Ontario .... TEL (416)340-2833

Tudhope Associates Inc
284 King St E Toronto Ontario .... TEL (416)366-7100

Turvey Associates
P.O. Box 1273 Guelph Ontario .... TEL (519)823-1075

Two Dimensions Inc
260 Sorauren Ave Toronto Ontario .... TEL (416)539-0766

TYCA Graphix Communications Inc
89A Sackville St Toronto Ontario .... TEL (416)923-5017

Type A Grafik
72 Fraser Ave #107 Toronto Ontario .... TEL (416)588-0447

Ungerman, Sharon Graphics
1519 Dupont St Toronto Ontario .... TEL (416)533-8723

Universal Communications
73 Laird Dr #402 Toronto Ontario .... TEL (416)423-4440

Unny, Gerhild
RR# 1 St Agatha Ontario .... TEL (519)699-5313

Uxbridge Communications
55 Wellesley St E #605 Toronto Ontario .... TEL (416)922-0807

Van Toch Designs Inc
66 Gloucester St Toronto Ontario .... TEL (416)926-9361

Victoria Graphics
9011 Leslie St #210 Richmond Hill Ontario .... TEL (416)886-9432

Visual Connection, The
886 Queen St W Toronto Ontario .... TEL (416)536-3427

Vital Design & Communications
72 Fraser Street, Unit III Toronto Ontario .... TEL (416)588-2689

Viva, Frank Design Limited
12 Birch Ave #205 Toronto Ontario .... TEL (416)923-6355

Vivid Design Group
931 Commissioners Rd E #200 London Ontario .... TEL (519)432-8212

Vopni & Parsons Design Ltd
522 Eglinton Ave E Toronto Ontario .... TEL (416)483-6557

Vosburgh & Associates
269 Richmond St W 2nd Fl Toronto Ontario .... TEL (416)585-9655

VS Design Ltd
72 Fraser Ave #125 Toronto Ontario .... TEL (416)530-1411

Wal, Gerry Professional Prod Promo Inc
321 Betty Ann Drive Willowdale Ontario .... TEL (416)222-6767

Walker, John & Associates
10 Walker Ave #103 Toronto Ontario .... TEL (416)968-3760

Wallis Studios Inc
600 King St W 4th Fl Toronto Ontario .... TEL (416)862-1444

Walsh, Mort & Associates Ltd
57 Charles St W # 1410 Toronto Ontario .... TEL (416)924-4583

Waplington, Forty, McGall Inc
49 Bathurst St #100 Toronto Ontario .... TEL (416)366-0466

Watt Group, The
300 Bayview Ave Toronto Ontario .... TEL (416)364-9384

Wellington & Wolfe Ltd
1030 Islington Ave Etobicoke Ontario .... TEL (416)233-3232

Werle Design Associates
740 Huron St Toronto Ontario .... TEL (416)927-7447

Westerside, Graham Graphic Design
60 Jeropme Cres #1405 Stoney Creek Ontario .... TEL (416)578-1817

Whelehan Design Associates Inc
388 King St W #220 Toronto Ontario .... TEL (416)979-9511

Whiteboard Studio
90 Winges Rd #22 Woodbridge Ontario .... TEL (416)850-3582

Whitecom
11 Boulton Ave Toronto Ontario .... TEL (416)469-0144

Whitney Graphics
3284 Yonge St Toronto Ontario .... TEL (416)485-8292

Whitton, H. Design Associates
332 Richmond St W Toronto Ontario .... TEL (416)591-7292

Windsor Art Studio Ltd
322 Antigua Rd Mississauga Ontario .... TEL (416)896-4020

Wolff Williams
67 Mowat Ave #353 Toronto Ontario .... TEL (416)531-2480

Word & Image Design Studio Inc
146 Laird Dr #307 Toronto Ontario .... TEL (416)429-1060

Wysiwyg Studio
20 Maud St #400 Toronto Ontario .... TEL (416)362-4348

Y.S. Design
37 Brentcliffe Rd Toronto Ontario .... TEL (416)422-3945

Yaneff, Chris Ltd
119 Isabella St Toronto Ontario .... TEL (416)924-6677

Yardley Productions Inc
69 Liberty St Toronto Ontario .... TEL (416)588-8695

Zeppelin Graphics
620 King St W Lower Level Toronto Ontario .... TEL (416)364-4146

Zimmerman Rose Inc
67 Mowat Ave #537 Toronto Ontario .... TEL (416)534-3444

Zoran Design Inc
25 Coronet Rd #1 Etobicoke Ontario .... TEL (416)236-1197

DESIGNERS — OTTAWA

246 5th Design Associated
246 5th Ave Ottawa Ontario .... TEL (613)231-3000

Aartvark
65 Bank St 2nd Fl Ottawa Ontario .... TEL (613)232-5133

Acart Graphics Services Inc
171 Nepean St #500 Ottawa Ontario .... TEL (613)230-7944

Aerographics Creative Services
75 Spark St #300 Ottawa Ontario .... TEL (613)235-2188

AL Associates Advertising & Mktg
404C Bank St Ottawa Ontario .... TEL (613)233-4331

BAC Communications Ltd
77 Gore St E Perth Ontario .... TEL (613)267-3734

Ball, Viki
P.O. Box 4758, Stn E Ottawa Ontario .... TEL (613)236-4136

Banfield-Seguin Ltd
887 Richmond Rd Ottawa Ontario .... TEL (613)722-6832

Bates, Donna Art & Design
246 Queen St #400 Ottawa Ontario .... TEL (613)232-3462

Bayne-Herrera Graphic Communication Ltd
155A MacLaren St #1 Ottawa Ontario .... TEL (613)233-5773

Bermingham Marketing Ltd
99 Brock St Box 1622 Kingston Ontario .... TEL (613)544-1380

Black Sheep Designs
11 Oakland Ave Ottawa Ontario .... TEL (613)235-0684

Boite Noire
125 Eddy St Hull Quebec .... TEL (819)778-0445

Cardinal Research & Design
Box 389 Manotick Ontario .... TEL (613)692-2961

Chalmers, Rae Associates Corp
880 Wellington St #806 Ottawa Ontario .... TEL (613)233-6425

Champagne, Chantel
808-1435 Prince of Wales Dr Ottawa Ontario .... TEL (613)723-0806

Charette, Jacques & Associates Ltd
77 Laurier St Hull Quebec .... TEL (819)771-0441

Cheriton Graphics Systems Ltd
432 Rideau St Ottawa Ontario .... TEL (613)238-3699

Communicado Associates
409 Queen St Ottawa Ontario .... TEL (613)238-6444

Danylevwich, Morris
349 Marshal Crt Ottawa Ontario .... TEL (613)733-9918

Desmarais, Donald
9 Lenore Pl Vanier Ontario .... TEL (613)745-6277

Eas Illustrators & Printers Ltd
171 Nepean St Ottawa Ontario .... TEL (613)236-7944

Ethier Fernand Graphiste
D101 - 131 Richer Hull Quebec .... TEL (819)777-1702

Fabian Marketing Systems
81 Auriga #13 Nepean Ontario .... TEL (613)232-9767

Fancott Associates
880 Wellington St #604 Ottawa Ontario .... TEL (613)594-3810

Gregory/Gregory Limited
1081 River Rd Ottawa Ontario .... TEL (613)741-4027

Griffe Design Inc
590 Rideau St Ottawa Ontario .... TEL (613)236-6040

Heath Horton Design Group
1081 River Rd Ottawa Ontario .... TEL (613)741-4027

Herrera, Bob
155a MacLaren St Ottawa Ontario .... TEL (613)233-5773

Hewitt, John
151 Bay St #905 Ottawa Ontario .... TEL (613)235-3301

Innovacom
72 Laval Hull Quebec .... TEL (819)771-6237

International Creative Marketing
458 Maclaren Ottawa Ontario .... TEL (613)230-9323

Labarthe, Christian
105 Putman Ave Ottawa Ontario .... TEL (613)746-0657

MacLeod, James B.
526 Gladstone Ave Ottawa Ontario .... TEL (613)593-4153

Marshall & Associates
126 York St #221 Ottawa Ontario .... TEL (613)567-7506

Maruska Studios
61A York St Ottawa Ontario .... TEL (613)230-1906

Matsumoto Advertising
620 Cummings Ave #12 Ottawa Ontario .... TEL (613)741-4807

McClure, Kathi
808-1435 Prince of Wales Dr Ottawa Ontario .... TEL (613)723-0806

McKenzie, George
2022 Kingsgrove Cres Ottawa Ontario .... TEL (613)741-7467

Mellor-Wheatley Associates Inc
179 Dalhousie St MW House Ottawa Ontario .... TEL (613)232-2413

Multimedia Design Group Inc
16 Beechwood Ave #202 Ottawa Ontario .... TEL (613)749-6663

Murray McFarlane Graphics
1356 Wellington St Ottawa Ontario .... TEL (613)729-6940

Noble Graphics
P.O. Box 190 Richmond Ontario .... TEL (613)838-3074

Noosong Graphics
D/22 Antares Dr Nepean Ontario .... TEL (613)226-8280

Nortext Information Design Ltd
200 - 16 Concourse Gate Nepean Ontario .... TEL (613)727-5466

Popelar, Jitka
440 Coventry Rd Ottawa Ontario .... TEL (613)933-0570

Productions Claude Savoie Inc
327 St. Joseph Blvd Hull Quebec .... TEL (819)776-6533

Quorum Graphics
200 - 1st Ave Ottawa Ontario .... TEL (613)232-5074

Rapid Grafic
410 Bank St Ottawa Ontario .... TEL (613)238-3303

Rolfe, George
32 Kennear St Ottawa Ontario .... TEL (613)998-8987

Rolfe, Shelagh
32 Kennear St Ottawa Ontario .... TEL (613)731-1831

Saint-Germain, Richard
National Arts Centre Ottawa Ontario .... TEL (613)996-5051

Scott, Mary
18 Bourgeau St Aylmer Quebec .... TEL (819)684-6379

Sheffield Graphics Ltd
1177 Newmarket Ave Ottawa Ontario .... TEL (613)741-1650

Shoreline Graphics Inc
316 Dalhousie St #200 Ottawa Ontario .... TEL (613)234-4000

Smith, Neville
131 Mayburry Skyridge, Alymer Quebec .... TEL (819)827-1832

Steele, Peggy Art & Design Ltd
246 Queen St #400 Ottawa Ontario .... TEL (613)233-6077

Takeuchi, Norman
310 Lindsay St Ottawa Ontario .... TEL (613)998-9485

Teitz, Carole
1924 Oakdean Cres Ottawa Ontario .... TEL (613)749-0090

The Advertising Dynasty Inc
190 Colonnade Rd S #6 Nepean Ontario .... TEL (613)727-5651

Vis.com Design
26 Woodlawn Ave Ottawa Ontario .... TEL (819)232-9917

Wang Graphics
P.O. Box 2917, Stn D Ottawa Ontario .... TEL (613)238-3254

Wawa Design
105 Putman Ave Ottawa Ontario .... TEL (613)746-0657

Way, Allen
392 Kenwood Ave Ottawa Ontario .... TEL (613)722-7430

Wendesigns
1B-150 Waverly St Ottawa Ontario .... TEL (613)232-5667

Wuff Designs
192 - 2nd Ave Ottawa Ontario .... TEL (613)232-8367

INDUSTRIAL DESIGNERS

Adamson Industrial Design
174 Avenue Rd Toronto Ontario .... TEL (416)963-9356

Almas & Associates Limited
2159 Alconbury Crescent Burlington Ontario .... TEL (416)336-1974

AM Studios
20 Eglinton Ave E #200 Toronto Ontario .... TEL (416)486-6279

Arato Design Associates Inc
135 Sparks Ave Willowdale Ontario .... TEL (416)492-0627

Arnott Design Group Inc
33 Davies Ave. Toronto Ontario .... TEL (416)778-8990

Association of Chartered Industrial Designers of Ontario
168 Bedford Rd 2nd Fl Toronto Ontario .... TEL (416)928-3069

Axis Group, The
65 Bellwoods Ave #2 Toronto Ontario .... TEL (416)364-3388

b&b design associates
5 Hermit Court Don Mills Ontario .... TEL (416)445-7563

D.I. Design & Development
110 Bond St Toronto Ontario .... TEL (416)595-9598

Designwerke
366 King St E Toronto Ontario .... TEL (416)362-6000

Dollery Rudman Design Associates Inc
600 King St W 3rd Fl Toronto Ontario .... TEL (416)362-0065

Etheric Line Designs
25 St Nicholas St #208 Toronto Ontario .... TEL (416)975-1511

Gidman Design Associates Limitee
Box 283, 55 McCaul St Toronto Ontario .... TEL (416)283-3003

Hetherington Welch Design
30 Wertheim Crt #27 Richmond Hill Ontario .... TEL (416)881-9243

Hubel, Vello
531 Soudan Ave Toronto Ontario .... TEL (416)486-1602

Hunter Straker Templeton Ltd
26 Overlea Blvd Toronto Ontario .... TEL (416)421-7880

Industrial Graphics
85 Bowes Rd #11 Concord Ontario .... TEL (416)660-2488

KAN Industrial Designers
76 Richmond St E Toronto Ontario .... TEL (416)362-7737

L'Image Design
7100 Warden Ave #1&2 Markham Ontario .... TEL (416)475-7703

Laskoski, Stephen Designers Inc
394 King St E Toronto Ontario .... TEL (416)863-1350

Marshall, Graham
48 Allen St W #3 Waterloo Ontario .... TEL (519)884-1710

Moffat Associates
98 Thornridge Dr Thornhill Ontario .... TEL (416)889-5252

Muller, Keith Ltd
56 The Esplanade #510 Toronto Ontario .... TEL (416)362-6446

Omniplan-Miller/Zell Inc
92 Church St S #108 Ajax Ontario .... TEL (416)427-2902

Ove Design Toronto Ltd
73 Laird Dr #302 Toronto Ontario .... TEL (416)423-6228

Percept Industrial Design Inc
480 Victoria St N Kitchener Ontario .... TEL (519)749-3186

Plewes, William Design
102 Atlantic Ave 2nd Fl Toronto Ontario .... TEL (416)538-3002

Price, Rene
812 Kenyon Cres Cornwall Ontario .... TEL (613)938-5886

Sambrook and Hermetz Industrial Designers Ltd
116 Viceroy Rd #D-9 Concord Ontario .... TEL (416)736-7619

Slade, Ross J.
39 Fern Ave Ottawa Ontario .... TEL (613)729-9313

Studio Innova Inc
8 Clarence Sq Toronto Ontario .... TEL (416)595-5991

Whalen, Robert Taylor Inc
77 Mowat Ave #505 Toronto Ontario .... TEL (416)532-2867

CORPORATE INTERIOR DESIGNERS

Anthony Meyrick-Eastick Design Group Inc
430 King St W #200 Toronto Ontario .... TEL (416)593-8844

Atkinson McKee Design Consultants Inc
360 Albert St #1415 Ottawa Ontario .... TEL (613)563-3797

B&H Interior Design
481 University Ave Toronto Ontario .... TEL (416)596-2299

Bjarnason & Associates
11 Church St #300 Toronto Ontario .... TEL (416)368-4040

Britacan Business Interiors Ltd
505 Consumers Rd #1010 Willowdale Ontario .... TEL (416)494-2007

Bullock, Jeffrey Design Consultants Inc
8 Market St #300 Toronto Ontario .... TEL (416)868-1616

Cecconi Eppstadt Simone Designers
663 Queen St E Toronto Ontario .... TEL (416)462-1445

Cheung Designs
722 Queen St W Toronto Ontario .... TEL (416)862-8282

Fielding & Associates
300 North Queen St #204 Etobicoke Ontario .... TEL (416)626-6767

Frankland Rusznyak Associates Ltd
228 Gerrard St E Toronto Ontario .... TEL (416)928-7422

Hefele Makowka Design Associates Inc
525 Adelaide St E Toronto Ontario .... TEL (416)367-3666

Holmberg Associates Inc
260 Richmond St E Toronto Ontario .... TEL (416)364-2950

Howlett Design Consultants Ltd
8 Market St #500 Toronto Ontario .... TEL (416)363-5281

Inger Bartlett & Associates Ltd
2a Gibson Ave Toronto Ontario .... TEL (416)926-8247

Interfac Inc - Facilities Design
255 Mathesson Blvd W Mississauga Ontario .... TEL (416)890-3000

Kubik Zdobinsky & Associates Inc
119 Spadina Ave #1103 Toronto Ontario .... TEL (416)977-4222

L'Image Design
7100 Warden Ave #1&2 Markham Ontario .... TEL (416)475-7703

McGregor Charbonneau Design Consultants Inc
507 King St E Toronto Ontario .... TEL (416)359-0002

McWatt Anderson Design Consultants Inc
28 Atlantic Ave Toronto Ontario .... TEL (416)530-4613

Mole-White & Associates Ltd
260 King St E #320 Toronto Ontario .... TEL (416)867-1414

Pulsann Commercial Interiors Inc
111 Queen St E #340 Toronto Ontario .... TEL (416)865-1196

Raymond Tipping Chiappetta Inc
550 Queen St E Toronto Ontario .... TEL (416)368-6819

Stocks, Paul A. Limited
35 Coldwater Rd Don Mills Ontario .... TEL (416)449-9733

Total Environmental Planning Limited
265 Hood Rd Markham Ontario .... TEL (416)474-0510

Yen, Chris Designs Inc, Planning & Design
120 Carlton St #315 Toronto Ontario .... TEL (416)323-3888

Zeidler Roberts Interiors Limited
315 Queen St W Toronto Ontario .... TEL (416)596-8300

ELECTRONIC GRAPHICS & SERVICES

Adcom Electronics Ltd
310 Judson St #1 Toronto Ontario .... TEL (416)251-3355

Advance Films & Video Limited
257 Norseman St Toronto Ontario .... TEL (416)231-2223

Advantech Animation Inc
181 Carlaw Ave #211 Toronto Ontario .... TEL (416)462-3662

Aniforms - The Audio Visualizers
410 Queens Quay W #420 Toronto Ontario .... TEL (416)363-4963

Animation Group Ltd
312 Adelaide St W #801 Toronto Ont .... TEL (416)593-0473

Animation House, The
162 Parliament St Toronto Ontario .... TEL (416)364-3556

Animette Canada
210 Romfield Circuit Thornhill Ontario .... TEL (416)881-2099

Ann-imation
179 John St 8th Fl Toronto Ontario .... TEL (416)971-9762

Arcca Animation Inc
800 Islington Ave Toronto Ontario .... TEL (416)863-9900

Ariel Computer Productions Inc
550 Queen St E Toronto Ontario .... TEL (416)863-9900

Associate Graphic Systems
5 Vata Crt #5 Aurora Ontario .... TEL (416)727-4261

Avcom Productions
228 King St E Toronto Ontario .... TEL (416)364-6238

Avenue Presentations
100 Richmond St E #216 Toronto Ontario .... TEL (416)367-9661

Avoid Graphics
6 Lakeshore Ave, Wards Island Toronto Ontario .... TEL (416)366-9735

Ballinger, Keith Illustration
61 St Clair Ave W #1706 Toronto Ontario .... TEL (416)924-6589

Beyond Graphics
29 McCaul St #304 Toronto Ontario .... TEL (416)340-1008

Bit Unlimited Computer Graphics
415 Horner Ave #9 Toronto Ontario .... TEL (416)252-1969

Blackbird Animated Productions
66 Portland St Lwr Level Toronto Ontario .... TEL (416)360-7857

Boxcar Animation Studios
19 Charlotte St #303 Toronto Ontario .... TEL (416)977-3111

Broadcast Productions Inc
77 Huntly St #2522 Toronto Ontario .... TEL (416)961-1776

Capstone Communications Group
15 Wilson St Markham Ontario .... TEL (416)472-2300

Cinera Productions Ltd
45c Hazelton Ave Toronto Ont .... TEL (416)972-1262

Cleave, Tony
165 Dixon Rd #1 Etobicoke Ontario .... TEL (416)242-8626

Computer Graphics Access Studio Toronto/Lightspeed
387 Richmond E Toronto Ontario .... TEL (416)367-8139

Computer Graphics Studio, The
4141 Yonge St #102 Toronto Ontario .... TEL (416)226-6629

Computer Grafix Inc
96 Carlaw Ave Toronto Ontario .... TEL (416)462-9070

Computer Imaging Services
550 Queen St E Toronto Ontario .... TEL (416)863-9900

Computer Slide Express
170 Donway W Don Mills Ontario .... TEL (416)449-6662

Corniche Corporate Communications
5400 Yonge St Willowdale Ontario .... TEL (416)733-2626

Creative Group
61 Cottonwood Crt Thornhill Ontario .... TEL (416)764-6024

Digital Magic House Ltd
58 Fraser Ave Toronto Ontario .... TEL (416)534-6154

Dome Productions
300 The Esplanade West #3400 Toronto Ontario .... TEL (416)341-2001

Electra Communications Inc
18-3455 Harvester Rd Burlington Ontario .... TEL (416)333-3399

Electricimages Inc
67 Lombard St Toronto Ontario .... TEL (416)366-1662

Express Computer Graphics Ltd
284 St Helens Ave #6 Toronto Ontario .... TEL (416)532-2517

Gelbert, Anna
100 Parkway Forest Dr #401 Willowdale Ontario .... TEL (416)490-8496

Graffects Inc
1200 Eglinton Ave E #302 Don Mills Ontario .... TEL (416)391-3123

Graphic Action
503 Adelaide St W Toronto Ontario .... TEL (416)367-4661

Greenlight Corporation
70 Richmond St E #302 Toronto Ontario .... TEL (416)366-5444

Here's How Productions
181 Carlaw Ave #216 Tronto Ontario .... TEL (416)469-8320

Hopp (Robert) Associates
196 Evans Ave Toronto Ontario .... TEL (416)252-9314

Image Group Canada Limited
26 Soho St Toronto Ontario .... TEL (416)591-1400

Image Technix
111 Queen St E #430 Toronto Ontario .... TEL (416)861-0032

Krech, Dan Productions Inc
48 River St Toronto Ontario .... TEL (416)861-9269

Lasercut Design
60 Granton Dr #9 Richmond Hill Ontario .... TEL (416)886-2787

Les Freres Proulx Brothers Inc
334 Churchill N Ottawa Ontario .... TEL (613)725-3743

Light & Motion Corporation, The
30 Northdale Blvd Toronto Ontario .... TEL (416)750-4112

Madole, Marlene
4 Barnstead Court Brampton Ontario .... TEL (416)459-9753

Mammoth Pictures Inc
67 Mowat Ave #146 Toronto Ont .... TEL (416)534-4229

Mason-Walden Computer Graphics Inc
227 MacPherson Ave Toronto Ontario .... TEL (416)924-9000

Meloche Communications Group Inc
236 Avenue Rd Toronto Ontario .... TEL (416)922-1361

Mobile Image Canada Ltd
26 Soho St Toronto Ontario .... TEL (416)591-1400

MS Art Services
410 Adelaide St W Toronto Ontario .... TEL (416)363-2621

Nissen-Drawings to Suit
72 Isabella St #31 Toronto Ontario .... TEL (416)960-9581

Nugraph Visual Inc
517 Wellington St W #203 Toronto Ontario .... TEL (416)977-7477

Pacesetter Communications
Toronto Creative Centre 225 Richmond W Toronto ...... TEL (416)977-9880

Pixel - The Computer Animation News People Inc
217 George St Toronto Ontario .... TEL (416)367-0088

Projections A.V. Ltd
205 Church St #100 Toronto Ontario .... TEL (416)862-0861

QPT Visual Expressions
Box 274 Thornhill Ontario .... TEL (416)886-4444

Statements Creative Services
95 Nugget Ave #204 Scarborough Ontario .... TEL (416)291-4710

Summerhill Group, The
18 Banigan Dr Toronto Ontario .... TEL (416)467-1211

Susan Sam
423 Vaughan Rd #1 Toronto Ontario .... TEL (416)658-6792

TOPIX-Computer Graphics & Animation
217 Richmond St W 2nd Fl Toronto Ontario .... TEL (416)971-7711

TYCA Graphix Communications Inc
89A Sackville St Toronto Ontario .... TEL (416)923-5017

SALES PROMOTION

Active Impressions In Mktg Inc
82 Queen St S Mississauga Ontario .... TEL (416)821-2446

Beakbane Marketing Inc
130 Bridgeland Ave #314 Toronto Ontario .... TEL (416)787-4901

Bird Promotions
145 Franklin Ave Willowdale Ontario .... TEL (416)226-9889

Checkmate Marketing Resources Ltd
2 Tarlton Rd Toronto Ontario .... TEL (416)482-2010

Communique Marketing
106 Front St E #301 Toronto Ontario .... TEL (416)365-7200

Concept In Ink
59 Division St Oshawa Ontario .... TEL (416)428-8193

Concept M2000/Millenium Promotions & Communication
135 West Beaver Creek Road Richmond Hill Ont. .... TEL (416)889-2000

Cumis Creative Services
3310 South Service Rd Burlington Ontario .... TEL (416)632-5390

Duncan McLaren Marketing
2200 Lakeshore Blvd W #300 Toronto Ontario .... TEL (416)253-5984

Earthmark Inc/Green Marketing
77 Mowat Ave #504 Toronto Ontario .... TEL (416)588-6488

Fedeli Advertising Corporation
719 Fisher St North Bay Ontario .... TEL (705)476-5044

Firewings Promotional & Design Group
87 Mowat Ave #207 Toronto Ontario .... TEL (416)538-6341

Gaylord Planned Promotions
39 Stoffel Dr Rexdale Ontario .... TEL (416)245-5252

GFS Consulting & Marketing Inc
139 Grand River St N Paris Ontario .... TEL (519)442-6626

Glavin & Associates
276 Merton St Toronto Ontario .... TEL (416)482-3030

Goldhall Group Inc, The
120 Trade Blvd E #105 Mississauga Ontario .... TEL (416)568-1500

Green, Milgrom & Associates Inc
111 Gerrard St E #300 Toronto Ontario .... TEL (416)340-1555

Hains Marketing Associates
34 Park Rd Toronto Ontario .... TEL (416)324-8240

Harrison Promotions Inc
637 The Queensway Peterborough Ontario .... TEL (705)743-2690

Huson Associations Ltd, The
200 Hudson Dr Toronto Ontario .... TEL (416)486-7993

IGI Communications Inc
50 Salome Ave Toronto Ontario .... TEL (416)293-0297

Innovators, Inc
One Yonge St #1801 Toronto Ontario .... TEL (416)365-1890

Ki Promotions
77 Mowat Ave #503 Toronto Ontario .... TEL (416)533-1147

L.E.L. Marketing Ltd
1037 McNicoll Ave Scarborough Ontario .... TEL (416)490-8995

Laine Marketing Group Inc The
621-B Mt Pleasant Rd Toronto Ontario .... TEL (416)485-2555

Logo Marketing Inc
604 Turner Dr Burlington Ontario .... TEL (416)681-0924

M Promotional Marketing Inc
11 Ontario St #2 Toronto Ontario .... TEL (416)359-0311

M.D.C. Sales Promotion Service
474 Bathurst St #300 Toronto Ontario .... TEL (416)968-0000

Marketcom
100 Lombard St #200 Toronto Ontario .... TEL (416)862-7733

Marketing & Promotion Group (M P & G)
92 Jarvis St Toronto Ontario .... TEL (416)862-8300

Marketing Opportunities
100 Steelcase Rd #205-A Markham Ontario .... TEL (416)479-3429

MG&A Mertens Gibson & Associates Inc
55 Avenue Rd #2700 West Tower Toronto Ontario .... TEL (416)922-4883

Michael Singer & Associates Inc
365 Bloor St E #1800 Toronto Ontario .... TEL (416)968-0172

Ocean Boulevard
1881 Yonge St #5 Toronto Ontario .... TEL (416)484-1840

Onyx Marketing Group Inc
245 Fairview Mall Dr #409 Toronto Ontario .... TEL (416)490-8155

Opticom Promotion Group Ltd
169 Dundas St E Mississauga Ontario .... TEL (416)276-6363

Phase III Promotions Ltd
1262 Don Mills Rd Toronto Ontario .... TEL (416)449-1971

Porter Marketing Group Inc
550 Queen St E #315 Toronto Ontario .... TEL (416)865-1984

Potter, Grahame Marketing Creative Services
40 Asquith Ave #1604 Toronto Ontario .... TEL (416)962-6749

Prestige Promotions
2550 Golden Ridge Unit 44 Mississauga Ontario .... TEL (416)622-3211

Program Design Group
579 Richmond St W #400 Toronto Ontario .... TEL (416)366-8464

Project Marketing
1425 Stoneybrook Trail Oakville Ontario .... TEL (416)540-2000

Promaction Corporation Inc
10 Bay St 10th Fl Toronto Ontario .... TEL (416)594-6370

Promo Marketing Canada Inc
5353 Dundas St W #400 Etobicoke Ontario .... TEL (514)288-5553

Promolink Marketing
5 Tallforest Cres Toronto Ontario .... TEL (416)620-7161

Promotion Blitz
8 Price St Lwr Lvl Toronto Ontario .... TEL (416)922-6434

Promotion House Inc The
20 Railside Rd Don Mills Ontario .... TEL (416)447-0055

Promotion Network
12 Bruce Park Ave 2nd Fl Toronto Ontario .... TEL (416)322-7611

Promotion Studio Ltd
4750 Yonge St #202 Willowdale Ontario .... TEL (416)226-6070

Promotional Campaigns
88 University Ave #9 Toronto Ontario .... TEL (416)979-0508

RDS Marketing Communications Group
637 The Queensway Peterborough Ontario .... TEL (705)743-2690

S.P.G. Promotions & Productions
188 Conti Cres Woodbridge Ontario .... TEL (416)856-6779

Sales & Merchandising Group
2700 Matheson Blvd E 2nd Fl W Twr Mississauga Ont .... TEL (416)238-8422

SGC Marketing Services Inc
145 Columbia St W Waterloo Ontario .... TEL (519)746-8767

Silver And Company
518 McNicol Ave Willowdale Ontario .... TEL (416)493-2323

Starboard Marketing Services Inc
391 Steelcase Rd W #22 Markham Ontario .... TEL (416)479-2250

Torsney Barnett Roberts Advertising
120 King St W #1075 Hamilton Ontario .... TEL (416)522-4662

Tri-Star Promotions Inc
60 Granton Dr Unit #6 Richmond Hill Ontario .... TEL (416)886-1616

Urban Associates
940 Main St W Hamilton Ontario .... TEL (416)525-7168

V & B Promotional Services
1133 Yonge St Toronto Ontario .... TEL (416)925-9393

Walker Promotions
3575 - 14th Ave Unit 16 Markham Ontario .... TEL (416)479-0272

Webbco
1181 Finch Ave W #210 Downsview Ontario .... TEL (416)665-2761

MULTIPLE FREELANCE SERVICES

Ad People Inc
55 Eglinton Ave E #805 Toronto Ontario .... TEL (416)486-1201

Freelancer, The
43 Thorncliffe Pk Dr #1516 Toronto Ontario .... TEL (416)425-5319

Freelancers Unlimited Inc
1491 Yonge St #203 Toronto Ontario .... TEL (416)969-9088

Graphic Assistant
391 Berkeley St #2 Toronto Ontario .... TEL (416)929-6333

PUBLIC RELATION FIRMS

Advance Planning & Communications Ltd
1910 Yonge St 4th Fl Toronto Ontario .... TEL (416)484-1363

Allen Cupples & Associates Communications Ltd
464 Castlefield Ave Toronto Ontario .... TEL (416)480-2828

Andrea Delvaille and Associates
1020 Brock Rd S. #2006 Pickering Ontario .... TEL (416)831-9550

Arato, Rona Communication Associates
135 Sparks Ave Willowdale Ontario .... TEL (416)492-0627

Argyle Communications Inc
6 Adelaide St E 5th Fl Toronto Ontario .... TEL (416)367-8760

Arts & Communications Counselors
55 Bloor St W #1200 Toronto Ontario .... TEL (416)966-3421

Ashpole, Barry & Associates
1 Yonge St #1801 Toronto Ontario .... TEL (416)362-4804

Aster Communications
48 Kenilworth Ave Toronto Ontario .... TEL (416)699-6442

Attache Communications
1500 Don Mills Rd #205 Don Mills Ontario .... TEL (416)445-5667

Balmoral Communications
401 Bay St #2710 Toronto Ontario .... TEL (416)364-0046

Barlow & Green
951 McBride Ave Mississauga Ontario .... TEL (416)276-7360

Baxter Communications
5468 Dundas St W #1900 Toronto Ontario .... TEL (416)530-4386

Beloff Group Inc, The
180 Bloor St W #100 Toronto Ontario .... TEL (416)323-9777

Berger & Associates Inc
100 University Ave #1004 Toronto Ontario .... TEL (416)599-8454

Blenheim Communications
2 St Clair Ave W #801 Toronto Ontario .... TEL (416)924-9361

Brisebois Communications
10 Morrow Ave #202 Toronto Ontario .... TEL (416)588-5553

Budman & Associates
505 Eglinton Ave W #303 Toronto Ontario .... TEL (416)484-9982

Burson-Marsteller
80 Bloor St W #1500 Toronto Ontario .... TEL (416)964-8300

Cheriton Communication Serv Ltd
1133 Yonge St Toronto Ontario .... TEL (416)920-4027

Chisholm Communications
101 Lawton Blve #108 Toronto Ontario .... TEL (416)482-6044

Clarke Marketing & Corporate Communications Inc
2021 Cliff Rd #311 Mississauga Ontario .... TEL (416)272-1122

CMG Public Relations
401 Richmond St W #369 Toronto Ontario .... TEL (416)593-4977

Cohn and Wolfe
80 Bloor St W #1400 Toronto Ontario .... TEL (416)924-5700

Communicaide Marketing Services Ltd
2857 Sherwood Heights-Dr #3 Oakville Ontario .... TEL (416)829-2966

Communication Initiatives Inc
179 John St 6th Fl Toronto Ontario .... TEL (416)595-5096

Communications Group Inc, The
85 Scarsdale Rd #301 Toronto Ontario .... TEL (416)447-8591

Communications Strategy
464 King St E Toronto Ontario .... TEL (416)359-0472

Continental PIR Communications
One Yonge St Toronto Ontario .... TEL (416)364-2154

Crocker International Communications Inc
49 Spadina Ave #500 Toronto Ontario .... TEL (416)597-8558

Cundari Group, The
160 Vanderhoof Ave #201 Toronto Ontario .... TEL (416)421-9900

Dalton McCabe Alaouze Inc
64 Jefferson Ave #6 Toronto Ontario .... TEL (416)537-8493

DCI-Daedal Communications Inc
425 University Ave #800 Toronto Ontario .... TEL (416)971-9140

Faye Clack Public Relations Inc
1454 Dundas St E #116 Mississauga Ontario .... TEL (416)276-7323

Gingko Public Relations
4950 Yonge St #600 North York Ontario .... TEL (416)221-2244

Good Relations Inc
1041 North Service Rd E #101 Oakville Ontario .... TEL (416)842-5610

Goodman Communications Inc
160 Bloor St E #924 Toronto Ontario .... TEL (416)924-9100

Harbinger Communications
160 Eglinton Ave E #606 Toronto Ontario .... TEL (416)322-7595

Hill & Knowlton (Cdn) Ltd
1 Eglinton Ave E #800 Toronto Ontario .... TEL (416)483-5228

Holman Communications Inc
The Keep, 250 The Esplanade Toronto Ontario .... TEL (416)362-7633

Houston Group Communications Ltd, The
900 Don Mills Rd Don Mills Ontario .... TEL (416)445-3531

Hunter Sommerfield Inc
135 Sheppard Ave W Toronto Ontario .... TEL (416)250-0400

Kerbel Communications Group, The
40 Holly St #602 Toronto Ontario .... TEL (416)489-1414

Knott, Leonard L. & Associates Inc
44 Hayden St Toronto Ontario .... TEL (416)921-2311

Langdon Starr PR & Promotion
20 Eglinton Ave W #1402 Toronto Ontario .... TEL (416)480-0533

Lewis Carroll Communications
68 Scollard St Toronto Ontario .... TEL (416)968-3845

Luppino & Associates Inc
602 Ridelle Ave #101 Toronto Ontario .... TEL (416)783-9484

Magil, David Communications
366 Adelaide St E #337 Toronto Ontario .... TEL (416)862-8461

McNeillie and Company
2 St. Clair Ave W #801 Toronto Ontario .... TEL (416)323-1997

Media Plus Total Communications
5770 Hurontario St #501 Mississauga Ontario .... TEL (416)568-3777

Media Profile
579 Richmond St W #400 Toronto Ontario .... TEL (416)366-8464

Melaine Communications Group Inc
33 Niagara St Toronto Ontario .... TEL (416)362-3900

National Public Relations Limited
2 Berkeley St #402 Toronto Ontario .... TEL (416)860-0180

OEB International
20 Toronto St #400 Toronto Ontario .... TEL (416)363-7101

Optimum
8 Price St Toronto Ontario .... TEL (416)922-3050

Pearce/Flannigan Communications Inc
2323 Yonge St #301 Toronto Ontario .... TEL (416)481-6317

Peckham McGirr Communications Ltd
260 Richmond St W #305 Toronto Ontario .... TEL (416)340-0244

Pegasus Communications Inc
111 Queen St E #456 Toronto Ontario .... TEL (416)364-9121

Pierce Communications
56 Scollard St Toronto Ontario .... TEL (416)961-5328

Pinnacle Group Inc, The
85 Scarsdale Rd #301 Toronto Ontario .... TEL (416)447-8591

Promacon Marketing Consultants Ltd
2857 Sherwood Heights Dr #3 Oakville Ontario .... TEL (416)829-2036

Reid/Burry/Young
20 Bay St #1603 Toronto Ontario .... TEL (416)367-3155

Sherman, Janet & Associates
1200 Sheppard Ave E #101 Willowdale Ontario .... TEL (416)591-8822

Smale, Joanne Productions Ltd
686 Richmond St W #2 Toronto Ontario .... TEL (416)961-3424

Special Assignment Inc
258 Carlton St Toronto Ontario .... TEL (416)964-6118

Strategic Objectives Inc
163 Sterling Rd Toronto Ontario .... TEL (416)536-7735

Tudhope and Company Ltd
2010 Yonge St #302 Toronto Ontario .... TEL (416)485-4688

Wafwot Communications
23 Brentcliffe Rd #325 Toronto Ontario .... TEL (416)467-9444

Warson, Albert Associates
77 Mowat Ave #522 Toronto Ontario .... TEL (416)530-4383

Warwick & Associates
1133 Yonge St Toronto Ontario .... TEL (416)961-3333

Wellington West Communications
151 John St #408 Toronto Ontario .... TEL (416)598-1937

Williams & Associates
77 Bloor St W #1106 Toronto Ontario .... TEL (416)323-9552

Wilson, Hilda Group, The
2200 Yonge St #1002 Toronto Ontario .... TEL (416)489-5864

Zed Communications
355 Adelaide St W #300 Toronto Ontario .... TEL (416)340-8275

WRITERS

Bashford Inc
165 Maple Ave Richmond Hill Ontario .... TEL (416)884-2441

Brewer, Wayne
894 Eglinton Ave E #202 Toronto Ontario .... TEL (416)425-3050

Browning Associates
105 Browning Ave Toronto Ontario .... TEL (416)465-9426

Bywood Communications
London Ontario .... TEL (519)272-0189

Crossen, John
23 Davies Cres Toronto Ontario .... TEL (416)422-2661

Devlin & Associates
123-D Berkeley St Toronto Ontario .... TEL (416)363-6316

Dial-A1-Resources
15 Bales Ave Willowdale Ontario .... TEL (416)730-9969

Final Draft Communications
23 Gresham Rd Toronto Ontario .... TEL (416)487-8147

Forrest, Diane
12 Birch Ave #210 Toronto Ontario .... TEL (416)924-7132

Foxman Communications
759 Marlee Ave Toronto Ontario .... TEL (416)783-5355

Freelancer, The/Joanne Ferriman
43 Thorncliffe Pk Dr Toronto Ontario .... TEL (416)423-5319

Goldberg, Rhonda
1689 Bathurst St Toronto Ontario .... TEL (416)487-6222

Hynes, Haslip & Partners Inc
151 John St #303 Toronto Ontario .... TEL (416)971-9706

Katz, Sidney Writing Enterprises
36 Servington Cr Toronto Ontario .... TEL (416)482-5115

Lidstone, William & Associates
58 Durie St Toronto Ontario .... TEL (416)767-7707

Lownsbrough, John
2 Temperance St #208 Toronto Ontario .... TEL (416)861-1981

MacMartin Corporate Services
RR #3 Schomberg Ontario .... TEL (416)859-5777

MacNaughton, John
1220 Bayview Ave #306 Toronto Ontario .... TEL (416)423-4394

Mastrodicasa, Tony
922 Sheppard Ave W North York Ontario .... TEL (416)636-5329

McEwen & Gordon
47 Worthington Cr Toronto Ontario .... TEL (416)766-9394

McIntyre, Grant
51 East Lynn Ave Toronto Ontario .... TEL (416)691-1939

MM Communications
59 Chudleigh Ave Toronto Ontario .... TEL (416)485-9494

Munroe, Ross
67 Mowat Ave Toronto Ontario .... TEL (416)538-2679

Orapith Creative
163 Buttermill #12 Concord Ontario .... TEL (416)764-7467

Scott, Douglas & Co
1231 Yonge St #202 Toronto Ontario .... TEL (416)964-2624

Word Works, The
1407 Yonge St #503 Toronto Ontario .... TEL (416)927-8001

Zinderdine Corporate Writing Services
258 Wallace Ave Toronto Ontario .... TEL (416)531-3193

Have you ever been sentenced to death?

(You
couldn't have been
reading my copy.)

I write to the point.

Tony Mastrodicasa, Writer
Advertising ~ Promotional ~ Corporate
922 Sheppard Avenue West
North York, Ontario M3H 2T6
Tel: 416 636 5329
Fax: 416 636 5315

EXHIBIT & DISPLAY

A & D Photo Lab Services Ltd.
27 Mobile Dr Toronto Ontario .... TEL (416)752-8586

Able Exhibits
6685 Tomken Rd #15B Mississauga Ontario .... TEL (416)670-2788

Adamson Industrial Design Assoc. Inc
174 Avenue Rd Toronto Ontario .... TEL (416)963-9356

Alphaform Exhibits & Design Inc
833 Oxford St Toronto Ontario .... TEL (416)253-9403

Apex Communications Inc
346 Wonderland Rd S London Ontario .... TEL (519)657-1841

Associated Display
1150 Northside Rd #10-14 Burlington Ontario .... TEL (416)827-4889

B C C Group
166 Norseman St Toronto Ontario .... TEL (416)237-0071

Best Displays
87 Bakersfield St Downsview Ontario .... TEL (416)635-8131

Bridgeford Dunn Associates
3281 Yonge St #200 Toronto Ontario .... TEL (416)481-1747

C & C Display & Florals Ltd
864 Eastern Ave Toronto Ontario .... TEL (416)469-5961

C.E.S. Exhibits Inc
7-29 Wabash Ave Toronto Ontario .... TEL (416)530-4411

CDA Industries
1430 Birchmount Road Scarborough Ontario .... TEL (416)752-2301

Chair-Man Mills
300 Consumers Rd Willowdale Ontario .... TEL (416)492-0400

Chair-Man Mills
470 Parkdale Ave N Hamilton Ontario .... TEL (416)547-6600

Chair-Man Mills
Metro Toronto Convention Centre 255 Front St E. ..... TEL (416)585-8000

Charlton & Gobuyan Design
392 Kent St Ottawa Ontario .... TEL (613)233-8053

Click Systems Canada Limited
2600 Matheson Blvd E Mississauga Ontario .... TEL (416)624-8844

Clint Freeman Display Limited
125 Vanderhoof Ave Toronto Ontario .... TEL (416)421-2652

Convex Exhibits
38 Riviera Dr Markham Ontario .... TEL (416)479-1493

Dann Dunn Designs Inc
856 Millwood Rd Toronto Ontario .... TEL (416)696-0366

Design Workshop
30 St Patrick #700 Toronto Ontario .... TEL (416)971-9970

Designamation Limited
60 Newcastle St Etobicoke Ontario .... TEL (416)252-0442

Disney Display
153 Dufferin St Toronto Ontario .... TEL (416)533-7911

Display Arts of Toronto
233 Carlaw Toronto Ontario .... TEL (416)461-2787

Display Service Co. Inc.
25 Dyas Rd Don Mills Ontario .... TEL (416)445-5120

Edge & Bratton Scenery & Display
258A Wallace Ave Toronto Ontario .... TEL (416)532-4451

Entertainment Technology
90 Thorncliffe Pk Dr Toronto Ontario .... TEL (416)422-4940

Exhibits Dimension Works
RR #1 Acton Ontario .... TEL (519)853-2228

Exhibits International
431 Horner Ave Etobicoke Ontario .... TEL (416)252-2818

Exhibits Plus/Kepac Canada
288 Judson St #13-14 Toronto Ontario .... TEL (416)252-3145

ExpoSystems Ltd
2161 Midland Ave Scarborough Ontario .... TEL (416)291-2932

Feature Factory Inc
137 Beaconsfield Ave Toronto Ontario .... TEL (416)537-6860

Fedor Expositions Inc
186 Strachan Ave Toronto Ontario .... TEL (416)362-4531

Fifty-One Design
101 Amber St #7&8 Markham Ontario .... TEL (416)475-7795

Geron Associates Limited
231 Bentley St Markham Ontario .... TEL (416)470-0205

Giltspur Toronto
120 Carrier Dr Rexdale Ontario .... TEL (416)674-0845

Goring Associates Inc
77 Mowat Ave #210 Toronto Ontario .... TEL (416)536-3509

Guibert Graphik Inc.
171 Jean Proulx Hull Québec .... TEL (819)771-9180

H. Piersig & Associates
290 Carlaw Ave Toronto Ontario .... TEL (416)462-9757

Hanna Design
16 Lesmill Rd Don Mills Ontario .... TEL (416)445-0950

Harding Display Corp
44 Metropolitan Rd Scarborough Ontario .... TEL (416)754-3215

Holman Design Ltd
160 Lesmill Rd Don Mills Ontario .... TEL (416)441-1877

J & O Exhibits Ltd
1450 The Queensway Toronto Ontario .... TEL (416)252-9575

Jeffrey Cowling & Associates
31 Alexander St #416 Toronto Ontario .... TEL (416)962-8188

Kadoke Display Limited
6155 Kestrel Rd Mississauga Ontario .... TEL (416)564-9790

Kuypers Norton Ltd
76 Richmond St E Toronto Ontario .... TEL (416)362-7737

M-Perial Display Group Inc.
108 Novan Dr Weston Ontario .... TEL (416)741-7891

McNicol Stevenson Ltd
2161 Midland Ave Scarborough Ontario .... TEL (416)291-2932

Mellor-Wheatley Associates Ltd
179 Dalhousie St Ottawa Ontario .... TEL (613)232-2413

Neat Woodworking & Display Ltd
4490 Chesswood Dr #1-2 Downsview Ontario .... TEL (416)630-1525

Nimlock Canada Ltd
70 Esna Park Dr Markham Ontario .... TEL (416)479-9511

Octanorm Canada Ltd
15 Lockport Ave Etobicoke Ontario .... TEL (416)233-2108

Odyssey Display
185 Gibson Dr #1 Markham Ontario .... TEL (416)475-1121

Panex Show Services Ltd
66 Akron Rd Toronto Ontario .... TEL (416)252-7806

Piddi Design Associates Ltd
1 Beaverdale Rd Toronto Ontario .... TEL (416)259-3768

PM Displays
1120 Old Innes Rd Ottawa Ontario .... TEL (613)748-7180

Quality Exhibits
3226 Wharton Way Mississauga Ontario .... TEL (416)238-1202

Sears & Russell Consultants
111 Avenue Rd #700 Toronto Ontario .... TEL (416)926-8242

Seven Continents Enterprises Inc
1 Atlantic Ave Toronto Ontario .... TEL (416)535-5101

Spectralite 70 Ltd.
50 McIntosh Dr #111 Markham Ontario .... TEL (416)474-0233

Spectrum Exhibits & Woodworking Limited
22 Taber Rd Rexdale Ontario .... TEL (416)745-9262

Stevens Signs & Display Ltd
23 Heather Cres London Ontario .... TEL (519)453-2040

Straight Line Design
42 Columbus Ave Toronto Ontario .... TEL (416)533-4437

Taber Exhibit Company Inc
1290 Aimco Blvd Mississauga Ontario .... TEL (416)238-5100

Taylor Manufacturing Industries Inc
55 Vansco Rd Etobicoke Ontario .... TEL (416)251-3155

The Exhibitors
41 Atomic Ave Toronto Ontario .... TEL (416)255-1156

Western Display Service Ltd
277 Lakeshore Rd E #406 Oakville Ontario .... TEL (416)338-1602

worden-watson ltd
12 Progress Ave Scarborough Ontario .... TEL (416)291-3432

PHOTOGRAPHERS — TORONTO

1323 Photo Studio/Bill Petro
1675 Sismet Rd #15 Mississauga Ontario .... TEL (416)624-6490

1323 Photo Studio/Harry Cantlon
1675 Sismet Rd #15 Mississauga Ontario .... TEL (416)624-6490

A Better Image Inc
10 Elora Rd Toronto Ontario .... TEL (416)762-7619

A.N.G.L.E.S. Photography
135 Lawton Blvd #801 Toronto Ontario .... TEL (416)322-3030

Abe, Masao Photography Ltd
445 King St W 4th Fl Toronto Ontario .... TEL (416)598-1011

Academy-Yamada Photography
1248 Bloor St W Toronto Ontario .... TEL (416)536-5675

Ad-Visual Communications
1350 Matheson Blvd E #1 Mississauga Ontario .... TEL (416)625-5665

Ajay Photographics
39 Cosentino Dr Scarborough Ontario .... TEL (416)293-0225

Allan, Richard and Associates Ltd
9 Davies Ave #302 Toronto Ontario .... TEL (416)778-6737

Alldrit, Philip Photography
219 Dufferin St #310 Toronto Ontario .... TEL (416)534-1945

Allen, Jim Photographics
57 Huntley St Toronto Ontario .... TEL (416)369-0391

Amberg, Lutz Photography Ltd
388 Carlaw Ave #107 Toronto Ontario .... TEL (416)463-3270

Amestoy, Juan
67 Mowat Ave #148 Toronto Ontario .... TEL (416)534-7729

Anast, Daniel
31 Brock Ave #205 Toronto Ontario .... TEL (416)534-9040

Anderson, Dawn Photography
9 Davies Ave #302 Toronto Ontario .... TEL (416)461-1234

Appleby, Paul Photography
1205 Bathurst St Toronto Ontario .... TEL (416)533-0007

Arc Light Studios
104 Howard Park Ave Toronto Ontario .... TEL (416)534-4009

Argue, Kevin Photography
10 Brian Ave St Catharines Ontario .... TEL (416)685-8853

Arsie, Laura Photography
22 Mowat Ave #300 Toronto Ontario .... TEL (416)588-8048

Ashton, Clinton Photography
219 Broadview Ave Toronto Ontario .... TEL (416)469-4062

Ashukian, Susan Photography
276 Carlaw Ave #301 Toronto Ontario .... TEL (416)778-7322

Assaly, Michael
17 Carlaw Ave #5 Toronto Ontario .... TEL (416)469-8202

Aura Photographics
481 North Service Rd W #9 Oakville Ontario .... TEL (416)847-7878

Avant Studios
45 Hannover Dr St Catharines Ontario .... TEL (416)641-0075

B. Creative Photography & Art Inc
2465 Dundas St W Toronto Ontario .... TEL (416)588-8111

Barber, Clive Photography Inc
629 Eastern Ave Toronto Ontario .... TEL (416)461-7144

Barr Photography
1275 Eglinton Ave E #44 Mississauga Ontario .... TEL (416)238-6081

Barratt, Bob Photography
4106 Martin Ave Niagara Falls Ontario .... TEL (416)357-2018

Barrington Photographic
445 King St W 4th Fl Toronto Ontario .... TEL (416)593-7173

Bart, Casimir Photographics
276 Carlaw Ave #220 Toronto Ontario .... TEL (416)469-0056

Bartosik, John Photography
63 Conroy Cres #58 Guelph Ontario .... TEL (519)763-0167

Batiuk, Ken Photography
219 Broadview Ave #101 Toronto Ontario .... TEL (416)465-6934

Becker, Brian Photography
67 Mowat Ave #335 Toronto Ontario .... TEL (416)534-7290

Behal, Steve
21 Beachview Cres Toronto Ontario .... TEL (416)699-3848

Bein, Ulf & Associates
1266 Queen St W #1 Toronto Ontario .... TEL (416)531-3433

Belisle-Eager
327 Winona Dr Toronto Ontario .... TEL (416)652-3832

Bell, Bert & Associates
52 Shaftesbury Ave Toronto Ontario .... TEL (416)961-9304

Bell, Richard & Associates
888 Don Mills #101 Toronto Ontario .... TEL (416)444-7425

Benard, Joel
372 Richmond St W #120 Toronto Ontario .... TEL (416)340-7435

Bentham, John Photography
137 Roncesvalles Ave #202 Toronto Ontario .... TEL (416)588-2904

Bentley, John Photographer
219 Dufferin St #302 Toronto Ontario .... TEL (416)536-2035

Bertelli, Jon Photography
77 Mowat Ave #222 Toronto Ontario .... TEL (416)533-7722

Berzins, Normunds Photography
RR#1 Orono Ontario .... TEL (416)696-5620

Bierwagen Photography Inc
50 Woodycrest Ave Toronto Ontario .... TEL (416)463-6560

Bignell, Bryon Photographer
56 The Esplanade #507 Toronto Ontario .... TEL (416)594-1515

Bird, Fred & Associates Ltd
202 Parkhurst Blvd Toronto Ontario .... TEL (416)421-4259

Bird, Mark
1179A King St W #200 Toronto Ontario .... TEL (416)533-9553

Biss, G. Photography Ltd
307 Bering Ave Toronto Ontario .... TEL (416)239-1637

Bochsler, Tom Mainway Studio
3514 Mainway Burlington Ontario .... TEL (416)336-7968

Bogner Photography Limited
28 West Main St Welland Ontario .... TEL (416)735-7551

Boothman, Nick Photography
219 Front St E Toronto Ontario .... TEL (416)861-0100

Boudreau, Ray Photography Inc
44 Sherbourne St 2nd Fl Toronto Ontario .... TEL (416)362-1509

Boyd, Virginia Photography
675 Euclid Ave Toronto Ontario .... TEL (416)537-8823

Boyes, Francis Photography
400 Avenue Rd # 201 Toronto Ontario .... TEL (416)921-5901

Boyko, Steve Associates
67 Mowat Ave #LL32 Toronto Ontario .... TEL (416)588-0090

Bradley Photographer
1775 Bayview Ave Main Toronto Ontario .... TEL (416)482-1160

Bradshaw, Douglas Photography Inc
99 Sudbury St #6 Toronto Ontario .... TEL (416)535-1771

Briand/Richarde Photography
111 Peter St #615 Toronto Ontario .... TEL (416)593-4198

Brieiro, John Photography
175 Catherine St S #16 Hamilton Ontario .... TEL (416)528-8323

Brigdens Studios
20 Railside Dr Don Mills Ontario .... TEL (416)447-0009

Brodie, Ralph Photographics
1499 Queen St W #304 Toronto Ontario .... TEL (416)536-9463

Brookside Studio/Janet Webb
1 Dufferin St #6 Millbrook Ontario .... TEL (705)932-2288

Brookside Studio/Wayne Eardley
1 Dufferin St #6 Millbrook Ontario .... TEL (705)932-2288

Brown, James Photographics
276 Carlaw Ave #310 Toronto Ontario .... TEL (416)462-9477

Brown, Richard Photography
205 Church St #100 Toronto Ontario .... TEL (416)862-0861

Bulmer, Randy Photography
1179A King St W #212 Toronto Ontario .... TEL (416)537-8896

Burke, John Photographer
140 Braidwood Ave #4 Peterborough Ontario .... TEL (705)748-3303

Campbell, Christopher Photography
202 Parkhurst Blvd Toronto Ontario .... TEL (416)421-4259

Campbell, Ian Photography
48 McGee St Toronto Ontario .... TEL (416)469-5247

Carroll & Carroll Photography Inc
104 Meadowbrook Dr #110 London Ontario .... TEL (519)652-9980

Carson PhotoProductions
680 Queen's Quay W #601 Toronto Ontario .... TEL (416)596-2275

Casselman, Paul Photography*Design
PO Box 288, Stn B Toronto Ontario .... TEL (416)596-7518

Cattoni, Renzo Photography
1 Gorevale Ave Toronto Ontario .... TEL (416)364-6534

Cavanagh, Brigitte
20 First Ave Toronto Ontario .... TEL (416)466-4318

CBF Photography Ltd
3015 Kennedy Rd #11 Scarborough Ontario .... TEL (416)292-2768

Champion Photography Ltd
1179A King St W #110 Toronto Ontario .... TEL (416)532-7304

Chan, Peter Photo
67 Mowat Ave #448 Toronto Ontario .... TEL (416)530-0489

Chapman Photography
2600 John St Unit 212 Markham Ontario .... TEL (416)474-1344

Chen, Ray Inc
40 Storey Pl Markham Ontario .... TEL (416)471-4369

Chou, Peter
46 McGee St Toronto Ontario .... TEL (416)469-4588

Christopher, Peter
PO Box 5802 Stn A Toronto Ontario .... TEL (416)928-9080

Clarke, Harold Photography
5945 Airport Rd #197 Mississauga Ontario .... TEL (416)672-0838

Clifford, Ian
106 Queen St E Toronto Ontario .... TEL (416)363-7938

Cole, Barbara Photography
176 John St #404 Toronto Ontario .... TEL (416)599-5822

Collier, Terry Photography
441 Queen St E Toronto Ontario .... TEL (416)869-3155

Collver, Gary & Associates
157 Wellesley St E Toronto Ontario .... TEL (416)960-5801

Commercial Frame and Photo
2901 Steeles Ave W #30 Downsview Ontario .... TEL (416)736-8450

Contact Photography
77 Mowat Ave #003 Toronto Ontario .... TEL (416)588-8107

Cooper, Michael Photographic
600 Queen St E 2nd Fl Toronto Ontario .... TEL (416)466-4474

Corbett, Linda Productions Inc
163 Sterling Rd Toronto Ontario .... TEL (416)537-5435

Corby, James N Photography
276 Carlaw Ave #206 Toronto Ontario .... TEL (416)463-1024

Courtney, Michael Photography
6487 Dixie Rd #36 Mississauga Ontario .... TEL (416)564-3694

Couto, Dan Photography
312 Adelaide St W #713 Toronto Ontario .... TEL (416)348-8783

Cox, Tracy Photographer
RR #1 Terra Cotta Ontario .... TEL (519)927-5093

Craig, Samuel Photography
1209 King St W #200 Toronto Ontario .... TEL (416)531-5428

Creative Images Photography
20 Admiral Rd St Catharines Ontario .... TEL (416)682-5161

Creative Photo Graphics
655 Dixon Rd/Skyline Hotel Rexdale Ontario .... TEL (416)247-9909

Creative Promotions
48 Tera Park Cres Brampton Ontario .... TEL (416)456-3526

Crysler, Ian R
7 Fraser Ave #6 Toronto Ontario .... TEL (416)588-4111

Cunningham, Bob Photography Ltd
PO Box 494 Don Mills Ontario .... TEL (416)447-3472

Daniels & Glionna Photography
378 Deloraine Ave Toronto Ontario .... TEL (416)783-4233

Danson, Andrew
300 Jones Ave Toronto Ontario .... TEL (416)466-2807

Davidson, John Photography
675 Auger St Sudbury Ontario .... TEL (705)566-6250

Davidson, Rob & Associates
390 Dupont St #202 Toronto Ontario .... TEL (416)922-5212

Davidson-Pilon Photography
340 Woodlawn Rd W #6 Guelph Ontario .... TEL (519)822-0783

Davies, Ken Photographer
11 Soho St #201 Toronto Ontario .... TEL (416)599-0240

Davies, Russell Photography
510B Eastern Ave Toronto Ontario .... TEL (416)461-4828

Daw, Rodney
42 Pickering St Toronto Ontario .... TEL (416)690-7737

Day, Fraser Photography
34 Barbara Cres Toronto Ontario .... TEL (416)463-9052

Day, Michael
264 Seaton St #101 Toronto Ontario .... TEL (416)920-9135

De Peers, George Photography
82 Bellevue Ave Toronto Ontario .... TEL (416)863-9836

de Visser, John Photographer
2 Hagerman St Port Hope Ontario .... TEL (416)885-6682

Dean Photographics Inc
9 Davies Ave #200 Toronto Ontario .... TEL (416)463-9516

Deluxe Photography
507 King St E #100 Toronto Ontario .... TEL (416)366-4477

Design Archive/Andre Beneteau
276 Carlaw Ave #219 Toronto Ontario .... TEL (416)466-0211

Design Archive/Robert Burley
276 Carlaw Ave #219 Toronto Ontario .... TEL (416)466-0211

Dickin, Doug Photographer
40 Gerrard St E #1611 Toronto Ontario .... TEL (416)340-2723

Dickson, Alan Photography
301 Simpson Street Thunder Bay Ontario .... TEL (807)623-5542

Dismatsek, Michael Photography
190 Locke St S Hamilton Ontario .... TEL (416)523-1112

Dixon, Don Photography
276 Carlaw Ave #205 Toronto Ontario .... TEL (416)465-3634

Dobson, Susan Photography
284 St Helens Ave #106 Toronto Ontario .... TEL (416)538-1783

Doda, Robert Photography
300 Jones Ave Toronto Ontario .... TEL (416)466-2807

Dojc, Yuri Inc
74 Bathurst St Toronto Ontario .... TEL (416)366-8081

Donohue, Mary Ann Photography
353 Eastern Ave #104 Toronto Ontario .... TEL (416)466-9270

Dorlandt, Mark Photography
65 Bellwoods Ave Toronto Ontario .... TEL (416)368-4091

Dorval, Didier
201 Humberside Ave Toronto Ontario .... TEL (416)767-7910

Dougal & Co Inc
114 Richmond St E #L101 Toronto Ontario .... TEL (416)365-0225

Dougherty, Daniel
60 Southvale Dr Toronto Ontario .... TEL (416)467-5498

Duarte, Carlos Photography
489 King St W #306 Toronto Ontario .... TEL (416)979-7107

Duff, Joseph Photography Inc
56 The Esplanade #509 Toronto Ontario .... TEL (416)363-7081

Dunbar, George Photography
39 Tralee Ave Scarborough Ontario .... TEL (416)439-2361

Dynamic Photography Inc
PO Box 201 Aurora Ontario .... TEL (416)773-2712

E Side Studios
106 Queen St E Toronto Ontario .... TEL (416)363-7938

Easy Grace Aerial Photography
48 Orchard Cres Toronto Ontario .... TEL (416)239-4087

Eco-Art Productions Inc
298 Queen St W Cambridge Ontario .... TEL (416)925-4323

Eco-Photo
66 Taunton Rd Toronto Ontario .... TEL (416)489-3202

Eekhoff & Muir Studios
67 Mowat Ave #335 Toronto Ontario .... TEL (416)538-3310

Eisenberg, David
1205 Bathurst St Toronto Ontario .... TEL (416)530-1655

Elephant Boy Productions
67 Mowat Ave #351 Toronto Ontario .... TEL (416)533-7740

Eligh, Gregg T. Photography
353 Eastern Ave #206 Toronto Ontario .... TEL (416)463-4955

Elliott, James N.
462 Woodland Ave Burlington Ontario .... TEL (416)632-7327

Elliott, Ken Photographer
56 The Esplanade #403 Toronto Ontario .... TEL (416)363-2974

Elmy, Ron Photography
353 Eastern Ave #205 Toronto Ontario .... TEL (416)463-9277

Emmerson, Peter Photography
517 Wellington St W #401 Toronto Ontario .... TEL (416)977-3302

Empire Photo & Art//Santiago Ku
807 St Clarens Ave Toronto Ontario .... TEL (416)538-1520

Empire Photo & Art/Joseph Ciancio
807 St Clarens Ave Toronto Ontario .... TEL (416)538-1520

Emrys, John P./The Giraffe Project Inc
259 Dufferin St #207 Toronto Ontario .... TEL (416)537-8680

Engler, Ivan Mitic Phototgraphy
80 St Patrick St #422 Toronto Ontario .... TEL (416)599-8040

Epstein, Stephen Photography
3388 Bathurst St #407 Toronto Ontario .... TEL (416)783-8763

Evans, Steven Photography
27 Davies Ave Toronto Ontario .... TEL (416)463-4493

Ewen, Scott Photography
302 Carlaw Ave #109 Toronto Ontario .... TEL (416)466-7900

F/22 Photography Inc/Ron Seto
77 Mowat Ave #003 Toronto Ontario .... TEL (416)588-8107

Fashion Photography
18 Mowat Ave 2nd Fl Toronto Ontario .... TEL (416)531-8910

FBM Photography
22 Mowat Ave #203 Toronto Ontario .... TEL (416)538-0276

Feather
67 Mowat Ave #547 Toronto Ontario .... TEL (416)588-4118

Feature Four Ltd
25 Connell Crt #3 Toronto Ontario .... TEL (416)252-6205

Feiler, Tom Photography
260 Wellesley St E #105 Toronto Ontario .... TEL (416)926-0089

Fifth Avenue Visual Communications Inc
391 Steelcase W #22 Markham Ontario .... TEL (416)940-0646

Filiou, Bill Photography
22 Mowat Ave #300 Toronto Ontario .... TEL (416)588-8048

First Light Associated Photographers
1 Atlantic Ave #204 Toronto Ontario .... TEL (416)532-6108

First Unit/Dave Hill
128 Berkeley St Toronto Ontario .... TEL (416)362-8285

First Unit/David Allen
128 Berkeley St Toronto Ontario .... TEL (416)362-8285

First Unit/Elizabeth Feryn
128 Berkeley St Toronto Ontario .... TEL (416)362-8285

First Unit/Greg Holman Photography
128 Berkeley St Toronto Ontario .... TEL (416)362-8285

First Unit/Paul Newberry Photography
128 Berkeley St Toronto Ontario .... TEL (416)362-8285

Fisher, Clare Photography
Spadina Ave #610 Toronto Ontario   TEL (416)362-4436

Flock, Ben Photography
219 Jarvis St #2 Toronto Ontario .... TEL (416)366-8998

Focal Point Ltd
2 Dorchester Ave Toronto Ontario .... TEL (416)252-9503

Focus Group Inc
235 Carlaw Ave 6th Fl Toronto Ontario .... TEL (416)469-5223

Focus Studio Ltd
35 Hogarth Ave Toronto Ontario .... TEL (416)465-4902

Fordham, Patrick Photography
464 Summerhill Ave #14 Toronto Ontario .... TEL (416)960-0950

Forester, Doug Photography
24 Brunswick Ave Toronto Ontario .... TEL (416)928-9311

Forrester, Robert Photography
472 Richmond St E Toronto Ontario .... TEL (416)362-6264

Foster, Michael Limited
9 Davies Ave 3rd Fl Toronto Ontario .... TEL (416)466-4740

Foto Shop
Timiskaming Sq New Liskard Ontario .... TEL (705)647-5436

Fougere, Francis
276 Carlaw Ave #312 Toronto Ontario .... TEL (416)465-8207

Francombe Photography
582 Davenport Rd Toronto Ontario .... TEL (416)972-6287

Fraser, Jamieson Photography
PO Box 147, Port Credit Stn Mississauga Ontario .... TEL (416)274-6661

Freda, Thomas Photography
104 Gothic Ave 2nd Fl Toronto Ontario .... TEL (416)766-3225

Freeway Visuals Inc
141 Bathurst St #100 Toronto Ontario .... TEL (416)362-0083

Freeze Frame Foto/Dan Roitner
43 Zenith Dr Scarborough Ontario .... TEL (416)269-6884

French, Graham Photography Inc
388 Carlaw Ave #303 Toronto Ontario .... TEL (416)778-7922

Frey, Antonin Photographer
16 Hawkedon Cres Etobicoke Ontario .... TEL (416)740-0802

Fuchs, Bernd Photography
150 James St St Catharines Ontario .... TEL (416)685-7883

G/W Photo Ltd
37 Melbourne Ave Toronto Ontario .... TEL (416)537-1225

Gabany, Peter/Limelight
73 Mlll St S Port Hope Ontario .... TEL (416)886-8853

Gadihoz Photographics
105 Dolomite Dr Downsview Ontario .... TEL (416)665-2233

Gajdel, Edward Photography
260 Adelaide St E #23 Toronto Ontario .... TEL (416)535-4773

Gayler, James Photographer
1941 Dundas St E Toronto Ontario .... TEL (416)691-1923

Gee, William
750 York Mills Rd #204 Don Mills Ontario .... TEL (416)441-2316

Geering, Hans Photography
16 Algonquin Ave Toronto Ontario .... TEL (416)536-6255

Gemini Enterprises
55 Parkhurst Blvd Toronto Ontario .... TEL (416)482-0883

Geo Graphics Inc
51 Borden St Toronto Ontario .... TEL (416)766-6690

Georgi, Henry Photography
PO Box 177 Beachburg Ontario .... TEL (613)582-3290

Gibson-Smith Photography/Kevin Smith
5080 Timberlea Blvd #8 Mississauga Ontario .... TEL (416)624-6033

Gibson-Smith Photography/Ted Gibson
5080 Timberlea Blvd #8 Mississauga Ontario .... TEL (416)624-6033

Gierszewski, John Photography
1350 Matheson Blve #7 Mississauga Ontario .... TEL (416)624-1668

Gilbert Studio
170 Davenport Rd Toronto Ontario .... TEL (416)923-1995

GM & Associates
1785 Matheson Blvd Mississauga Ontario .... TEL (416)625-1734

Goodall, Ruby
149 Rhodes Ave Toronto Ontario .... TEL (416)465-9796

Graphic Artists Photographers
58 Stewart St 2nd Fl Toronto Ontario .... TEL (416)362-0737

Green, Sharon/Windward Productions
682 North Shore Blvd E Burlington Ontario .... TEL (416)523-1313

Gridwork
20 Amber St #202 Markham Ontario .... TEL (416)479-8505

Griffiths, Derek Inc
3045 South Creek Rd #37 Mississauga Ontario .... TEL (416)960-3736

Gruggen, David Photography
55 Glen Rd Hamilton Ontario .... TEL (416)522-1031

Halenko, John Photography
89 Sackville St Toronto Ontario .... TEL (416)863-9624

Harbron, Patrick Photography
586 Gerrard St E #200 Toronto Ontario .... TEL (416)462-0128

Harquail, John Photography Inc
67 Mowat Ave #340 Toronto Ontario .... TEL (416)535-1620

Hart, Jean Florence Photography
77 Rosehill Blvd Oshawa Ontario .... TEL (416)576-0152

Harvey, Gail Photography
57 Beech Ave Toronto Ontario .... TEL (416)691-1445

Harvey, Shane Photography
272 Fairlawn Ave Toronto Ontario .... TEL (416)480-0578

Haslinger, Allen Photography
100 Queen St N Kitchener Ontario .... TEL (519)745-8860

Hauser, Tony V. Photography
55 Front St E Toronto Ontario .... TEL (416)862-7082

Hawk Productions
445 King St W 4th Fl Toronto Ontario .... TEL (416)598-3515

Hay, Gordon Photography Inc
95 Berkeley St Toronto Ontario .... TEL (416)862-1955

Hayes, Kerry
318 Willow Ave Toronto Ontario .... TEL (416)698-0511

Heidel, W.H. Photographer
PO Box 2201 Stn B Kitchener Ontario .... TEL (519)748-4551

Heinecke, Rolf Photography
983 Queen St E Toronto Ontario .... TEL (416)463-6657

Henderson, Greg/Ad-Lib
67 Mowat Ave #351 Toronto Ontario .... TEL (416)533-2004

Hendrick, Karen Photography
1209 King St W #200 Toronto Ontario .... TEL (416)530-1110

Heringa, Dan Photography
349 Queen St W #202 Toronto Ontario .... TEL (416)586-0444

Hessel, Dieter
302 Carlaw Ave #108 Toronto Ontario .... TEL (416)466-2685

Heyfron, Richard Photography
60 Sumach St 3rd Fl Toronto Ontario .... TEL (416)594-9144

Hill, Richard Photographer
10 Morrow Ave Toronto Ontario .... TEL (416)533-6634

Hodder, Mark Photographer
299 Mullen Dr #27 Thornhill Ontario .... TEL (416)298-0955

Hodgson, Bruce
3 MacDonnell Ave Toronto Ontario .... TEL (416)531-2364

Holtom, Herbert J
20 Hexham Dr Scarborough Ontario .... TEL (416)755-9404

Hood, Archie Photography Ltd
97 Burgar St Welland Ontario .... TEL (416)735-4477

Horn, Bruce Photography
60 Sumach St Toronto Ontario .... TEL (416)864-1314

Horvath, Peter Photography
600 Queen St E 2nd Fl Toronto Ontario .... TEL (416)461-7210

Howard Photographic Studios Inc
1 West Glen Cres Islington Ontario .... TEL (416)622-4300

Hoy, David Photography
205 Richmond St W #602 Toronto Ontario .... TEL (416)340-2341

Hubbs, Cameron
1266 Queen St W #1 Toronto Ontario .... TEL (416)347-9665

Hughes, Brian Photography
888 Don Mills #102 Toronto Ontario .... TEL (416)444-6720

Humber College/Creative Arts Dept
205 Humber College Blvd Rexdale Ontario .... TEL 675-3111x4491

Hunter, George
PO Box 272 Stn A Mississauga Ontario .... TEL (416)828-2486

Hutchings, Peter Photography
170 Heward Ave Toronto Ontario .... TEL (416)462-1546

Hynds, Robyn Photographer
2445 Homelands Dr #22 Mississauga Ontario .... TEL (416)823-0099

Icon Photography Inc
395 Michener Rd #2 Guelph Ontario .... TEL (519)836-4266

Image Photographics/Dwayne Coon
214 St Paul St St Catharines Ontario .... TEL (416)682-0063

Image Photographics/Robert Nowell
214 St Paul St St. Catharines Ontario .... TEL (416)682-0063

Image Professional Photography
281 Roncesvalles Ave Toronto Ontario .... TEL (416)537-9572

Images Photographic
52 Nina St Toronto Ontario .... TEL (416)533-4917

In Camera Studios/Clive Barber
629 Eastern Ave Toronto Ontario .... TEL (416)461-7144

In Camera Studios/Doug Hall
629 Eastern Ave Toronto Ontario .... TEL (416)461-7144

In Camera Studios/Mark Shapiro
629 Eastern Ave Toronto Ontario .... TEL (416)461-7144

Infinity Graphics Limited
744 Dundas St E Toronto Ontario .... TEL (416)363-3251

Ingersoll, Bill Photography
228 Audrey Ave Scarborough Ontario .... TEL (416)698-0525

Instil Productions Inc
489 Wellington St W Toronto Ontario .... TEL (416)596-6587

Ivy, Bill
PO Box 127 Don Mills Ontario .... TEL (416)444-7221

Iwanowski, Andrew
10 Tangreen Crt #2503 Willowdale Ontario .... TEL (416)579-4400

Jac, Steven Photogaphy
77 Mowat Ave #405 Toronto Ontario .... TEL (416)537-5814

Jackson Klomstad Partnership
77 Mowat Ave #305 Toronto Ontario .... TEL (416)531-7003

Jackson, Stephen Studios
71 Pembroke St Toronto Ontario .... TEL (416)469-1173

Jacobs, Tim/Studio North
11 Leroy Ave Toronto Ontario .... TEL (416)462-0988

Jacobson Photographics
131 Bloor St W #1107 Toronto Ontario .... TEL (416)922-2532

Jamieson Photography
1121 Invicta Dr #12 Oakville Ontario .... TEL (416)844-8146

Johnson, Bryon Photography
105 Rowena Dr #1011 Don Mills Ontario .... TEL (416)449-9102

Johnson, Raymond Photography
7251 Copenhagen Rd #62 Mississauga Ontario .... TEL (416)567-1493

Josko Photography
PO Box 942 Stn A Scarborough Ontario .... TEL (416)751-1875

Joy Studios
70 Six Point Rd Toronto Ontario .... TEL (416)231-4724

Kaj, Luis Photographer
74 Stilecroft Dr Downsview Ontario .... TEL (416)633-0439

Kamdar Studios Ltd
439 Wellington St W Toronto Ontario .... TEL (416)591-1188

Kelly, Arnold G.-Shoot!
334 King St E #403 Toronto Ontario .... TEL (416)961-5333

Kelly, Kevin Photography
89 McCaul St #922 Toronto Ontario .... TEL (416)340-6377

Kendrick, Arthur/CIA Photography Services
2055 Duncan Rd Oakville Ontario .... TEL (416)844-2296

Kennedy, Patrick Photography
524 Wellington St W Toronto Ontario .... TEL (416)593-9266

Kennedy, Paul J. Photographer
1643 Jalna Rd Mississauga Ontario .... TEL (416)823-1942

Kessler, Jeremy Photographer
9 Caines Ave Willowdale Ontario .... TEL (416)250-1909

Kilburn, Elaine Photography
296 Richmond St W #300 Toronto Ontario .... TEL (416)593-7282

Kimat Photography
216 Neal Dr Richmond Hill Ontario .... TEL (416)884-3701

Kirkwood Communications
20 Valleywood Dr #112 Markham Ontario .... TEL (416)479-1790

Kisin Studios
250 Shields Ct #27 Markham Ontario .... TEL (416)475-6533

Klotzek, Andre Studio
888 Don Mills Rd #102 Don Mills Ontario .... TEL (416)445-4426

Knetsch, William
79 Regal Rd #3A Guelph Ontario .... TEL (519)763-3099

Knoll, Brian
22a Austin Terrace Toronto Ontario .... TEL (416)960-3896

Knox, Patrick Photography
132 Berkeley St Toronto Ontario .... TEL (416)368-3307

Kohn, Michael/Oyster Studio
67 Mowat Ave #332 Toronto Ontario .... TEL (416)588-1889

Kruger, Trevor Photography
11 Soho St #202 Toronto Ontario .... TEL (416)979-7427

Krysztofiak, Mark Photography
3590 Kaneff Cres #213 Mississauga Ontario .... TEL (416)279-9527

Kuryluk, William Photography
69 Bessemer Rd #45 London Ontario .... TEL (519)681-2767

Kutnahorsky, Wolf Photography
69 Harding Blvd Scarborough Ontario .... TEL (416)691-5160

Kwoi, Gin
474 Bathurst St #401 Toronto Ontario .... TEL (416)924-4883

LaCroix, Pat Photographer
25 Brant St Toronto Ontario .... TEL (416)864-1858

Lafond, Michael J. Photography
272 Avenue Rd Toronto Ontario .... TEL (416)927-8383

Lansdale, Robert Photography
18 Ashfield Dr Etobicoke Ontario .... TEL (416)621-8788

Lant, Michael Photography
67 Mowat Ave #230 Toronto Ontario .... TEL (416)535-2690

Lantinga, Curtis Photography
67 Mowat Ave #143 Toronto Ontario .... TEL (416)532-6241

Lavigne & Smale Photography
73 Laird Dr Toronto Ontario .... TEL (416)429-3686

Law, Graham Photography
206 St George St Penthouse A Toronto Ontario .... TEL (416)963-4359

Lawson, Greg & Associates
2182A Queen St E Toronto Ontario .... TEL (416)469-5222

Layton, Mary Photography
RR#1 Black Creek Rd Fullarton Ontario .... TEL (519)229-6810

Lear, Robert Photography Inc
64 Fraser Ave Toronto Ontario .... TEL (416)536-2038

LeBourdais, Julien Photography
379 Adelaide St W #306A Toronto Ontario .... TEL (416)862-2417

Leduc, Andre Pierre
5 Soho St #101 Toronto Ontario .... TEL (416)596-7779

Leibrecht, Nicholas Photography
533 College St #401 Toronto Ontario .... TEL (416)925-9447

Leith, Ian & Associates
17 Carlaw Ave Toronto Ontario .... TEL (416)462-2966

Lenscape Incorporated
222 Eastern Ave Toronto Ontario .... TEL (416)368-9567

Les Com-Pals Photography
1161 Victoria Park Ave Toronto Ontario .... TEL (416)757-9911

Levy Studios Ltd
200 Steelecase Rd E #3 Markham Ontario .... TEL (416)474-1363

Levy, Karen Photography
276 Carlaw Ave #305 Toronto Ontario .... TEL (416)778-6372

Light Wise, The Studio, Inc
30 Wertheim Crt #24 Richmond Hill Ontario .... TEL (416)764-6420

Lightwaves/Francine Dick
134 Peter St #400 Toronto Ontario .... TEL (416)598-4827

Lightwaves/John Ashton
134 Peter St #400 Toronto Ontario .... TEL (416)598-4827

Lim, Dan Photography
64 Fraser Ave Toronto Ontario .... TEL (416)536-1080

Link/Arlene Collins
2 Berkeley St #206 Toronto Ontario .... TEL (416)369-9442

Link/Russell Monk
2 Berkeley St #206 Toronto Ontario .... TEL (416)369-9442

Little, Robert Photographer
110 Spadina Ave #610 Toronto Ontario .... TEL (416)941-9751

Livingston, Rick Photography
9 Davies Ave #201 Toronto Ontario .... TEL (416)778-8970

Lo, Lionel Photographer
270 Queens Quay W #1805 Toronto Ontario .... TEL (416)591-7317

Loates, Darcy Photography
272 Richmond St E 3rd Fl Toronto Ontario .... TEL (416)863-0002

Location Photography
2465 Cawthra Rd #112 Mississauga Ontario .... TEL (416)273-7143

Longo, Paul Photography
129 Midland Ave Scarborough Ontario .... TEL (416)261-5892

Loren Group Inc, The
9 Davies Ave 2nd Fl Toronto Ontario .... TEL (416)366-8081

Loynd, Mel Studios
2592 Oshkin Court Mississauga Ontario .... TEL (416)821-0477

Lumina Photography/Drew Williamson
357 Rusholme Rd #105 Toronto Ontario .... TEL (416)532-9371

Macaulay, Bruce Photography
115 Browning Ave Toronto Ontario .... TEL (416)463-2654

MacDonald, Brian/Maleda Ltd
135 West Beaver Creek Richmond Hill Ontario .... TEL (416)889-2000

MacDonell, Dean Photography
278 Eglinton Ave W Toronto Ontario .... TEL (416)481-4600

MacKay, Sandy Photography
35 Cumberland Dr Mississauga Ontario .... TEL (416)271-4146

MacMillan & Associates Photography Ltd
77 Mowat Ave #302 Toronto Ontario .... TEL (416)534-9243

MacNeill, Deborah Photography
400 Markham St Toronto Ontario .... TEL (416)920-5407

Madau, Mario Photo Communications
70 Dumart Pl Kitchener Ontario .... TEL (519)743-1135

Mahogany Stills Photography
2220 Midland Ave #88 Scarborough Ontario .... TEL (416)321-1536

Mahovlich, Michael Photography
1179A King St W #206 Toronto Ontario .... TEL (416)537-7935

Majesky, Bill R Photography
153 Colbeck St Toronto Ontario .... TEL (416)763-1079

Malakian, Arline Photography
77 Mowat Ave #405 Toronto Ontario .... TEL (416)532-5762

Malcolm, Blake Photography
738a Queen St E Toronto Ontario .... TEL (416)461-6705

Maloney, Dennis Photography
77 Mowat Ave #405 Toronto Ontario .... TEL (416)537-5814

Manco, Jerry Photography
1114 Queen St E Toronto Ontario .... TEL (416)461-8460

Mandel, Howard Photography
319 Queen St E Toronto Ontario .... TEL (416)368-0783

Marti, H.P. Photography
146 Brock Ave #302 Toronto Ontario .... TEL (416)536-5824

Masson, Alain Photographer
164 Albertus Ave Toronto Ontario .... TEL (416)482-0776

Maurer, Charles
31 Forsyth Ave S Hamilton Ontario .... TEL (416)528-7604

Mauro Abballe
19 Katie Court North York Ontario .... TEL (416)248-9290

Mavrikis, Dimitri Photography
1209 King St W #200 Toronto Ontario .... TEL (416)537-1999

Mayes, Victor Photography
132 Berkeley St Toronto Ontario .... TEL (416)368-3307

McCormick Photographic Illustration
235 Carlaw Avenue Toronto Ontario .... TEL (416)469-5223

McCormick, Suzanne Photography
183 Bathurst St #402 Toronto Ontario   TEL (416)361-3111

McCrae Studios Inc
2 Thorncliffe Pk Dr #21 Toronto Ontario .... TEL (416)467-9659

McCrum, Guy Photography
258 Wallace Ave Toronto Ontario .... TEL (416)535-2152

McGregor, Kirk Photography
443 King St W 3rd Fl Toronto Ontario .... TEL (416)599-2991

McIntyre, Robert Photography
73 Delaware Ave Toronto Ontario .... TEL (416)598-1011

McKenna, Monica Photographer
205 Richmond St W #603 Toronto Ontario .... TEL (416)977-6247

McKenzie, Alan Photography
420 Camden Circle Mississauga Ontario .... TEL (416)890-3333

McKenzie-Darg Limited
717 Church St 2nd Fl Toronto Ontario .... TEL (416)923-3579

McKim, Andrew Photography
88 Wellesley St E #401 Toronto Ontario .... TEL (416)968-6718

McLaren, Hugh Photography
77 Mowat Ave #106 Toronto Ontario .... TEL (416)535-1557

McLoughlin, Guy
PO Box 519, Stn A Toronto Ontario .... TEL (416)532-7866

McQueen, John & Associates
152 Heward Ave Toronto Ontario .... TEL (416)465-8257

McRann & Malone Commercial Studio Inc
388 Carlaw Ave Toronto Ontario .... TEL (416)469-3444

Meinecke G. Photography
198 Merton St Toronto Ontario .... TEL (416)484-1580

Mellows, Iain Photographer
56 The Esplanade #509 Toronto Ontario .... TEL (416)363-7081

Michaels, Paul Photography
10 Morrow Ave Toronto Ontario .... TEL (416)534-9900

Michel, Brian Photographer
7 Fraser Ave #6 Toronto Ontario .... TEL (416)588-4111

Millar, Kean Studio
22 Mowat Ave #201 Toronto Ontario .... TEL (416)538-8167

Miller, Don Photography
489 King St W #100a Toronto Ontario .... TEL (416)596-7883

Miller, Larry Photography
259 Dufferin St 2nd Fl Toronto Ontario .... TEL (416)536-8787

Milne, Gilbert & Co. Ltd
3080 Yonge St Toronto Ontario .... TEL (416)486-1131

Miszczyk, Paul Photography
556 Chiddington Ave London Ontario .... TEL (519)649-7808

Mizuyabu, Gordon Photography
1179A King St W #212 Toronto Ontario .... TEL (416)531-8756

Moehrle, Wolf Photography
460 Winona Dr #404 Toronto Ontario .... TEL (416)330-1414

Moonlight Studios
77 Mowat Ave #015 Toronto Ontario .... TEL (416)532-1649

Moore, Thomas Photography
5 Albermarle Ave Toronto Ontario .... TEL (416)465-6694

Morfey, Robert Photographer
77 Mowat Ave #402 Toronto Ontario .... TEL (416)530-0777

Morrison, John W Photography
99 Sudbury St #2 Toronto Ontario .... TEL (416)588-2746

Mulcahey, Gary Photography
101 Niagara St #400 Box 45 Toronto Ontario .... TEL (416)367-9180

Mulveney, Ken & Assoc. Photography Ltd
204 Parkhurst Blvd Toronto Ontario .... TEL (416)421-2285

Narvali, John
5 Soho St Toronto Ontario .... TEL (416)593-0813

Nasmith, Peter & Co
97 Maclean Ave Toronto Ontario .... TEL (416)362-3770

Network Studios
1030 Islington Ave Etobicoke Ontario .... TEL (416)233-3232

New Age Productions
11 Mulham Place Toronto Ontario .... TEL (416)246-0840

Newton, Ralph Photography
600 Queen St E 2nd Fl Toronto Ontario .... TEL (416)466-4474

Niagara Studio/Dennis Hall
1553 Knareswood Dr Mississauga Ontario .... TEL (416)278-0354

Nicholls, Chris Photography
276 Carlaw Ave #305 Toronto Ontario .... TEL (416)469-0812

Nigro, Giorgio Photography
555 Richmond St W 8th Fl Toronto Ontario .... TEL (416)520-7061

Noel, Claude Photography
276 Carlaw Ave #216 Toronto Ontario .... TEL (416)469-8112

Noguchi, Vincent Photography
52 Shaftsbury Ave Toronto Ontario .... TEL (416)961-9304

Northern Studio/Rob Mitchell
205 Richmond St W #602 Toronto Ontario .... TEL (416)977-5887

Noto, Rino Photography
276 Carlaw Ave #306 Toronto Ontario .... TEL (416)465-8094

Nova Illustrative Photography Inc
150 Britannia Rd E #4 Mississauga Ontario .... TEL (416)890-0088

O'Brien, John Photography
56 The Esplanade #508 Toronto Ontario .... TEL (416)862-2871

Oasis Art & Photography
5 Polson St Toronto Ontario .... TEL (416)461-7518

Oasis/Philip Gallard
5 Polson St Toronto Ontario .... TEL (416)461-7518

Odesse Photography
PO Box 457 Penetang Ontario .... TEL (705)526-0212

Ohashi, David Photographer
10 Morrow Ave Toronto Ontario .... TEL (416)533-6634

Olson, Mark Photography
192 Spadina Ave #312 Toronto Ontario .... TEL (416)366-6608

OOStudio Photography
118 Berkeley St Toronto Ontario .... TEL (416)862-7973

Orenstein, Paul Photography Ltd
317 Adelaide St W #603 Toronto Ontario .... TEL (416)593-9200

P.A.U. Photography
43 Laing St Toronto Ontario .... TEL (416)423-3007

Paisley Studio
11 Benary Cres Scarborough Ontario .... TEL (416)439-4573

Palmer Photographic
276 Carlaw Ave #309 Toronto Ontario .... TEL (416)465-3634

Panda/Patrick Kennedy
524 Wellington St W Toronto Ontario .... TEL (416)593-9266

Panou, Jim Photography
80 Spadina Ave #207 Toronto Ontario .... TEL (416)531-7721

Pariselli, Joseph Photographer
468 Roxton Rd Toronto Ontario .... TEL (416)536-1811

Parkes, Ted Photography
276 Carlaw Ave #202 Toronto Ontario .... TEL (416)465-4556

Paterson Photographic Works
6 Croft St Toronto Ontario .... TEL (416)968-6696

Paul, Dan Photography
276 Carlaw Ave #305 Toronto Ontario .... TEL (416)778-6327

Paulson, Todd
80 Aberdeen Rd S Cambridge Ontario .... TEL (519)623-6685

Pawlowski, Richard
66 Oakmount Rd #1211 Toronto Ontario .... TEL (416)769-7868

Pearson, Marcus
850 Palmerston Ave #2 Toronto Ontario .... TEL (416)348-0134

Perlmutter, Karen Photography
183 Bathurst St #402 Toronto Ontario .... TEL (416)361-3111

Petersen, Barry Photography
512 Lansdowne Ave Toronto Ontario .... TEL (416)531-0617

Petrelli, Sergio
9 Davies Ave #300 Toronto Ontario .... TEL (416)469-3727

Philip-Jon Studios
6790 Kitimat Rd #6 Mississauga Ontario .... TEL (416)826-1300

Phillips, John Photographics
25 Liberty St #208 Toronto Ontario .... TEL (416)536-9442

Photo Engravers & Electrotypers Ltd.
2250 Islington Ave Toronto Ontario .... TEL (416)743-8920

Photo Images
1179A King St W #105 Toronto Ontario .... TEL (416)531-3997

Photo Stetics
76 Hazelton Ave Toronto Ontario .... TEL (416)925-7887

Photo Works
45 South Shields Ave Agincourt Ontario .... TEL (416)293-3292

Photo's By James
4036 Rushton Cres Mississauga Ontario .... TEL (416)828-7599

Photo/Design Associates Inc/Ivan Otis
409 Front St E Toronto Ontario .... TEL (416)368-1031

Photographic Arts
60 La France Rd Brampton Ontario .... TEL (416)450-5854

Photographic Excellence
Toronto Ontario .... TEL (416)962-5364

Photographic Illustration
1114 Queen St E Toronto Ontario .... TEL (416)461-8460

Photographic Visions
51 Crestwood Rd Thornhill Ontario .... TEL (416)731-2111

Photography by Babak
124 Baby Point Road Toronto Ontario .... TEL (416)766-4973

Photography By Dene
487 Adelaide St W #103 Toronto Ontario .... TEL (416)362-4142

Photography Place Incorporated
2350 Haines Rd Bldg #2 Mississauga Ontario .... TEL (416)848-5703

PhotoPlex
73 Laird Dr #301 Toronto Ontario .... TEL (416)429-4007

Pickett Photography
1087 Queen St W Toronto Ontario .... TEL (416)531-2545

Picton, Richard Photogaphy
60 Sumach St Toronto Ontario .... TEL (416)864-1314

Pierre, Richard
21 Fairview Blvd Toronto Ontario .... TEL (416)466-4063

Plexman, Matthew Photography Ltd
146 First Ave Toronto Ontario .... TEL (416)463-3914

Plow, John
7 Longbow Sq Agincourt Ontario .... TEL (416)497-1967

Plum Studios
70 Villarboite #7 Concord Ontario .... TEL (416)660-2491

Pokorchak, James
31 Progress Crt #5 Scarborough Ontario .... TEL (416)289-4477

Porter, John Photography
235 Carlaw Ave #6000 Toronto Ontario .... TEL (416)469-5223

Prelude Photography
55 West Beaver Creek #3 Richmond Hill Ontario .... TEL (416)764-9391

Pringle & Booth Ltd
1133 Leslie St Don Mills Ontario .... TEL (416)447-5121

Prost, B Photography Inc
1680 Midland Ave #7 Scarborough Ontario .... TEL (416)752-0186

Protter, Karl Photography
25 George St #505 Toronto Ontario .... TEL (416)594-1126

Proudfoot, Jill Photography
53 Golfview Ave Toronto Ontario .... TEL (416)698-8986

Psotka, Walter Photography
1430 Yonge St Toronto Ontario .... TEL (416)922-1979

QPT Inc
2220 Midland Ave #118 Toronto Ontario .... TEL (416)299-6911

QPT Visual Expressions Inc.
Box 274 Thornhill Ontario .... TEL (416)886-4444

Quaile, Jamie Photography
99 Sudbury St #2 Toronto Ontario .... TEL (416)537-7939

Quest for Image Photography
1947 Dundas St W #B8 Toronto Ontario .... TEL (416)532-5803

Quirk, Colin
3066 Merritt Ave Mississauga Ontario .... TEL (416)677-1652

Quon, Kint Photogaphy
276 Carlaw Ave #223 Toronto Ontario .... TEL (416)463-0789

R.D.H. Photographic Services
70 Hogarth Ave North York Ontario .... TEL (416)361-3163

Raamat, Rein P & Co Inc
9 Davies Ave #202 Toronto Ontario .... TEL (416)778-8800

Rafelson, Michael Photography
553 Queen St W #300 Toronto Ontario .... TEL (416)368-2487

Ragsdale, Robert C. Limited
21 Avenue Rd (Four Seasons)Lwr Toronto Ontario .... TEL (416)967-3326

Rainbow Productions
7150 Torbram Rd Mississauga Ontario .... TEL (416)678-6596

Rand Photography Co
388 Carlaw Ave #203 Toronto Ontario .... TEL (416)461-5576

Randall, Walley Photography
400 Eastern Ave #220 Toronto Ontario .... TEL (416)462-3062

Ranford, Barry
Kaywood Mills RR#1 Palgrave Ontario .... TEL (519)942-1262

Rava, Robert Photography
353 Eastern Ave #104 Toronto Ontario .... TEL (416)466-9270

Redhead Studios
60 Fraser Ave Toronto Ontario .... TEL (416)588-7218

Reeves, John
33 St Paul St Toronto Ontario .... TEL (416)362-5223

Reichwein, Glen Photogapher
1114 Queen St E Toronto Ontario .... TEL (416)461-8460

Rhijnsburger, Gary Photography
12 Logan Ave Toronto Ontario .... TEL (416)461-5100

Riccio & Associates Photography
2400 Finch Ave W #2 North York Ontario .... TEL (416)748-0878

Richardson, Don Photography
1412 Tyandaga Pk Dr Burlington Ontario .... TEL (416)336-0012

Richter, Karl Photography
163 Sterling Rd, N Entrance Toronto Ontario .... TEL (416)532-5863

Rolagraphic Images
1264 York Mills Rd #209 Don Mills Ontario .... TEL (416)446-1755

Rolfe, Roger
180 Delaware Ave Toronto Ontario .... TEL (416)536-5291

Rommel Life Style Productions
1 Babington Crt Toronto Ontario .... TEL (416)239-6300

Rondel, Benjamin Photography
155 Marlee Ave #604 Toronto Ontario .... TEL (416)785-8680

Roth, Hal Photography Inc
56 The Esplanade E #402 Toronto Ontario .... TEL (416)365-9898

Rough Layout
46 Noble St #212 Toronto Ontario .... TEL (416)535-0288

Roxy Photography
109 Vanderhoof Ave Toronto Ontario .... TEL (416)424-1270

Rozario, Paul J. Photography
77 Mowat Ave #305 Toronto Ontario .... TEL (416)537-3047

Rubesa, Alen Photography
60 Sumach St Toronto Ontario .... TEL (416)864-1314

Rudner, Sheldon Photography Inc
219 Front St E Toronto Ontario .... TEL (416)367-2443

Ruelens, Brad Photography
741 Queen St E Toronto Ontario .... TEL (416)463-0943

Russell-Carib Photo Studio
607 St Clair Ave W Toronto Ontario .... TEL (416)657-1598

Ryan, Pete
135 High Park Ave Toronto Ontario .... TEL (416)230-2552

Ryerson Polytechnical Institute
350 Victoria St Toronto Ontario .... TEL (416)979-5167

Sakulensky, Lisa Photography
650 Crawford St Toronto Ontario .... TEL (416)661-9290

Sampson, Ridge
10 Morrow Ave Toronto Ontario .... TEL (416)537-8700

Samson, Ian Productions
100 Whitehorn Cres Willowdale Ontario .... TEL (416)493-1131

Samuel, Craig Photography
1209 King St W #200 Toronto Ontario .... TEL (416)531-5428

Sanders, Richard Photography Ltd.
200 Steelcase Rd E #3 Markham Ontario .... TEL (416)474-0712

Sandor, Michael Photography Inc
252 Glengrove Ave #3 Toronto Ontario .... TEL (416)480-0918

Santillo Photography
1044 Bathurst St Toronto Ontario .... TEL (416)535-8200

Saunders, Tim & Associates
163 A Manning Ave Toronto Ontario .... TEL (416)368-1611

Schnepel Photography Inc
9 Davies Ave #300 Toronto Ontario .... TEL (416)466-1461

Schofield, Arnold Photography
200 Gage Ave S #102 Hamilton Ontario .... TEL (416)547-5902

SCL Visual Marketing Group
190 Milner Ave Scarborough Ontario .... TEL (416)293-9943

Scott, David Photography
99 Sudbury St #4 Toronto Ontario .... TEL (416)531-7484

Scrivano Photography
4040 Steeles Ave W #41 Woodbridge Ontario .... TEL (416)856-4010

Select Communications
6967 Pacific Circle Mississauga Ontario .... TEL (416)670-5240

Sensibility/Anne Zbitnew
7 Fraser Ave #7 Toronto Ontario .... TEL (416)531-8181

Sensibility/Karrie Gayer
7 Fraser Ave #7 Toronto Ontario .... TEL (416)531-8181

Shainbaum, Barry Photography
148 Arlington Ave Toronto Ontario .... TEL (416)656-0482

Shanoff, Nancy & Associates Ltd
688 Richmond St W Toronto Ontario .... TEL (416)863-1774

Sharp, Liam Photography Inc
186 Brunswick Ave Toronto Ontario .... TEL (416)922-4401

Sharpshooter Studios Inc
524 Queen St E Toronto Ontario .... TEL (416)860-0300

Sharpshooter/Brian Smale
524 Queen St E Toronto Ontario .... TEL (416)860-0300

Sharpshooter/Michel Pilon
524 Queen St E Toronto Ontario .... TEL (416)860-0300

Sharpshooter/Peter Leverman
524 Queen St E Toronto Ontario .... TEL (416)860-0300

Sibbald, Peter
671 Huron St Toronto Ontario .... TEL (416)928-6605

Sinclair, Ian
21 Polson St Toronto Ontario .... TEL (416)463-5706

Singh, Walter
120 Cowan Ave #20 Toronto Ontario .... TEL (416)533-3653

Singleton, Colin Photographer
99 Sudbury St #5 Toronto Ontario .... TEL (416)530-4634

Sippel, Hal G. Photographer
410 - 4 The Donway E Toronto Ontario .... TEL (416)446-1400

Sirant, Olga Photography
22 Soho St Toronto Ontario .... TEL (416)595-7195

Skinner, Cliff
RR#1 Queensville Ontario .... TEL (416)478-2327

Skyart Productions
RR#3 Elmwood Ontario .... TEL (416)363-5785

Sloan Shoots
65 Bellwoods Ave Toronto Ontario .... TEL (416)368-4112

Smith, Andy
6 Allison Dr Toronto Ontario .... TEL (416)239-4995

Smith, Kevin Photography
87 Mowat Ave #305 Toronto Ontario .... TEL (416)532-9462

Smith, Paul J./Gallery 12
1058 Gerrard St E Toronto Ontario .... TEL (416)469-4820

Smith, Ronald Baxter Photography Ltd
11 Carlaw Ave #4 Toronto Ontario .... TEL (416)365-1429

Smith, Thomas M.
393 Ridge Rd. Ridgeway Ontario .... TEL (416)894-3047

Spalding-Smith, Fiona
70 Hogarth Ave Toronto Ontario .... TEL (416)463-5073

Spectrum Studios
900 Pond View Rd #118 London Ontario .... TEL (519)681-2299

St-Pierre, Marcel Photography
86 Parliament St Studio C Toronto Ontario .... TEL (416)361-5885

Stage Four Productions
328 Roxton Rd Toronto Ontario .... TEL (416)588-2285

Stamenov, Robert Photography
1383 Danforth Ave Toronto Ontario .... TEL (416)461-9646

Stegel, Mark Photography
9 Davies Ave #300 Toronto Ontario .... TEL (416)462-3244

Stephen, Craig Photography
32 Curzon St #8 Toronto Ontario .... TEL (416)461-1948

Sterling Group, The
221 Sterling Rd #5 Toronto Ontario .... TEL (416)533-3650

Sterling Group, The/David Michael Allen
221 Sterling Rd #5 Toronto Ontario .... TEL (416)533-3650

Sterling Group, The/Gary Gerovac
221 Sterling Rd #5 Toronto Ontario .... TEL (416)533-3650

Sterling Group, The/Kevin Sparkman
221 Sterling Rd #5 Toronto Ontario .... TEL (416)533-3650

Sterling Group, The/R. Averill Lehan
221 Sterling Rd #5 Toronto Ontario .... TEL (416)533-3650

Stewart, Bob Photography Inc
60 Sumach St #100 Toronto Ontario .... TEL (416)359-1190

Stiegler, Jaro Photography Inc
221 Dufferin St #304A Toronto Ontario .... TEL (416)532-6445

Stober, Steve Photography
20 Maud St #205 Toronto Ontario .... TEL (416)360-1226

Stokal, Robert Photography
445 Rosewell Ave #1 Toronto Ontario .... TEL (416)364-7551

Stott, Greg Photography
181 Beech Ave Toronto Ontario .... TEL (416)698-9824

Strada Photography Inc
42 Mowat Ave Ground Level Toronto Ontario .... TEL (416)533-5132

Street, David Photographer
9 Davies Ave 3rd Fl Toronto Ontario .... TEL (416)466-9994

Stringer, Brad Photographer
44 Kippendavie Ave Toronto Ontario .... TEL (416)691-9054

Struan Photography Inc
567 Queen St W 4th Fl Toronto Ontario .... TEL (416)366-6000

Strube, Peter Photography
725 King St W #705 Toronto Ontario .... TEL (416)594-0110

Struthers Photographics
1398 Queen St E Toronto Ontario .... TEL (416)465-8763

Studio 37 Incorporated
86 Yorkville Ave 3rd Fl Toronto Ontario .... TEL (416)967-6416

Studio Northwest Inc
2 Melanie Dr #5 Bramalea Ontario .... TEL (416)792-3682

Studio Two Photographers Inc
1297 Matheson Blvd Mississauga Ontario .... TEL (416)624-6322

Studio, The/David Leadbitter
2 Berkeley St #502 Toronto Ontario .... TEL (416)862-0605

Studio, The/Elie Moussalli
2 Berkeley St #502 Toronto Ontario .... TEL (416)862-0605

Sugino, Shin & Associates Inc
46 McGee St Toronto Ontario .... TEL (416)469-4588

Summers, Brian Photography
4 Boulton Ave Toronto Ontario .... TEL (416)469-0144

Svarre Productions Ltd
426 Dundas St E Toronto Ontario .... TEL (416)964-8974

Swiecki, Richard Photography
4 Boulton Ave Toronto Ontario .... TEL (416)466-7502

Szuba, Tom Photographer
9 Davies Ave #302 Toronto Ontario .... TEL (416)461-1234

Szurkowski, Les Photography
124 Fox Run Barrie Ontario .... TEL (705)726-4521

Tabak, Sid Photography
353 Eastern Ave #206 Toronto Ontario .... TEL (416)463-5718

Tanaka, Ron
67 Mowat Ave #540 Toronto Ontario .... TEL (416)536-9440

Tancredi, Frank Photography Inc
533 College St #401 Toronto Ontario .... TEL (416)922-7092

Taub, Ellen Photography
20 Maud St #205 Toronto Ontario .... TEL (416)866-8295

Taylor Photographics
223 Bagot St Kingston Ontario .... TEL (613)541-1098

TDF Artists Ltd/Photographic Div
980 Yonge St 2nd Fl Toronto Ontario .... TEL (416)924-3371

Templeton Studios Ltd
1595 McCowan Rd Scarborough Ontario .... TEL (416)292-2490

Teschel, Joseph
235 Carlaw Ave 6th Fl Toronto Ontario .... TEL (416)861-1247

The Cove/Dave Starrett
140 Milner Ave #48 Scarborough Ontario .... TEL (416)297-1200

The Cove/George Mashinter
140 Milner Ave #48 Scarborough Ontario .... TEL (416)297-1200

The Reliance Group
42 Industrial St Toronto Ontario .... TEL (416)425-5750

Thomaidis, Chris Photography
85 Ravina Cres Toronto Ontario .... TEL (416)465-7635

Thomas, Fred Photography
287 Crawford St Toronto Ontario .... TEL (416)766-3225

Thomassian, Edmond
62 Fraser Ave Toronto Ontario .... TEL (416)535-9097

Tigani, Doug Photography
15 Lower Sherbourne St #6 Toronto Ontario .... TEL (416)368-0950

Timberwolf Productions
PO Box 2779 Sudbury Ontario .... TEL (705)566-0433

Tinios, Jim Photography
22 Mowat Ave #300 Toronto Ontario .... TEL (416)588-8048

To, John Photography
89 Sackville St Toronto Ontario .... TEL (416)861-0965

Tofflemire Photographics
317 Adelaide St W #603 Toronto Ontario .... TEL (416)593-9200

Tom, Kam Photography
17 Carlaw Ave #6 Toronto Ontario .... TEL (416)462-2966

Toma, Miki Photography
160 Huron St #315 Toronto Ontario .... TEL (416)340-7610

Toronto Image Works
80 Spadina Ave Toronto Ontario .... TEL (416)363-1999

Toronto Photogroup Ltd
584 Gordon Baker Rd Willowdale Ontario .... TEL (416)497-3127

Trevor, David & Associates
276 Carlaw Ave #308 Toronto Ontario .... TEL (416)466-2650

Tri Imagery
91 Parliament St Toronto Ontario .... TEL (416)367-4052

Triple M Photo Ltd
220 Duncan Mills Rd #307 Don Mills Ontario .... TEL (416)422-1919

Trussler, Eric Photography Ltd
961 Eglinton Ave E Toronto Ontario .... TEL (416)429-7222

Tuffner, Deborah Photography
22 Mowat Ave #300 Toronto Ontario .... TEL (416)588-8048

Tulloch, Janet/Visual Artist
517 Hurd Ave Burlington Ontario .... TEL (416)634-3514

Twan, Joseph
204 Brunswick Ave Toronto Ontario .... TEL (416)921-7786

Tyler-Clarke Studios
264 Seaton St #208 Toronto Ontario .... TEL (416)923-6025

Umbrella Communications
90 Northline Dr Toronto Ontario .... TEL (416)288-8739

Vanderkooy, Wim Photographer
272 Richmond St E Toronto Ontario .... TEL (416)368-5224

Vecera, Anthony Photography Ltd
264 Avenue Rd Toronto Ontario .... TEL (416)922-4397

Vella, Charles
2200 St Clair Ave W Toronto Ontario .... TEL (416)761-4138

Venus Photography
21 Penhurst Ave Toronto Ontario .... TEL (416)252-8849

Villeneuve, Ken
14 Markham St 3rd Fl Toronto Ontario .... TEL (416)363-9581

Visser, Mike Photography
1179A King St W #307 Toronto Ontario .... TEL (416)536-7718

Vistorino, Mark Photography
1179A King St W #316 Toronto Ontario .... TEL (416)531-2218

Visual Associates
474 Bathurst St #401 Toronto Ontario .... TEL (416)465-1400

Visual Dynamics Photography
1276 Playford Rd Mississauga Ontario .... TEL (416)823-2157

Visual Impact/Christopher So
272 Richmond St E #300 Toronto Ontairo .... TEL (416)863-0002

Visual Impact/Darcy Loates
272 Richmond St E #300 Toronto Ontairo .... TEL (416)863-0002

Wadano, Yoshi Photography
29 Firth Cres Scarborough Ontario .... TEL (416)431-5250

Walker, Peter Photography
221 Dufferin St #304A Toronto Ontario .... TEL (416)588-6168

Wallace, Michael Photography
3 MacDonell Ave Toronto Ontario .... TEL (416)537-1887

Walley, Ken Photography Inc
441 Queen St E Toronto Ontario .... TEL (416)869-3155

Walter's PG & Associates Inc
385 Richmond St E Toronto Ontario .... TEL (416)364-9859

Walton, David Photography
205 Richmond St W #603 Toronto Ontario .... TEL (416)977-6247

Waring, Michael Photography
276 Carlaw Ave #216 Toronto Ontario .... TEL (416)469-0107

Watson, Budd
P.O. Box 579 Midland Ontario .... TEL (416)925-4323

Watson, Robert Photography
60 Sumach St Toronto Ontario .... TEL (416)864-1314

Webster, Clive Photography Inc
56 The Esplanade #502 Toronto Ontario .... TEL (416)363-7081

Wescam Photographic
97 Davisville Ave Toronto Ontario .... TEL (416)483-7195

Westside Ariel Photography
33 Jefferson Ave Toronto Ontario .... TEL (416)535-1955

Westside/Garth Grosjean
33 Jefferson Ave Toronto Ontario .... TEL (416)535-1955

Westside/George Simhoni
33 Jefferson Ave Toronto Ontario .... TEL (416)535-1955

Westside/James Elliott
33 Jefferson Ave Toronto Ontario .... TEL (416)535-1955

Westside/Jean Desjardins
33 Jefferson Ave Toronto Ontario .... TEL (416)535-1955

Westside/Liz Crofton
33 Jefferson Ave Toronto Ontario .... TEL (416)535-1955

Westside/Olga Tracy
33 Jefferson Ave Toronto Ontario .... TEL (416)535-1955

Westside/Rick McKechnie
33 Jefferson Ave Toronto Ontario .... TEL (416)535-1955

Westside/Silvio Calcagno
33 Jefferson Ave Toronto Ontario .... TEL (416)535-1955

Westside/William McLeod
33 Jefferson Ave Toronto Ontario .... TEL (416)535-1955

Whillians, Richard Photography
150 Longboat Ave #404 Toronto Ontario .... TEL (416)868-0563

White, Don Carleton & Associates
PO Box 6664 Stn A Toronto Ontario .... TEL (416)363-5320

White, Gary Photography
99 Sudbury St #5 Toronto Ontario .... TEL (416)530-4634

White, Robert/Whitecom Studio
4 Boulton Ave Toronto Ontario .... TEL (416)469-0144

Whiteside, George Photographer
58 Stewart St Toronto Ontario .... TEL (416)360-7147

Whittaker, David Photography
276 Carlaw Ave #307 Toronto Ontario .... TEL (416)466-0558

Wigington, Robert Photographer Ltd
4 Clinton Pl Toronto Ontario .... TEL (416)533-7938

Wild Photography Inc
6 Church St 3rd Floor Toronto Ontario .... TEL (416)863-6875

Wiley, Matthew Photography
483 Eastern Ave Toronto Ontario .... TEL (416)462-0112

Wilkins, George Photography Ltd
456 Wellington St W Toronto Ontario .... TEL (416)596-6530

Wittman, Bill
2161 Yonge St #200 Toronto Ontario .... TEL (416)482-3768

Wohlfahrt, David Photography
483 Eastern Ave Toronto Ontario .... TEL (416)462-0112

Wolk, Lorne Photography Inc
111 Davisville Ave #306 Toronto Ontario .... TEL (416)961-8935

Wong, Robin Photography
22 Mowat Ave #300 Toronto Ontario .... TEL (416)532-9291

Wong, Stanley Pictures Inc
225 Richmond St W #400 Toronto Ontario .... TEL (416)585-9366

Wright, Dan Photography
3100 Ridgeway Dr #10 Mississauga Ontario .... TEL (416)828-0666

Wu, David Photography
235 Carlaw Ave Toronto Ontario .... TEL (416)466-4722

Yarwood, Ted Photography
1179A King St W #302 Toronto Ontario .... TEL (416)531-4615

Yee, Allen & Assoicates
300 Jones Ave 1st Fl Toronto Ontario .... TEL (416)462-9327

Yip, Roger Photography
275 Leslie St Toronto Ontario .... TEL (416)462-0202

Zabol, Myron Photographer
219 Dufferin St #301 Toronto Ontario .... TEL (416)530-4924

Zanetti Photography
221 Dufferin St #310 Toronto Ontario .... TEL (416)531-6215

Zelea Photography
334 King St E #525 Toronto Ontario .... TEL (416)361-0204

Zelinski, Mark Photographics Design
35 Roxborough St W Toronto Ontario .... TEL (416)928-9682

Zinger Photographics
77 Florence Ave #304 Toronto Ontario .... TEL (416)536-8119

Zipper Studios
31 Progress Crt #5 Scarbourgh Ontario .... TEL (416)289-4477

Zoli Photographic
489 King St W #306 Toronto Ontario .... TEL (416)979-7107

Zoom Professional Photography
427A Queen St W 3rd Fl Toronto Ontario .... TEL (416)593-0690

PHOTO ASSISTANTS

Coussin, Jeff/Photo Assistant
32 Draper St Toronto Ontario .... TEL (416)599-9468

Cowie, Kathryne
1640 Beaudry Montreal Quebec .... TEL (514)524-7581

Field, Heather
18 Humphrey Dr Ajax Ontario .... TEL (416)686-0075

Peter Gordon for Photo Assistant
Box 334 Stn A Vancouver B.C. .... TEL (604)669-1959

Tucker, Diana/Photo Assistant
22 Palmerston Gardens Toronto Ontario .... TEL (416)534-7008

PHOTOGRAPHERS — OTTAWA

Andrews-Newton Photographers
151 Sparks St Ottawa Ontario .... TEL (613)234-4144

Balfour, Andrew Photography
286 Frost Ave Ottawa Ontario .... TEL (613)230-8887

Baum, Curtis Photography
9 Foster St #1 Ottawa Ontario .... TEL (613)728-1552

Beaudry, Anna Photography Ltd
205 Catherine St #202 Ottawa Ontario .... TEL (613)567-0628

Bedford, Michael
63 Sparks St #100 Ottawa Ontario .... TEL (613)232-4335

Belinge, Marie-Lys
21 des Erables Hull Quebec .... TEL (819)771-3668

Beninger Photography Inc
Fifth Ave Court Ottawa Ontario .... TEL (613)233-9952

Black, Garry
1083 St Emmanuel Terrace Gloucester Ontario .... TEL (613)824-9295

Boite Noir Eng.
125 Eddy St 2nd Fl Hull Quebec .... TEL (819)778-0445

Camicioli, Albert M. Photography
5006 River Rd Manotick Ontario .... TEL (613)822-6084

Carter, Garry Photography Ltd
Box 116 RR#2 Manotick Ontario .... TEL (613)728-9377

Cattroll/Ritcey Photo Associates
335 Catherine St Ottawa Ontario .... TEL (613)235-3686

Cochrane Photography
126 York St #406 Ottawa Ontario .... TEL (613)234-3099

Couvrette, Paul Photography Inc
54 Florence St Ottawa Ontario .... TEL (613)238-5104

Cretney, Clive
43 Plateau Du Reservoir Gatineau Quebec .... TEL (819)243-4467

Desmarais, Richard
205 Catherine St #300 Ottawa Ontario .... TEL (613)238-1943

Devries - Mikkelson Photography
6-555 Gilmour St Ottawa Ontario .... TEL (613)722-5137

E&K Productions
234 Slater St Ottawa Ontario .... TEL (613)563-1134

Evans, John Photography Ltd
519 Sussex Dr Ottawa Ontario .... TEL (613)237-1044

Fenn, Stephen Photographer
359 Terry Fox Dr Kanata Ontario .... TEL (613)233-4415

Foto Blohm Associates Ltd
64 Avonlea Rd Ottawa Ontario .... TEL (613)226-4212

Ginn, Kenneth Photographer
205 Catherine St Ottawa Ontario .... TEL (613)238-5377

Green Audio Visual Ltd
404 Bank St Ottawa Ontario .... TEL (613)326-2919

Greer, Brian Photography
1045 Morrison Dr #23 Ottawa Ontario .... TEL (613)829-5765

Grogan, Roy Photographer
44 - 710 Coronation Nepean Ontario .... TEL (613)526-4090

Harquail, Randy/Overall Design
245 Strafford Rd W Nepean Ontario .... TEL (613)596-6591

Heritage & Industrial Recording Services
190 Bronson Ave Ottawa Ontario .... TEL (613)563-4549

Horan Photography
14 Pinehurst Ave Ottawa Ontario .... TEL (613)729-0724

Horvath, Walter J. Photography
1647 Bank St Ottawa Ontario .... TEL (613)737-3331

Image House/John McQuarrie
107 York St Ottawa Ontario .... TEL (613-236-1833

Imagem Societe Audio-Visuelle Inc
365-A Bd. St-Joseph Hull Quebec .... TEL (819)778-1626

King, Gordon Photography
111-A Rideau St Ottawa Ontario .... TEL (613)230-8180

Kocsis Photography
49E Woodfield Dr Ottawa Ontario .... TEL (613)226-2600

Landreville, Philippe Photographe Inc
2630D Lancaster Rd Ottawa Ontario .... TEL (613)738-5045

Le Blanc, Andrew Photography
134 Clarence St Ottawa Ontario .... TEL (613)230-8887

Lux Photographic Services Inc.
20 Foster St Ottawa Ontario .... TEL (613)728-4515

MacGowen, Murray
330 Booth St Ottawa Ontario .... TEL (613)232-3994

Main Street Studios
359 Terry Fox Dr Kanata Ontario .... TEL (613)591-0357

Major, John Photographer
537 Blair St Ottawa Ontario .... TEL (613)521-4995

Marquis Photographers Ltd
115 Flora St Ottawa Ontario .... TEL (613)236-5182

Maruska Studios
61A York St Ottawa Ontario .... TEL (613)230-1906

McElligott, William P. Photography Ltd.
146 Dalhousie St Ottawa Ontario .... TEL (613)594-5955

Merrithew, Jim Photography
RR#2 (Middleville) Lanark Ontario .... TEL (613)259-3331

Metropolis Studio
34 Noel St Ottawa Ontario .... TEL (613)744-1337

Mirsky, Phillip
104 - 124 Springfield Rd Ottawa Ontario .... TEL (613)745-2243

Overall Design Associates
245 Stafford Rd W Nepean Ontario .... TEL (613)596-6591

Patterson Photographic
100 - 151 Slater St Ottawa Ontario .... TEL (613)236-7678

Perigree Productions
92 Spruce St Ottawa Ontario .... TEL (613)234-9665

Photo Features Ltd
160 Richmond Rd Ottawa Ontario .... TEL (613)729-9076

Photo Kouri Ltd
15 Boucher Hull Quebec .... TEL (819)770-3264

Photo-Graphics
P.O. Box 1180 Richmond Ontario .... TEL (613)838-2288

Proulx, Francois
361 Winston Ave Ottawa Ontario .... TEL (613)596-2848

Przybytek, John Photography
51 Sumac St #9 Ottawa Ontario .... TEL (613)564-4318

Remembrance Photo
430 Preston St Ottawa Ontario .... TEL (613)232-0361

Richter, Ewald Photography Ltd
1297 Woodroffe Ave Ottawa Ontario .... TEL (613)727-8155

Searle, Adrian Photography
880 Grenon Ave Ottawa Ontario .... TEL (613)820-7478

St. Jacques, Pierre
237 King Edward Ottawa Ontario .... TEL (613)233-0970

Tarp, Steven Photography
9-333 McCarthy Rd Ottawa Ontario .... TEL (613)523-9509

The Focus Centre
254 Bank St Ottawa Ontario .... TEL (613)232-5368

Toomey Photography
5900 Hazeldean Rd Stittsville Ontario .... TEL (613)831-1603

Volpel, Douglas
308 Legget Dr Kanata Ontario .... TEL (613)591-0357

White, Christopher Photographs
181 Gilmour St #1 Ottawa Ontario .... TEL (613)237-5930

Wolf Professional Photo Services
800 Bank St Ottawa Ontario .... TEL (613)232-5521

Zarysky, Larry & Associates
45-3240 Southgate Rd Ottawa Ontario .... TEL (613)731-1734

STOCK PHOTOGRAPHY

Canapress Photo Service
36 King St E 4th Fl Toronto Ontario .... TEL (416)364-0321

Cinémanima Inc.
56 rue St. Pierre #306 Québec, Québec .... TEL (418)692-0352

Creative Stock Agencies Inc
70 Scollard St #202 Toronto Ontario .... TEL (416)324-9800

First Light Associated Photographers
1 Atlantic Ave #204 Toronto Ontario .... TEL (416)532-6108

Focus Stock Photography Inc
950 Yonge St #409 Toronto Ontario .... TEL (416)968-6619

Image Bank Canada, The
40 Eglinton Ave E #307 Toronto Ontario .... TEL (416)322-8840

Image Finders Photo Agency Inc
134 Abbott St Vancouver B.C. .... TEL (604)688-9818

Mach 2 Stock Exchange, The
1409 Edmonton Trail NE #200 Calgary Alberta .... TEL (403)230-9363

Masterfile
415 Yonge St #200 Toronto Ontario .... TEL (416)977-7267

Miller/Comstock
180 Bloor St W #1102 Toronto Ontario .... TEL (416)925-4323

Mosiac Stock Photo Agency
836 Yonge St Toronto Ontario .... TEL (416)499-2936

Petkov, Marin Photographer
MPO Box 2431 Vancouver B.C. .... TEL (604)941-1190

Photo Artists Canada
620 Richmond St W #1 Toronto Ontario .... TEL (416)367-9770

Publiphoto Inc.
797 av Champagneur Outremont Québec .... TEL (514)273-4322

Stock Market Inc, The
93 Parliament St #228 Toronto Ontario .... TEL (416)362-7767

Superstock - Four x Five
512 King St E #300 Toronto Ontario .... TEL (416)860-1518

Take Stock Inc
705,603-7th Ave SW Calgary Alberta .... TEL (403)233-7487

Timmermann, John Photography
41 Meadowbank Dr Nepean Ontario .... TEL (613)729-9076

Valan Photos
490 Dulwich Ave St. Lambert Québec .... TEL (514)465-2557

Viewpoints West Photofile Ltd
1252 Burrard St #101 Vancouver B.C. .... TEL (604)685-8381

PHOTO LABORATORIES

A&D Photo Lab Services Ltd
27 Mobile Dr Toronto Ontario .... TEL (416)752-8586

Absolute Color Slides
197 Dundas St E Toronto Ontario .... TEL (416)868-0413

Alden Photographic Inc
401 Alden Rd #10 Markham Ontario .... TEL (416)477-5161

Aperture
319 Queen St E Toronto Ontario .... TEL (416)368-0583

B&W Custom Photo Lab
155 George St Toronto Ontario .... TEL (416)368-3840

Benjamin Film Laboratories Ltd
287 Richmond St Toronto Ontario .... TEL (416)863-1166

BGM Colour Laboratories
497 King St E Toronto Ontario .... TEL (416)947-1325

Colour Prints
119 Vanderhoof Ave Toronto Ontario .... TEL (416)421-4136

Colour Projects Laboratories
2 Thorncliffe Park Ave #6 Toronto Ontario .... TEL (416)429-2700

Colour Scripts Ltd
504 Wellington St W Toronto Ontario .... TEL (416)596-6517

Contempo Colour Laboratories
155 George St Toronto Ontario .... TEL (416)868-1206

Custom Colour Labs
890 Caledonia Rd Toronto Ontario .... TEL (416)781-4615

D-Max Studio Lab
489 Queen St W Toronto Ontario .... TEL (416)867-8745

Etna Colour Laboratory Inc
1561 Keele St Toronto Ontario .... TEL (416)651-7770

F.K. Photo Finishers Ltd
90 Northline Rd Toronto Ontario .... TEL (416)285-9883

Galbraith Reproductions Ltd
201 Dufferin St Toronto Ontario .... TEL (416)531-6913

House of Brown
474 Richmond St E Toronto Ontario .... TEL (416)863-1121

Jones & Morris Photo-Enlarging Ltd
24 Carlaw Ave Toronto Ontario .... TEL (416)465-5466

Light Spectrum
473 Acherd St Toronto Ontario .... TEL (416)921-7149

Madison Photo Murals Ltd
272 Richmond St E Toronto Ontario .... TEL (416)368-9777

MCPL
4 Gilead Place Toronto Ontario .... TEL (416)362-6586

McRae Custom Colour Laboratories Ltd
76 Stafford St Toronto Ontario .... TEL (416)368-3401

MediaColour Photo Lab Inc
16 Lesmill Rd Don Mills Ontario .... TEL (416)441-9999

Northern Artist Film Labs
2362 A Yonge St Toronto Ontario .... TEL (416)484-1660

PAS Vanguard Photo Services
244 Queen St E Toronto Ontario .... TEL (416)869-0000

Photmaxx Canada Inc
19 Milliken Blvd Scarborough Ontario .... TEL (416)754-3167

Photo 123
13 Charles St W Toronto Ontario .... TEL (416)920-3844

Photo One Film Lab
18 Richmond Blvd Napanee Ontario .... TEL (613)354-3309

Photo-Enlarging Plus
73 Railside Rd Don Mills Ontario .... TEL (416)446-1578

Photo-Pro Labs Ltd
3100 Ridgeway Dr #10 Mississauga Ontario .... TEL (416)828-0666

Photofinishing Plus
11 Irwin Ave Don Mills Ontario .... TEL (416)922-5486

Photomethods Custom Colour Lab
433 Queen St E Toronto Ontario .... TEL (416)868-1390

Positive Images
1383 Danforth Ave Toronto Ontario .... TEL (416)461-9646

Pringle & Booth Ltd
1133 Leslie St Don Mills Ontario .... TEL (416)447-5121

Qualicolor Systems Limited
109 Vanderhoof Ave #1 Toronto Ontario .... TEL (416)422-1015

RC Colour Lab Ltd
1177 Queen St E Toronto Ontario .... TEL (416)461-3078

Riley's Colourlab
272 Richmond St E Toronto Ontario .... TEL (416)365-1100

Scarborough Colour Labs
190 Milner Ave Scarborough Ontario .... TEL (416)293-9943

Silvano Color Laboratories Limited
355 Weston Rd Toronto Ontario .... TEL (416)766-4131

Starlab Photo Finishing Services Inc
2300 Bloor St W Toronto Ontario .... TEL (416)769-7003

Steichenlab Ltd
500 Richmond St E Toronto Ontario .... TEL (416)366-8745

Studies In Light
RR#1 Thornton Ontario .... TEL (705)436-5186

System 4 Photofinishing Lab
214 Oakdale Rd Downsview Ontario .... TEL (416)741-5547

The Fine Print
259 Dufferin St #209 Toronto Ontario .... TEL (416)535-5227

TNT Colour Laboratories Ltd
5 Soho St Toronto Ontario .... TEL (416)340-0381

Toronto Image Works
80 Spadina Ave #207 Toronto Ontario .... TEL (416)363-1999

Transparency Processing Service Ltd
324 Richmond St W Toronto Ontario .... TEL (416)593-0434

Trend Colour Lab
1194 D Caledonia Rd Toronto Ontario .... TEL (416)781-3547

West Camera
514 Queen St W Toronto Ontario .... TEL (416)865-9432

Yee, Henry Photography
473 Cosburn Ave Toronto Ontario .... TEL (416)423-4883

Profoto Inc
155 boul St-René o. Gatineau Québec .... TEL (819)663-8850

Techniphoto Ltd
234 Slater St #102 Ottawa Ontario .... TEL (613)234-7136

STUDIO RENTALS

Wallace Studios
258 Wallace Ave Toronto Ontario .... TEL (416)537-3471

RETOUCHERS

Abbey Photo Restoration
255 Waverly Rd Toronto Ontario .... TEL (416)699-4400

Air Force Ink
16 Brighton St London Ontario .... TEL (519)672-6740

Bartholomew Retouching
30 Simmons Bramalea Ontario .... TEL (416)456-2321

Burnt Arrow Artworks
1492 Dupont St Bldg 5 Toronto Ontario .... TEL (416)531-5633

Colour Collaborators
114 Parliament St Toronto Ontario .... TEL (416)368-3073

Colour It Rose
28 John Garland Blvd Rexdale Ontario .... TEL (416)741-5733

Compack Productions
433 Queen St E Toronto Ontario .... TEL (416)362-4054

Fellini, Michael
31 Hunt Club Dr Toronto Ontario .... TEL (416)690-1105

Hills, Ron Digital Retouching
165 East Beaver Creek Rd #10 Richmond Hill Ont. .... TEL (416)886-0006

Karman, Robert
5 Polson St Toronto Ontario .... TEL (416)466-0812

Light Spectrum/Retouching & Framing
473A Church St Toronto Ontario .... TEL (416)921-7149

Meecham, Robert Ltd
20 Carleton St #120 Toronto Ontario .... TEL (416)581-1298

Partners III Graphics
109 Vanderhoof Ave #202 Toronto Ontario .... TEL (416)425-5162

Pfeiffer, Rolf
2465 Cawthra Rd #112 Mississauga Ontario .... TEL (416)273-7143

Psotka, Walter
1430 Yonge St Toronto Ontario .... TEL (416)922-1979

Sardinha, Anthony
16 Sparta Rd Toronto Ontario .... TEL (416)249-0285

Smith, Paul
320 Westminister Ave #29 London Ontario .... TEL (519)438-1300

SNG Retouching Studio Ltd
275 Renfrew Dr #102 Markham Ontario .... TEL (416)940-9029

W.T.S./Transparency Retoucher
52 Widmer St Toronto Ontario .... TEL (416)599-8816

FILM/VIDEO/AV

A.L.P. Communications
183 Avenue Rd Toronto Ontario .... TEL (416)927-8800

Absolute Productions
380 Bathurst St 2nd Fl Toronto Ontario .... TEL (416)366-3214

Accuphoto Company Ltd
436 Adelaide St W Toronto Ontario .... TEL (416)366-9318

Ad-Venture Sight & Sound
390 Parliament St Toronto Ontario .... TEL (416)923-9424

Adair, Trayton Productions
103 Charles St E 4th Fl Toronto Ontario .... TEL (416)922-2930

Advance Films & Video Ltd
257 Norseman St Toronto Ontario .... TEL (416)231-2223

Advanced F/X
140 Broughdale Ave London Ontario .... TEL (519)438-4312

Alndon Group Productions Inc
111 Queen St E 4th Fl Toronto Ontario .... TEL (416)361-5800

ALP Communications
183 Avenue Rd Toronto Ontario .... TEL (416)927-8800

Aniforms - The Audio Visualizers
410 Queens Quay W #420 Toronto Ontario .... TEL (416)363-4963

Animation House Ltd, The
162 Parliament St Toronto Ontario .... TEL (416)364-3556

Apor, Gabor & Company Ltd
12 Cluny Dr Toronto Ontario .... TEL (416)923-9228

Arcana Productions
132 Tamarack Dr Thornhill Ontario .... TEL (416)731-8806

Arto-Pelli Motion Pictures
33 Prince Arthur Ave Toronto Ontario .... TEL (416)928-0164

Atlantis Films Ltd.
65 Heward Ave Toronto Ontario .... TEL (416)462-0246

AV Force Inc, The
49 Spadina Ave #200 Toronto Ontario .... TEL (416)340-7036

AV House, The
409 King St W 2nd Fl Toronto Ontario .... TEL (416)591-1770

AV International
3495 14th Ave Markham Ontario .... TEL (416)479-2582

AV Works, The
17 St Joseph St #315 Toronto Ontario .... TEL (416)967-4711

Avatar Communications
2740 Matheson Blvd E #3 Mississauga Ontario .... TEL (416)629-8900

Avcom Productions
228 King St E Toronto Ontario .... TEL (416)364-6238

Avcor
189 Dufferin St Toronto Ontario .... TEL (416)531-2113

AVENU Presentation
100 Richmond St E #216 Toronto Ontario .... TEL (416)367-9661

Avtek Audio Visual
122 Sherbourne St Toronto Ontario .... TEL (416)361-1812

Bascombe Group Inc, The
489 Queen St E Toronto Ontario .... TEL (416)868-6818

Bell Production Services
507 Queen St E Toronto Ontario .... TEL (416)362-8700

Berman, Reva
251 Bedford Rd Toronto Ontario .... TEL (416)925-8829

Black Tie Productions
65 Harbour Sq #807 Toronto Ontario .... TEL (416)462-1742

Blue Eyes Productions
505 Queen St E 2nd Fl Toronto Ontario .... TEL (416)366-4055

Boardwalk Motion Pictures Ltd
46 Power St Toronto Ontario .... TEL (416)362-3155

Bongard Films Inc
59 Mutual St Toronto Ontario .... TEL (416)368-4593

Bowen & Associates
45 South Shields Ave Agincourt Ontario .... TEL (416)293-3292

Broadcast Productions Inc
77 Huntley St #2522 Toronto Ontario .... TEL (416)961-1776

Broadview Motion Pictures
219 Broadview Ave #103 Toronto Ontario .... TEL (416)469-4062

C Productions Ltd
53 Niagara St Toronto Ontario .... TEL (416)367-3711

Cait, Robert Productions Inc
300 Eglinton Ave E #904 Toronto Ontario .... TEL (416)440-1490

Canned Films
312 Adelaide St W #808 Toronto Ontario .... TEL (416)599-3350

Canvas Productions
96 Caroline Ave Toronto Ontario .... TEL (416)469-3809

Capstone Communications Group
15 Wilson St Markham Ontario .... TEL (416)472-2330

Cardinal Studios
43 Railside Rd Don Mills Ontario .... TEL (416)447-9126

Carter, Mike Productions Ltd
447 Rosewell Ave #2 Toronto Ontario .... TEL (416)483-0595

CFA Video
782 King St W Toronto Ontario .... TEL (416)363-5071

Champagne Motion Pictures Co. Ltd.
437 Sherbourne St Toronto Ontario .... TEL (416)928-3001

Chetwynd Productions Inc.
214 Gerard St E Toronto Ontario .... TEL (416)926-9551

Cineplus Inc
44 Charles St W #4311 Toronto Ontario .... TEL (416)929-3874

Cineservice Ltd.
99 Queen St E Toronto Ontario .... TEL (416)363-4301

Command Post and Transfer
179 John St 8th Fl Toronto Ontario .... TEL (416)585-9995

Communication Oasis Ltd, The
885 Don Mills Rd #222 Don Mills Ontario .... TEL (416)444-6944

Communique
106 Front St E Toronto Ontario .... TEL (416)365-7200

Coney, Peter Associates Ltd
465 King St E #7 Toronto Ontario .... TEL (416)363-3086

Corniche Corporate Communications Ltd
5400 Yonge St 3rd Floor Toronto Ontario .... TEL (416)733-2626

Corporate Images
5355 Fairview St Burlington Ontario .... TEL (416)366-1234

Corporate Slide Inc
479A Wellington St W Toronto Ontario .... TEL (416)597-2333

Crackerjack Production Inc
179 Carlton St Toronto Ontario .... TEL (416)961-8559

Creava Communications
4 New St Toronto Ontario .... TEL (416)964-2922

Creative Group, The
61 Cottonwood Crt Thornhill Ontario .... TEL (416)764-6024

Crombie, Rod
PO Box 564, Stn B Sudbury Ontario .... TEL (705)674-4345

Directors Film Company, The
179 John St Toronto Ontario .... TEL (416)585-9255

Duocom
380 Finchdene Sq #1&2 Scarborough Ontario .... TEL (416)321-2922

Eaglevision
550 Spadina Cres Toronto Ontario .... TEL (416)658-0345

Emerson Screen Productions Ltd
Box 204 Stn "S" Toronto Ontario .... TEL (416)481-1965

Entertainment Technology
90 Thorncliffe Pk Dr Toronto Ontario .... TEL (416)422-4940

F & M Productions Ltd.
282 Richmond St E 3rd Fl Toronto Ontario .... TEL (416)364-3034

Fabulous Footage Inc
12 Mercer St Toronto Ontario .... TEL (416)591-6955

Film Shop, The
77 Mowat Ave #507 Toronto Ontario .... TEL (416)531-4999

Ford Productions
187 Kirk Dr Thornhill Ontario .... TEL (416)532-4096

Foresight Visual Communications
489 Queen St E #201 Toronto Ontario .... TEL (416)367-9136

Freeway Visuals Inc
141 Bathurst St Toronto Ontario .... TEL (416)362-0083

Frischkorn Associates Inc
128 Fewster Dr Mississauga Ontario .... TEL (416)624-5599

G O Productions
RR#1 Gowanstown Ontario .... TEL (519)335-6173

Gabinet Studios Inc
77 Mowat Ave #407 Toronto Ontario .... TEL (416)536-0650

Global Communications Ltd
81 Barber Greene Rd Don Mills Ontario .... TEL (416)482-6200

Greenlight Corporation
70 Richmond St E #302 Toronto Ontario .... TEL (416)366-5444

Gylon Productions
190 Britannia Rd E #11 Mississauga Ontario .... TEL (416)890-0608

Hart Sound
212 Martins Rd Pickering Ontario .... TEL (416)831-3849

Hayman Prod'n Network, The
461 Sackville St Toronto Ontario .... TEL (416)928-9398

Heartstar Productions Ltd.
439 Wellington St W Toronto Ontario .... TEL (416)597-1868

Henry Less Productions Inc
1196 Queen St W Toronto Ontario .... TEL (416)532-1116

Henteleff, David L.
70 Cambridge Ave #523 Toronto Ontario .... TEL (416)461-2856

Holman Communications Inc
The Keep 250 The Esplanade Toronto Ontario .... TEL (416)362-7633

Hulme Productions
2 Tippett Rd #400 Downsview Ontario .... TEL (416)653-6933

Hyde Park Film Productions
216 Ashworth Ave Toronto Ontario .... TEL (416)535-7281

Image Corporation, The
427 Albert St Waterloo Ontario .... TEL (519)885-6291

Imax Systems
38 Isabella St Toronto Ontario .... TEL (416)960-8509

Innovation Two
79 Kenninghall Cres Mississauga Ontario .... TEL (416)821-1906

Intergraphics 2000
481 North Service Rd W #27 Bldg A Oakville Ontario .... TEL (416)847-5829

Invisions Productions Inc
525 Adelaide St W #401 Toronto Ontario .... TEL (416)360-0075

Jatco Film Services Inc
266 Adelaide St W Toronto Ontario .... TEL (416)591-6761

Josko Photo-Graphic-Video
PO Box 942, Stn A Scarborough Ontario .... TEL (416)751-1875

L&K International Videotraining
295 Evans Ave Box 940 Stn U Toronto Ontario .... TEL (416)252-6407

Lawrence Marshall Productions Ltd
76 Gerrard St E Toronto Ontario .... TEL (416)585-9373

Leader Media Productions Ltd
72 Frazer Ave #203 Toronto Ontario .... TEL (416)538-6369

Les Freres Proulx Brothers Inc
334 Churchill Ave North Ottawa Ontario .... TEL (613)725-3743

Less, Henry Productions Inc
1196 Queen St W Toronto Ontario .... TEL (416)532-1116

Lightbox Studios Inc
422 Dundas St E Toronto Ontario .... TEL (416)323-3215

Lighthouse Video Inc
67 Mowat Ave #440 Toronto Ontario .... TEL (416)588-7952

LTB Productions
78 Berkley St Toronto Ontario .... TEL (416)360-0053

M & M Productions Ltd
189 Dupont St Toronto Ontario .... TEL (416)968-9300

MacGuffin Films Limited
489 Queen St W 2nd Fl Toronto Ontario .... TEL (416)359-0000

MAE Studios
511 King St W #300 Toronto Ontario .... TEL (416)977-5308

Mammoth Picturers Inc
67 Mowat Ave #146 Toronto Ontario .... TEL (416)534-4229

Mariposa Communications Inc
147 Liberty St Toronto Ontario .... TEL (416)588-6699

McCleery, Cameron Productions Ltd
424 Lakefront 2nd Fl Toronto Ontario .... TEL (416)690-3451

McDonald Productions
190 Clark Blvd #703 Brampton Ontario .... TEL (416)457-7656

McWaters Film
491 King St E Toronto Ontario .... TEL (416)366-9158

Meloche Communications Group, The
70 Yorkville Ave Toronto Ontario .... TEL (416)922-1361

Mercel Productions
22 Donino Ave North York Ontario .... TEL (416)489-1217

MIJO Productions Ltd
1491 Yonge St #201 Toronto Ontario .... TEL (416)964-7539

Mind's Eye Productions
212 St George St #210 Toronto Ontario .... TEL (416)968-7373

Mistral Films Ltd
445 King St E Toronto Ontario .... TEL (416)867-9000

MS Art Services
410 Adelaide St W Toronto Ontario .... TEL (416)363-2621

Multiple Images Inc
218 Adelaide St W Toronto Ontario .... TEL (416)595-1566

New Ledgend Films Inc
25 Merton St 2nd Fl Toronto Ontario .... TEL (416)488-7866

Now On Video
15 Doris Dr Toronto Ontario .... TEL (416)285-1400

Oasis
120 Parliament St Toronto Ontario .... TEL (416)369-1072

Optical Resolution, The
235 Carlaw Ave Toronto Ontario .... TEL (416)469-5127

Partners' Film Co. Ltd.
508 Church St Toronto Ontario .... TEL (416)966-3500

Pascoe Productions Ltd
15 Draper St Toronto Ontario .... TEL (416)593-0409

Pathe Video Inc.
720 King St W #1002 Toronto Ontario .... TEL (416)364-6720

PM Creative Services Inc
169 Gerrard St E Toronto Ontario .... TEL (416)925-1806

Portside Films
63 Mutual St Toronto Ontario .... TEL (416)360-8376

PR Video Productions
134 Florence St #1 Hamilton Ontario .... TEL (416)523-0270

Pro Video Services
1 Golden Blvd St. Catharines Ontario .... TEL (416)562-4819

Producers Group International Inc
199 Avenue Rd #300 Toronto Ontario .... TEL (416)972-0555

Propeller
153 Logan Ave Toronto Ontario .... TEL (416)462-1144

QPT Visual Expressions
2220 Midland Ave #118 Toronto Ontario .... TEL (416)299-6911

Quadravision Communications
3 Polson St Toronto Ontario .... TEL (416)461-3542

Rawi Sherman Film Co Inc
41 Peter St Toronto Ontario .... TEL (416)593-5969

Rexford Films Inc
144 Henderson Ave #5 Thornhill Ontario .... TEL (416)886-0333

Rhombus Media Inc
14 Belmont St Toronto Ontario .... TEL (416)962-9131

Richardson, Don J.
PO Box 1550, Stn B Burlington Ontario .... TEL (416)336-0012

Sauder-Harris AV Productions
250 Merton St Toronto Ontario .... TEL (416)485-8881

Shooters Film Company, The
95 Berkeley St Toronto Ontario .... TEL (416)862-1955

Sincinkin Ltd
198 1/2 Davenport Rd Toronto Ontario .... TEL (416)920-5735

Slack, Ian & Associates Ltd
288 Airdrie Rd Toronto Ontario .... TEL (416)421-6369

Smartketics
205 Church St #100 Toronto Ontario .... TEL (416)862-0861

SOMA Film Producers
65 Heward Ave Bldg A #202 Toronto Ontario .... TEL (416)466-0822

Stancon Video Inc
37 River St Toronto Ontario .... TEL (416)360-3933

Stone Film
197 Queen St E Toronto Ontario .... TEL (416)860-1265

Stracuzzi Videography
6182 Dixon St Niagara Falls Ontario .... TEL (416)358-8094

Strategic Corporate Communications
169 Gerrard St E Toronto Ontario .... TEL (416)961-7987

Strauss & Associates
40 Lombard St #303 Toronto Ontario .... TEL (416)362-1555

Stringer Ltd.
196 Hallam St Toronto Ontario .... TEL (416)533-6085

Stronco Audio Visuals Ltd.
189 Dufferin St Toronto Ontario .... TEL (416)588-8282

Studio 4.2.2. Inc
530 Richmond St W Rear Toronto Ontario .... TEL (416)362-0422

Summerhill Group, The
18 Banigan Dr Toronto Ontario .... TEL (416)467-1211

Synergex
124 Merton St 5th Fl Toronto Ontario .... TEL (416)484-6275

The Directors Film Company
179 John St #202 Toronto Ontario .... TEL (416)585-9255

The Slide Factory
253 Cranbrooke St Toronto Ontario .... TEL (416)482-6212

The St. John Group
132 Jarvis St Toronto Ontario .... TEL (416)364-3884

The Videoart Group
100 Lombard St #202 Toronto Ontario .... TEL (416)360-1456

Timberwolf Productions
PO Box 2779 Sudbury Ontario .... TEL (705)566-0433

Toronto Creative Centre
225 Richmond St W 5th Fl Toronto Ontario .... TEL (416)977-7666

Toronto Video Services
41 Bellefair Ave Toronto Ontario .... TEL (416)587-7930

Total Eclipse
3 Carlaw Ave Toronto Ontario .... TEL (416)462-1400

Trickett Productions Inc.
530 Richmond St W Rear Toronto Ontario .... TEL (416)366-6658

Triune Productions Inc
24 Ryerson Ave #304 Toronto Ontario .... TEL (416)362-9120

United AVSR
1770 Mattawa Ave Mississauga Ontario .... TEL (416)275-6010

V.C.G. Visual Communications Group
103 Church St #401 Toronto Ontario .... TEL (416)368-1192

Van Lint, Derek and Associates Inc
55 Sudbury St Toronto Ontario .... TEL (416)588-6041

VCR Duplications
3121 Universal Drive Mississauga Ontario .... TEL (416)629-2553

Video Events
6 Withrow Ave #6 Toronto Ontario .... TEL (416)461-7725

Video Newsrelease
107 Church St #301 Toronto Ontario .... TEL (416)363-4456

Video Ventures
1500 Don Mills Rd #205 Don Mills Ontario .... TEL (416)447-8899

Video Works
100 Lodge St Waterloo Ontario .... TEL (519)885-5800

Videoart Group, The
100 Lombard St #202 Toronto Ontario .... TEL (416)360-1456

Videogenic Corporation
179 Richmond St W Toronto Ontario .... TEL (416)593-7500

Viscom Limited
99 Sumach St Toronto Ontario .... TEL (416)366-6400

Visual Productions '80 Ltd
101 Niagara St #2 Toronto Ontario .... TEL (416)868-1535

VTR/Eastern Sound
47 Scollard St Toronto Ontario .... TEL (416)968-1822

Weaver, Tanner & Miller Inc Adv
300 Ardelt Ave Kitchener Ontario .... TEL (519)578-5910

Wellington West Communication
151 John St #408 Toronto Ontario .... TEL (416)598-1937

Yorkville Films Inc
193 Seaton St Toronto Ontario .... TEL (416)964-7880

Visual Innovative Productions
3807 Bertie Rd Streetsville Ontario .... TEL (416)382-2402

PHOTO/VIDEO EQUIPMENT & SUPPLIES

Adcom Electronics Limited
310 Judson St #1 Toronto Ontario .... TEL (416)251-3355

Agfa-Gevaret Cdn Ltd
69 Viceroy Rd Concord Ontario .... TEL (416)667-0700

Amplis
22 Telson Rd Markham Ontario .... TEL (416)477-4111

Applied Electronics
299 Evans Ave Toronto Ontario .... TEL (416)252-3761

AV Rent-All/Super 8 Centres
308 Adelaide St W Main Fl Toronto Ontario .... TEL (416)977-3075

Bader Brothers Ltd
1300 Alness St Concord Ontario .... TEL (416)738-3838

Bell & Howell Ltd
230 Barmac Dr Weston Ontario .... TEL (416)746-2200

Black's Camera's
371 Gough Rd Markham Ontario .... TEL (416)475-2777

Booth Photographic Ltd
3440 Pharmacy Ave #4 Scarborough Ontario .... TEL (416)497-8511

Canadian AV Communications
4237 Dundas St W Toronto Ontario .... TEL (416)236-1811

Canadian Motion Picture Rentals
35 Granby St Toronto Ontario .... TEL (416)977-7113

Canon Canada Inc
6390 Dixie Rd Mississauga Ontario .... TEL (416)678-2730

Carson, W Co Ltd
151 Telson Rd Markham Ontario .... TEL (416)479-4104

Chinon/Kingsway Film Equipment
1665 Enterprise Rd Mississauga Ontario .... TEL (416)672-2880

Cinequip Inc
275 Macpherson Ave Toronto Ontario .... TEL (416)920-5424

Clark, Alex L Ltd
30 Dorchester Ave Toronto Ontario .... TEL (416)255-8594

Concord AV
1594 Dundas St W Toronto Ontario .... TEL (416)534-2605

Continent-Wide Enterprises Ltd
41 Bertal Rd Toronto Ontario .... TEL (416)762-8101

Corvis Communications
400 Esna Pk Dr Markham Ontario .... TEL (416)497-8661

Daymen Photo Marketing Ltd
3241 Kennedy Rd #22 Scarborough Ontario .... TEL (416)298-9644

DeVere (Sales) Canada Inc
1093 Britannia Rd E Mississauga Ontario .... TEL (416)673-8711

Downtown Camera
55 Queen St E Toronto Ontario .... TEL (416)363-1749

Duocom Ontario Inc
380 Finchdene Sq #1 Scarborough Ontario .... TEL (416)321-2922

Edcom Multimedia Products
1773 Mattawa Ave Mississauga Ontario .... TEL (416)275-6010

Elmo Canada Mfg Corp
44 West Dr Brampton Ontario .... TEL (416)453-7880

Film+ Photo Supply Inc
116 Atlantic Ave Toronto Ontario .... TEL (416)535-3747

Fuji Photo Film Cdn
5915 Coopers Ave Mississauga Ontario .... TEL (416)890-6611

Gabrial A/V Ltd
188 Pearl St Toronto Ontario .... TEL (416)977-7474

General Films
1350 Birchmount Rd Scarborough Ontario .... TEL (416)759-9301

Henry's
119 Church St Toronto Ontario .... TEL (416)868-0872

Hitachi Denshi Ltd (Cdn)
65 Melford Dr Scarborough Ontario .... TEL (416)299-5900

Ilford Photo (Canada) Ltd
2751 John St Markham Ontario .... TEL (416)494-2810

Imax Systems
38 Isabella St Toronto Ontario .... TEL (416)960-8509

J-Mar Electronics
6 Banigan Dr Toronto Ontario .... TEL (416)421-9080

Japan Camera Centre
150 Lesmill Rd Don Mills Ontario .... TEL (416)445-1481

JVC Canada Inc
21 Finchdene Sq Scarborough Ontario .... TEL (416)293-1311

Kodak Canada Inc (Consumer Centre)
3500 Eglinton Ave W Toronto Ontario .... TEL (416)766-8233

Konica Canada Inc
1329 Meyerside Dr Mississauga Ontario .... TEL (416)677-7722

Kyocera Canada Inc
7470 Bath Rd Mississauga Ontario .... TEL (416)671-4300

Lisle-Kelco Ltd
3525 Nashua Dr Mississauga Ontario .... TEL (416)672-6661

Mackenzie Equipment
26 Duncan St Toronto Ontario .... TEL (416)977-8266

Manta Electronics Group
185 Frederick St Toronto Ontario .... TEL (416)868-0513

Matsushita Electric
5770 Ambler Dr Mississauga Ontario .... TEL (416)624-5010

Minolta Camera Inc
369 Brittania Rd E Mississauga Ontario .... TEL (416)890-6600

Multivision Exectrosonic
517 Wellington St W Toronto Ontario .... TEL (416)585-9500

Nikon Canada Inc
1366 Aerowood Dr Mississauga Ontario .... TEL (416)625-9910

Noritsu Canada Ltd
6155 Tomken Rd #10 Mississauga Ontario .... TEL (416)670-0137

Optex Corporation
52 Lesmill Rd Don Mills Ontario .... TEL (416)449-6470

Palette Productions
340 Gerrard St E Toronto Ontario .... TEL (416)921-8987

Panavision Canada Ltd
793 Pharmacy Ave Scarborough Ontario .... TEL (416)752-7670

Peachtree Marketing Inc
3410 Midland Ave #8 Scarborough Ontario .... TEL (416)293-0200

Pentax Canada Inc
3131 Universal Dr Mississauga Ontario .... TEL (416)625-4930

Photo Chalet Inc
219 Front St #210 Belleville Ontario .... TEL (613)966-3511

Photo Shop
145 St Paul St Box 1570 St Catharines Ontario .... TEL (416)688-4450

Photoquip Systems Ltd
29 Polson St Toronto Ontario .... TEL (416)465-4644

Polaroid Canada Inc
350 Carlingview Dr Rexdale Ontario .... TEL (416)675-3680

Precision Camera Inc
181 Carlaw Ave Toronto Ontario .... TEL (416)461-3411

Procam
58 Scarsdale Rd Don Mills Ontario .... TEL (416)391-1314

PS Production Service
65 Heward Ave Bldg B Toronto Ontario .... TEL (416)466-0037

Ricoh of Canada Ltd
150 Lesmill Rd Don Mills Ontario .... TEL (416)445-7813

Rosco Laboratories
1271 Denison St #66 Markham Ontario .... TEL (416)475-1400

Rutherford Photo Ltd
189 Dufferin St Toronto Ontario .... TEL (416)534-6622

Schotsman Enterprises Ltd
498 Glancaster Rd RR#1 Mount Hope Ontario .... TEL (416)679-3255

Sharp Electronics of Canada Ltd
335 Brittania Rd W Mississauga Ontario .... TEL (416)890-2100

Slide Mount Cdn Ltd
17 Main St Streetsville Ontario .... TEL (416)826-7413

Sony of Canada Ltd
411 Gordon Baker Rd Willowdale Ontario .... TEL (416)499-1414

St Clair Camera
568A St Clair Ave W Toronto Ontario .... TEL (416)652-2515

Strand Lighting Ltd
6490 Viscount Rd Mississauga Ontario .... TEL (416)677-7130

Studio Specialties Ltd
39 Orfus Rd #B Toronto Ontario .... TEL (416)787-1813

Supreme Audio-Visual & Video Inc
PO Box 1557, Stn A London Ontario .... TEL (519)668-9631

Technigraph Equipment Ltd
496 McNicoll Ave Willowdale Ontario .... TEL (416)497-2232

Torontel Technology Systems Ltd
296 Richmond St W Toronto Ontario .... TEL (416)971-5880

Toronto Camera
340 Yonge St 3rd Fl Toronto Ontario .... TEL (416)597-1891

Treck Hall Photographic Canada Inc
71 Adessa Rd Concord Ontario .... TEL (416)738-4255

Triathlon Equipment Leasing
2300 Yonge St #2800 Toronto Ontario .... TEL (416)488-2310

VGC of Canada Ltd
103 The East Mall Toronto Ontario .... TEL (416)234-5000

Vision Marketing
56 Nably Court Scarborough Ontario .... TEL (416)298-5999

Vistek Ltd
100 Queen St E Toronto Ontario .... TEL (416)365-1777

Vivitar Canada Ltd
5211 Creekbank Rd Mississauga Ontario .... TEL (416)624-1761

W.A. Bynum Sales
57 Tally Ho Rd Dundas Ontario .... TEL (416)628-8249

William F White Ltd
36 Parklawn Rd Toronto Ontario .... TEL (416)252-7171

ILLUSTRATORS — TORONTO

Acorn Illustration & Art Studio
260 King St E 3rd Fl Toronto Ontario .... TEL (416)369-1707

Aldrich, David
143 Amelia St Toronto Ontario .... TEL (416)960-6005

AM Studios
20 Eglinton Ave E #200 Toronto Ontario .... TEL (416)486-6279

Amedeo, Rich Cartoon Illustration
1864 Roy Ivor Cres Mississauga Ontario .... TEL (416)828-0961

Angry Cow
379 Adelaide St W #404 Toronto Ontario .... TEL (416)368-2559

Angus, Jennifer
246 Bessborough Dr Toronto Ontario .... TEL (416)322-6877

Anne-Marie Seguin
38 Glenholme Ave Toronto Ontario .... TEL (416)656-5404

Anno Domini Inc
197 Church St 2nd Fl Toronto Ontario .... TEL (416)364-2144

Armstrong, Shelagh
342 Avenue Rd #544 Toronto Ontario .... TEL (416)323-1684

Arnould, Grahame/Cartoonist
15 Spruce St Toronto Ontario .... TEL (416)925-2805

Art & Design Studios Ltd
68 Merton St Toronto Ontario .... TEL (416)481-6461

Artlab Communications Inc
14 College St #500 Toronto Ontario .... TEL (416)922-8822

Artworks/Kevin Barrett
235 Avenue Rd Richmond Hill Ontario .... TEL (416)884-6330

Aru, Agnes
498 Manning Ave Toronto Ontario .... TEL (416)532-9861

Au, Jamie
132 Gates Gill St Brampton Ontario .... TEL (416)450-3392

B&W Studios
77 Davisville Ave #2603 Toronto Ontario .... TEL (416)322-3931

Ballinger, Keith Illustration
61 St Clair Ave W #1706 Toronto Ontario .... TEL (416)924-6589

Band, William
815 Fletcher Valley Cres Mississauga Ontario .... TEL (416)823-1537

Bandera, Emilio
99 Woodpark Pl Newmarket Ontario .... TEL (416)756-0171

Barnett, Deborah
46 Harbord St Toronto Ontario .... TEL (416)977-0769

Barry & Elva Show, The
82 O'Hara Ave 2nd Fl Toronto Ontario .... TEL (416)531-8322

Baviera Illustration
51 Firenze St Hamilton Ontario .... TEL (416)385-0047

Belair Creative Concepts
PO Box 174 Stn L Toronto Ontario .... TEL (416)967-9195

Belmore, Jay G.
96 Spadina Ave 9th Fl Toronto Ontario .... TEL (416)365-9965

Berg, Ron Illustration
71 Hewitt Ave Toronto Ontario .... TEL (416)537-4069

Berger, Bob/Illustrator
52 McNairn Ave Toronto Ontario .... TEL (416)485-8555

Berkowitz, Sandra
2100 Bathurst St #303 Toronto Ontario .... TEL (416)781-8855

Besco, Don Illustrations
266 Riverdale Ave Toronto Ontario .... TEL (416)466-7191

Biddle, William Illustration
91 Little John Rd Dundas Ontario .... TEL (416)672-7532

Bill Michelis
188 Mortimer Ave Toronto Ontario .... TEL (416)422-4545

Bindon, John
79 Elizabeth St S Brampton Ontario .... TEL (416)457-1400

Birdsnest Productions
156A Arthur St N Guelph Ontario .... TEL (519)821-0793

Bjarnason, Tom Inc
63 Yorkville Ave Toronto Ontario .... TEL (416)960-0834

Blanchard, Marie
69 White Heather Blvd Toronto Ontario .... TEL (416)292-3527

Blanchfield, Sharon
RR #1 Cedar Valley Ontario .... TEL (416)473-2193

Bloss, Larry Illustration
4387 Spruce Ave Burlington Ontario .... TEL (416)681-7041

Blue Train Illustration
77 Mowat Ave #207 Toronto Ontario .... TEL (416)538-3375

Bohemicae Art Studio
138 Longboat Ave Toronto Ontario .... TEL (416)947-0537

Boldt, Jennifer
1179A King St W #307 Toronto Ontario .... TEL (416)588-7093

Bond, Jocelyne Illustration
158 Connaught Ave N Hamilton Ontario .... TEL (416)547-7756

Borody, Patrick
807 St Clarens Ave Toronto Ontario .... TEL (416)538-1520

Bowes, Stephan Studios Inc
34 Noble St #203 Toronto Ontario .... TEL (416)538-0354

Brad Black + Fringe Limited
99 Glendale Ave Toronto Ontario .... TEL (416)588-9162

Brennan, Daniel J.
21 Brookside Dr #2 Toronto Ontario .... TEL (416)698-1547

Breznik, Helen
974 Vera Cruz Dr Mississauga Ontario .... TEL (416)272-0920

Brunato, Joe
20 Dallner Rd Downsview Ontario .... TEL (416)242-3841

Bui, Thach
128 Stephenson Ave Toronto Ontario .... TEL (416)694-8147

Burden, Walter Illustration Ltd
495 Davenport Rd Toronto Ontario .... TEL (416)922-8658

Burke, Linda/Perceptive Images
20 Rectory Rd Weston Ontario .... TEL (416)240-9460

Burnt Arrow Artworks
77 Florence #307 Toronto Ontario .... TEL (416)531-5633

Caico, Robert Illustration
45 Indian Rd Cres Toronto Ontario .... TEL (416)538-1290

Calder, Jean (Medical)
214 Fairlawn Ave Toronto Ontario   TEL (416)484-6349

Campbell, Kim
161 Collier St #A Barrie Ontario .... TEL (705)739-1449

Carter, Mike/Mc2
36 Madison Ave Toronto Ontario .... TEL (416)925-3271

Cavlovision Illustration
48 Wright Ave Toronto Ontario .... TEL (416)537-5509

Chan, Harvey Illustration
2 Clinton Pl Toronto Ontario .... TEL (416)533-6658

Chapman, Bill
175 Roslin Ave Toronto Ontario .... TEL (416)485-1679

Chapman, David
400 Eastern Ave #270 Toronto Ontario .... TEL (416)778-4600

Chatwin, Robert/Clay Illustration
25 Winnett Ave Toronto Ontario .... TEL (416)657-8133

Chen, Paul
72 Lincoln Green Dr Markham Ontario .... TEL (416)294-9205

Chestnutt, David
87 Glen Rd Toronto Ontario .... TEL (416)921-8700

Christie, Janet
503 Palmerston Blvd Toronto Ontario .... TEL (416)532-2657

Cinquemani, John
4 Glendale Ave S Hamilton Ontario .... TEL (416)545-4080

Ciss, Julius Illustration Inc
446 Lawrence Ave W #1 Toronto Ontario .... TEL (416)784-1416

Clancy, Frances
59 Sammon Ave Toronto Ontario .... TEL (416)463-5826

Clark, Blair
361 Sorauren Ave Toronto Ontario .... TEL (416)531-4806

Clark, Brenda G.
RR #1 Scugog Point Estates Nestleton Ontario .... TEL (416)986-4080

Clemmer Ad Images
128 Parliament St Toronto Ontario .... TEL (416)364-4054

Colbert, Peter
22 Walmer Rd #302 Toronto Ontario .... TEL (416)964-3882

Collis, James
126 Confederation St Glen Williams Ontario .... TEL (416)363-4700

Colquhoun, Eric
379 Adelaide St W #404 Toronto Ontario .... TEL (416)360-7282

Condy, Roy/Cartoonist
1562 Alwin Circle Pickering Ontario .... TEL (416)427-8430

Cook, Richard J
8 Agar Cresent Islington Ontario .... TEL (416)231-0743

Cooper, David
1061 Fair Birch Dr Mississauga Ontario .... TEL (416)271-4460

Cooper, Heather Illustration
2 Gloucester St #302 Toronto Ontario .... TEL (416)966-3604

Coulas, Mick/Mc2
36 Madison Ave Toronto Ontario .... TEL (416)925-3271

Coulton, Joanne
3459 Cawthra Rd Mississauga Ontario .... TEL (416)276-4857

Craig, David
120 Matheson Blvd E #101 Mississauga Ontario .... TEL (416)570-0200

Creative Images Illustration Studio
439 Wellington St W Toronto Ontario .... TEL (416)599-8080

Creativity Plus
RR 2 MacPherson Dr Corbeil Ontario .... TEL (705)752-3297

Cruchaga, Gloria
3373 Fellmore Dr Mississauga Ontario .... TEL (416)270-3899

Csafordi & Associates
2 Clinton Pl Toronto Ontario .... TEL (416)530-1951

Csakany, Gabriel
25 Leith Hill Rd North York Ontario .... TEL (416)495-7465

Cselko Associates Inc.
115 Balliol St Toronto Ontario .... TEL (416)486-9731

D'Arcy, Adele
175 Elm St #201 Toronto Ontario .... TEL (416)591-7037

D'Souza, Helen/The Basement
487 Mortimer Ave Toronto Ontario .... TEL (416)466-0630

Da Mota, Richard
2 Clinton Pl Toronto Ontario .... TEL (416)539-0678

Daigneault, Sylvie
415 Wellesley St E Toronto Ontario .... TEL (416)961-0681

Dang, Hong C./Computer Illustrator
49 Lotherton Pathway Toronto Ontario .... TEL (416)785-6575

Dannenberg, Thomas Illustrator
154 Crestwood Rd Thornhill Ontario .... TEL (416)731-8038

Davies, Will
63 Yorkville Ave Toronto Ontario .... TEL (416)925-8191

Dawson, John Illustration
116 Bedford Rd #1 Toronto Ontario   TEL (416)926-0730

de Verteuil, Suzanne
450 Walmer Rd #907 Toronto Ontario .... TEL (416)923-9198

Dedika Art House
3 Massey Square #1204 Toronto Ontario .... TEL (416)699-0663

Deines, Brian
551 Logan Ave Toronto Ontario .... TEL (416)463-9920

Dell, Lori Illustration
412 Coxwell Ave Toronto Ontario .... TEL (416)461-6849

DeWolfe, Richard Illustrator
625 Yonge St Toronto Ontario .... TEL (416)923-8334

Dickson, Bill
411 Richmond St E #204 Toronto Ontario .... TEL (416)862-7773

Diduch, Luba Illustration
6 Grenadier Rd Toronto Ontario .... TEL (416)588-4773

Dionisi, Sandra
859 King St W Toronto Ontario .... TEL (416)867-1771

Disensi, Joanne
431 Brunswick Ave Toronto Ontario .... TEL (416)925-2215

Dolcini, Catherine
RR# 1 Carrying Place Ontario .... TEL (613)392-7797

Donec, Julie
2301 Cavendish Dr #62 Burlington Ontario .... TEL (416)335-4077

Donnelly, Mike (Technical)
23 Kilkenny Dr St. Catharines Ontario .... TEL (416)937-4476

Dorsett Design
3644 Kelso Cres Mississauga Ontario .... TEL (416)828-8538

Doty, Kevin
3245 Huxley Dr Mississauga Ontario .... TEL (416)972-6140

Douglas, Alexandra
381 Richmond St E #200 Toronto Ontario .... TEL (416)767-8426

Dovaston, Terry
51 Broadview Ave Mississauga Ontario .... TEL (416)278-1401

Drever, Charles
482 Huron St #1A Toronto Ontario .... TEL (416)924-3395

Drew, Lionel
199 Rouge Hills Dr Scarborough Ontario .... TEL (416)281-6032

Drew-Brook-Cormack
81 Garthdale Crt #102 Toronto Ontario .... TEL (416)636-5744

Duda, Jenny
240 Northcliffe Blvd #113 Toronto Ontario .... TEL (416)653-3045

Duffy, Amanda
1200 York Mills Rd #912 Don Mills Ontario .... TEL (416)444-9862

Dumas-Hudecki, Pat
124 Delaware Ave Toronto Ontario .... TEL (416)536-2284

Dynamic Air
1621 McEwen Dr #9 Whitby Ontario .... TEL (416)723-7175

Dywelska, Michael
56 The Esplanade #503 Toronto Ontario .... TEL (416)363-1440

Edmunds, David Studio
1312 Monmouth Dr Burlington Ontario .... TEL (416)332-6047

Elephant Works Inc
57 Charles St W Toronto Ontario .... TEL (416)923-5712

Elsom, Vicky (FABRIC)
95 Lawton Blvd Toronto Ontario .... TEL (416)489-6453

Empire Photo & Art Studios Inc
807 St. Clarens Ave Toronto Ontario .... TEL (416)538-1530

English, Sarah Jane
23 Hepworth Dr Toronto Ontario .... TEL (416)247-7336

Esk, Michael
175 Elm St #1205 Toronto Ontario .... TEL (416)596-6435

Etheridge, John
110 Oriole Pkwy #204 Toronto Ontario .... TEL (416)486-1465

Eyolfson, Norman
379 Adelaide St W #404 Toronto Ontario .... TEL (416)368-2559

Farley, Catherine & Associates
100 Galt Ave Toronto Ontario .... TEL (416)463-3075

Feline/Julie Carlisle
221 Sterling Rd #3B Toronto Ontario .... TEL (416)534-1638

Fellini, Michael Aerographics
31 Hunt Club Dr Toronto Ontario .... TEL (416)690-1105

Ferguson, John/Hand Tinting
84 Wilson Park Rd Toronto Ontario .... TEL (416)588-8653

Fernandes, Henry
R.R. #1 Peterborough Ontario .... TEL (705)657-1545

Ferringo, Joseph J.
15 Dufferin St Guelph Ontario .... TEL (519)836-4937

Fisch, Charles
33 Isabella #2115 Toronto Ontario .... TEL (416)927-9997

Fitzgerald, Joanne
11 Temple Rd Georgetown Ontario .... TEL (416)877-5966

Fleming, Joe/The Basement
487 Mortimer Ave Toronto Ontario .... TEL (416)466-0630

Flockhart, Doug
22 Rosevear Ave Toronto Ontario .... TEL (416)690-2579

Fong, Patrick/Chinese Calligraphy
22 Clematis Rd Willowdale Ontario .... TEL (416)491-1567

Fortin, Pierre
42 Glen Manor Dr Brampton Ontario .... TEL (416)840-4798

Frampton, Bill
49 Henderson Ave Toronto Ontario .... TEL (416)535-1931

Fraser, John Studio
379 Adelaide St W #404 Toronto Ontario .... TEL (416)368-2559

Freire, Carlos
393 King St E #204 Toronto Ontario .... TEL (416)594-0687

Furmanczyk, Gregory
10 Alhambra Ave Toronto Ontario .... TEL (416)766-8953

Galleria Aphrodite
30 Hess St S Hamilton Ontario .... TEL (416)572-7276

Garbett, Paul
100 Broadview Ave #322 Toronto Ontario .... TEL (416)778-0805

Gardos Illustration
115 Balliol St Toronto Ontario .... TEL (416)486-9731

Geras, Audra Illustration Inc
53a Gloucester St Toronto Ontario .... TEL (416)928-2965

Ghiglione, Kevin N.
96 Spadina Ave 9th Fl Toronto Ontario .... TEL (416)365-9965

Giancontieri, Philippa
511 The West Mall #1912 Etobicoke Ontario .... TEL (416)621-6298

Giovannina Illustration & Design
31 Massey Grove Crt Rexdale Ontario .... TEL (416)745-0069

Goldman, Linda R.
244 Howland Ave Toronto Ontario .... TEL (416)534-2515

Gorczynski, Wojtek
29 Valleywoods Rd #175 Don Mills Ontario .... TEL (416)449-8156

Gordon, Donna
32 Roosevelt Rd Toronto Ontario .... TEL (416)463-8869

Graham, Heather
132 St Clements Ave Toronto Ontario .... TEL (416)483-5584

Grainge, Ian
280 Southcrest Dr London Ontario   TEL (519)471-6852

Gray, A.J. Illustration
Box 34 Dwight Ontario .... TEL (705)633-5615

Greaves & Allen Studios Limited
151 Esna Park Dr #30 Markham Ontario .... TEL (416)474-1666

Green, Dennis
5590 Yonge St #21 Willowdale Ontario .... TEL (416)730-0546

Grice, Mark
RR#1 Inglewood Ontario .... TEL (416)584-2116

Griffin, Barbara
36 Erindale Ave Toronto Ontario .... TEL (416)461-5745

Grigor, Rod
67 Mowat Ave #339 Toronto Ontario .... TEL (416)537-1210

Gunthardt, Walt
140 Broadview Ave Toronto Ontario .... TEL (416)465-1086

Gwilliams, Scott R.
243 MacDonell Ave #5 Toronto Ontario .... TEL (416)533-4370

Hambly & Woolley Inc.
152 King St E Toronto Ontario .... TEL (416)867-1622

Hamilton, Keith
477A Dupont St 2nd Fl Toronto Ontario .... TEL (416)533-1739

Hamilton, Tony
797 Manning Ave Toronto Ontario .... TEL (416)588-6433

Hammond, Franklin
219 Dufferin St #203 Toronto Ontario .... TEL (416)538-4387

Harley, Evaline
312 Maple Ave Oakville Ontario .... TEL (416)845-1704

Hart, Kimberly
Vogrie Farm RR #2 Port Hope Ontario .... TEL (416)885-4790

Hathaway, Loi
76 Glen Rd Toronto Ontario .... TEL (416)924-3891

Hawgood, W.R.
545 The West Mall #1103 Etobicoke Ontario .... TEL (416)626-8613

Hayes, Chris
2170 Bromsgrove Rd #13 Mississauga Ontario .... TEL (416)823-5918

Headlight Productions Inc
17 Combermere Cres Waterloo Ontario .... TEL (519)756-3185

Heagle, Barbara Diane
44 Dunfield Ave #1502 Toronto Ontario .... TEL (416)483-0976

Heda, Jackie
60 Sparkhall Ave #1 Toronto Ontario .... TEL (416)463-8692

Henderson, Patricia
8 Anndale Rd Scarborough Ontario .... TEL (416)699-8590

Hendry, Linda G.
125A Indian Rd Toronto Ontario .... TEL (416)538-4128

Heron, Tony Illustration
7 Fraser Ave #14 Toronto Ontario .... TEL (416)535-4665

Hewgill, Jody
89 Burnaby Blvd 2nd Fl Toronto Ontario .... TEL (416)487-4642

High Noon Studio
34 Noble St #206 Toronto Ontario .... TEL (416)537-1164

Hill, Roger
63a Yorkville Ave Toronto Ontario .... TEL (416)923-5933

Hish, Jerry Cartoonist
86 Orphir Rd Hamilton Ontario .... TEL (416)561-0122

Hladin, Brian
161 Clearbrooke Circle Rexdale Ontario .... TEL (416)741-9879

Hoffman, Robert
173 Parkside Dr Toronto Ontario .... TEL (416)588-8359

Holdcroft, Tina
75 Midland Ave Toronto Ontario .... TEL (416)698-3577

Holmes, Martin
79A Roncesvalles Ave Toronto Ontario .... TEL (416)588-0580

Hoople, Jane (Editorial)
14 Neilson Dr #904 Etobicoke Ontario .... TEL (416)620-1833

Horback, Kim
88 University Ave 9th Fl Toronto Ontario .... TEL (416)593-1375

Houston, Steve Sports Illustrator
25 Whitecap Blvd Scarborough Ontario .... TEL (416)265-1585

Hrabuwiak, Angela
173 London St S Hamilton Ontario .... TEL (416)547-3343

Hutching, Stephen
79A Roncesvalles Ave Toronto Ontario .... TEL (416)588-0580

Hutchings Cartoons Inc
4 Webb Ave Toronto Ontario .... TEL (416)762-1427

Ianzzo, Virginia
3413 Homark Dr Mississauga Ontario .... TEL (416)270-9959

Illustrators Plus Inc
822 Dundalk Dr London Ontario .... TEL (519)685-5913

Imagers Art Direction
52 Shaftesbury Ave Toronto Ontario .... TEL (416)964-2262

Irwin, Brock
95 Vaughan Rd Toronto Ontario .... TEL (416)656-2956

Irwin, Dorothy
68 Henry St Toronto Ontario .... TEL (416)596-7194

Jacobson/Fernandez
115 Belhaven Rd Toronto Ontario .... TEL (416)462-3842

Jansen-Buhr, Mary-Louise
86 Twenty Sixth St Toronto Ontario .... TEL (416)259-6065

Jay's Airworks
22 Broadleaf Rd Don Mills Ontario .... TEL (416)449-7985

Jenkins, Sarie
106 Balsam Ave Toronto Ontario .... TEL (416)699-9822

Jobson, Kellie Illustrator
484 Oriole Parkway #306 Toronto Ontario .... TEL (416)481-2397

Johannsen, Robert
7251 Copenhagen Rd #62 Mississauga Ontario .... TEL (416)567-1493

Johnson, Lee Studio Inc
503A Adelaide St W Toronto Ontario .... TEL (416)947-0623

Jones, Danielle
55 Charles St W #1003 Toronto Ontario .... TEL (416)968-6277

Jones, Richard
Box 1182 Copper Cliff Ontario .... TEL (705)522-8548

Jurgen, Stella
2100 Lynchmere Ave Mississauga Ontario .... TEL (416)279-6672

Kangas, Dan Illustration
104 Park Home Ave Willowdale Ontario .... TEL (416)222-2942

Kearns, Cliff Inc
392 Murray St London Ontario .... TEL (519)672-9090

Kebic, Bob Illustration Inc
69 Sherbourne St #223 Toronto Ontario .... TEL (416)363-7934

Keen, Trevor
1473 Bunsden Ave Mississauga Ontario .... TEL (416)274-4974

Kempkes, Jim
1052 Mt Pleasant Rd Toronto Ontario .... TEL (416)489-9814

Kercheff, Stacey Illustration
23 Brentcliffe Rd Toronto Ontario .... TEL (416)467-1669

Kinnes, Peter Alexander Greenlaw
10 Lewis Rd Belleville Ontario .... TEL (613)962-6704

Klunder, Barbara
12 First St Toronto Ontario .... TEL (416)360-7431

Korhonen Studios Inc
106 Berkeley St Toronto Ontario .... TEL (416)363-0150

Kotack Kustom Art & Mural
1176 Strathy Ave Mississauga Ontario .... TEL (416)274-8301

Kovalik, Peter
725 King St W #310 Toronto Ontario .... TEL (416)362-4253

Kovalski, Maryann
16 Monteith St Toronto Ontario .... TEL (416)923-6542

Kucharski, Zigi
965 Iverhouse Dr #601 Mississauga Ontario .... TEL (416)822-2912

Kunz, Anita
230 Ontario St Toronto Ontario .... TEL (416)364-3846

Kunz, Frank
32 Windy Golfway Don Mills Ontario .... TEL (416)429-5349

Kurisu, Jane
97 Airdrie Rd Toronto Ontario .... TEL (416)424-2524

Kveta Jelinek
27 Brisbourne Grove Scarborough Ontario .... TEL (416)286-0584

La Fave, Kim
96 Castlewood Rd Toronto Ontario .... TEL (416)538-4398

Lafrance, Laurie
164 Oakwood Ave Toronto Ontario .... TEL (416)658-0263

Laishes, James
55 Charles St W Toronto Ontario .... TEL (416)921-1709

Lam, Chris
14 Sandy Haven Dr Scarborough Ontario .... TEL (416)756-0206

Lau, Bernadette
25 Redheugh Cres Scarborough Ontario .... TEL (416)491-6753

Lau, Josephine
129 Apache Trail Willowdale Ontario .... TEL (416)495-9685

Lavelle, Patty
139 Duncairn Rd Don Mills Ontario .... TEL (416)444-0514

Lawrason, June
43 Springbrook Gdns Etobicoke Ontario .... TEL (416)234-0540

Lax, Leila
446 Russell Hill Rd Toronto Ontario .... TEL (416)488-2868

Leach, Jay
1162 Queen St W 2nd Fl Toronto Ontario .... TEL (416)534-9921

LeClerc, Denis Illustration Graphic Design
1179A King St W #111 Toronto Ontario .... TEL (416)538-8037

Lee, Charmain
54 Maitland St #402 Toronto Ontario .... TEL (416)324-9472

Lee, Wendy J.
161 Huron St Toronto Ontario .... TEL (416)591-6879

Leopold, Susan Studios
135 Marlee #804 Toronto Ontario .... TEL (416)782-0947

Lettering Services Inc
40 Wellington St E 3rd Fl Toronto Ontario .... TEL (416)364-8260

Levona, Avner/Yehros
130 Neptune Dr #810 Toronto Ontario .... TEL (416)782-5685

Lewis, Andrew L.G.
47 Windsor Ave London Ontario .... TEL (519)660-1118

Link/Blair Clark
2 Berkeley St #206 Toronto Ontario .... TEL (416)369-9442

Link/Brian Deines
2 Berkeley St #206 Toronto Ontario .... TEL (416)369-9442

Link/Doug Fraser
2 Berkeley St #206 Toronto Ontario .... TEL (416)369-9442

Link/Jay Leach
2 Berkeley St #206 Toronto Ontario .... TEL (416)369-9442

Link/June Steube
2 Berkeley St #206 Toronto Ontario .... TEL (416)369-9442

Link/Mike Constable
2 Berkeley St #206 Toronto Ontario .... TEL (416)369-9442

Link/Nina Berkson
2 Berkeley St #206 Toronto Ontario .... TEL (416)369-9442

Link/Normand Cousineau
2 Berkeley St #206 Toronto Ontario .... TEL (416)369-9442

Link/Paul Rivoche
2 Berkeley St #206 Toronto Ontario .... TEL (416)369-9442

Lintzen, Frank
PO Box 261 Streetsville Stn Mississauga Ontario ...... TEL (416)749-3791

Lionsgate 3-D Illustration
255 Robina Ave Toronto Ontario .... TEL (416)537-3696

Liota, Karen
1448 Dewbourne Cres Burlington Ontario .... TEL (416)270-2501

Lo, Stephen
54 Johnbutton Blvd Unionville Ontario .... TEL (416)470-1733

Lopez, Emmanuel/Crackers
192 Spadina Ave #510 Toronto Ontario .... TEL (416)359-0024

Lowe, Wesley
46 Murison Blvd Scarborough Ontario .... TEL (416)284-2522

Lung, Yick-Wan
3300 Don Mills Rd #2404 Willowdale Ontario ...... TEL (416)4974359

Lupo, Frank
420 Edgehill Dr Barrie Ontario .... TEL (705)721-4123

MacDonald, Norman
RR # 2 Erin Ontario .... TEL (519)833-9011

MacDougall, Rob
2049 Lakeshore Rd W Oakville Ontario .... TEL (416)847-7663

MacKenzie, Helen
14 Seymour Ave Toronto Ontario .... TEL (416)465-1226

Maclachlan, Neil
45 Earswick Dr Toronto Ontario .... TEL (416)269-8141

MacQuarrie, Lynn
101 Vaughan Rd #18 Toronto Ontario .... TEL (416)658-3390

MacRae, Jock
590 Alden RD #213 Markham Ontario .... TEL (416)470-8919

Madrick, David
10 Savarin St Scarborough Ontario .... TEL (416)266-0159

Malaguti, Peter
3827 Lawrence Ave E #506 Scarborough Ontario ...... TEL (416)439-6488

Mallette, Philip
18 Winston Ave Scarborough Ontario .... TEL (416)694-2060

Mansfield, Renee
379 Adelaide St W #404 Toronto Ontario .... TEL (416)594-3787

Mantha, John Design
9 Hanna Ave Box 49 Toronto Ontario .... TEL (416)530-0065

Marc L. Tec Inc
2727 Armstrong Ave Windsor Ontario .... TEL (519)948-0863

Mardon, John
27 Colonsay Rd Thornhill Ontario .... TEL (416)881-5854

Marioncu, Helen
16 Freeman St Scarborough Ontario .... TEL (416)698-4070

Martin, Deirdre
37 Coe Drive Ajax Ontario .... TEL (416)686-8771

Martin, Dennis Stillwell
221 Gledhill Ave Toronto Ontario .... TEL (416)975-9750

Martin, Doug
285 Waverley Rd Toronto Ontario .... TEL (416)690-0055

Martin, John
56 Wheeler Ave Toronto Ontario .... TEL (416)698-0626

Mason, Roger/Mason Adv Ltd
15 Wertheim Crt #204 Richmond Hill Ontario .... TEL (416)731-7593

Match Art Inc
219 Dufferin St #200B Toronto Ontario .... TEL (416)534-4227

Matson, Sharon
50 Stephanie St #609 Toronto Ontario .... TEL (416)599-5548

Matthews, Dave
437 McRoberts Ave Toronto Ontario .... TEL (416)651-3509

McCann, Michael Assoc. Ltd
2 Gibson Ave (rear) Toronto Ontario .... TEL (416)964-7532

McCullough, Shane
106 Goodwood Pk Ct #306 Toronto Ontario .... TEL (416)690-0226

McEvoy, Greg Illustration
25 Defries St Toronto Ontario .... TEL (416)863-0093

McEwan, Peg
450 Winona Dr #403 Toronto Ontario .... TEL (416)653-2548

McGarvey, Nancy
RR #2 Wasaga Beach Ontario .... TEL (705)429-5040

McGaw, Laurie
RR #2 Shelburne Ontario .... TEL (519)925-5134

McGhee, Tom
1346 Sycamore Dr Burlington Ontario .... TEL (416)335-3425

McGraw, Sheila
665 Carlaw Ave Toronto Ontario .... TEL (416)465-8274

McGregor, James
117 Sorauren Ave #2 Toronto Ontario .... TEL (416)535-6394

McKee, Jon
165 Shaw St Toronto Ontario .... TEL (416)537-6806

McKeever, Mike
7 Yuen Yuen St 3/F Happy Valley Hong Kong .... TEL (011)5-745087

McLaughlin, Gary Illustrator Inc
RR #2 Mount Forest Ontario .... TEL (519)323-3252

McNair, Debbie
20 Aitken Pl Toronto Ontario .... TEL (416)367-0507

McNeely, Tom
63a Yorkville Ave Toronto Ontario .... TEL (416)925-1929

Meechan, Robert
20 Carlton St #120 Toronto Ontario .... TEL (416)581-1298

Meers, Tony Illustration
4637 Dundas St W Toronto Ontario .... TEL (416)239-9097

Meldazy, Monte Angelo
3546 Bathurst St #204 Toronto Ontario .... TEL (416)783-1755

Meyers, Anne (Children's Books)
2186 Hurontario St #4F6 Mississauga Ontario .... TEL (416)276-9887

Michener, Ted Limited
12 Sullivan St Toronto Ontario .... TEL (416)971-6491

Miele, John Illustration
104 Chipwood Cres North York Ontario .... TEL (416)493-1927

Miller, Jean
380 Esna Pk Dr Markham Ontario .... TEL (416)883-4114

Milligan, Dan
88 University Ave 9th Fl Toronto Ontario .... TEL (416)593-1375

Milne, Jonathan/Papersculptureworks
277 Eglinton Ave E Toronto Ontario .... TEL (416)487-3275

Milot, Rene
221 Balliol St #1723 Toronto Ontario .... TEL (416)485-8641

Mitchell, Dean
1684 John St Thornhill Ontario .... TEL (416)881-8251

Mixed Nuts Inc
9 Clarence Sq #4 Toronto Ontario .... TEL (416)593-0845

Mogensen, Suzanne
7 Heath St E #1 Toronto Ontario .... TEL (416)968-6768

Mogg, Tim Illustrator
504 Fairlawn Ave Toronto Ontario .... TEL (416)782-3712

Molnar, John
25 St Mary St Toronto Ontario .... TEL (416)864-0811

Monkman, Kent Illustration
17 Paton Rd Toronto Ontario .... TEL (416)588-2255

Montague, Desmond
4185 Wheelwright Cres Mississauga Ontario .... TEL (416)820-4921

Montesano, Sam
23 High Park Toronto Ontario .... TEL (416)531-7901

Montgomery, Linda
20 D'Arcy St Toronto Ontario .... TEL (416)977-4002

Moreau, Keith Illustration & Design
108 Eldomar Ave Brampton Ontario .... TEL (416)459-2683

Morin, Paul
RR#4 Rockwood Ontario .... TEL (519)833-9906

Morrison & Hershfield Ltd.
45 Lansing St North York Ontario .... TEL (416)499-3110

Mulock, Julian
105 Montgomery Ave Toronto Ontario .... TEL (416)484-4677

Murata, San
489 Parliament St Toronto Ontario .... TEL (416)967-3492

Murphy, Bill
23 Copeland Ave Toronto Ontario .... TEL (416)698-1214

Murphy, John William
22 Woodvale Cres Toronto Ontario .... TEL (416)469-4111

Nicholls, Calvin Paper Sculpture
83 Norton Ave North York Ontario .... TEL (416)223-1743

Nidenoff, Michele
110 Erskine Ave #1203 Toronto Ontario .... TEL (416)482-5348

Nitto, Tomio
25 The Esplanade #1310 Toronto Ontario .... TEL (416)366-2567

Noble, Mary
28 Chesham Crt Brampton Ontario .... TEL (416)846-7247

Noodle Studio
37 Strathmore Blvd Toronto Ontario .... TEL (416)461-9793

Norwell, Jeff
196 Sunnyside Ave Apt 1 Toronto Ontario .... TEL (416)536-6729

O'Young, Leoung
36 Woodycrest Ave Toronto Ontario .... TEL (416)462-3388

One A.M.
33 Wasdale Cres #9 Toronto Ontario .... TEL (416)782-5113

Oni - Illustration
17728 Leslie St RR#5 Newmarket Ontario .... TEL (416)895-7839

P.R. Melbacom
25 Mutual St #702 Toronto Ontario .... TEL (416)364-5041

Pace, Richard
3 Lipton Ave Toronto Ontario .... TEL (416)778-7740

Paine, Jonathan
220 Rose Park Dr Toronto Ontario .... TEL (416)489-6754

Pandora Illustration Designs
80 Nashdene Rd #107 Scarborough Ontario .... TEL (416)297-8036

Panton, Doug Inc
341 Wellesley St E Toronto Ontario .... TEL (416)920-5612

Pao, Derick/Calligrapher
23 Becca Hall Trail Scarborough Ontario .... TEL (416)321-1907

Paper Chameleon
911 Wonderland Rd #122 London Ontario .... TEL (519)657-5057

Park, Jun/Illustrator
1385 Midland Ave #703 Scarborough Ontario .... TEL (416)757-9927

Parker, Eric
550 Jarvis St #1104 Toronto Ontario .... TEL (416)927-0655

Parker, Lewis
R.R. #1 Sunderland Ontario .... TEL (416)852-3793

Patkau, Karen Illustration
980 Broadview Ave #203 Toronto Ontario .... TEL (416)461-9747

Paxton, Maureen
1472 King St W #4 Toronto Ontario .... TEL (416)536-6733

Peets, Vince
36 Linelle St North York Ontario .... TEL (416)225-2130

Peng, Leif
88 University Ave 9th Fl Toronto Ontario .... TEL (416)593-1375

Pennaertz, Charles
2342 Devon Rd Oakville Ontario .... TEL (416)842-2357

Perna, Debi Illustrator
34 Little Norway Cres #508 Toronto Ontario .... TEL (416)593-7757

Petroski, Daniel
35 Wynford Heights Cres #2401 Don Mills Ontario .... TEL (416)391-1667

Philipovich, Bill
277 Woodbine Ave Toronto Ontario .... TEL (416)699-1925

Phillips, Louise
201 Glebeholme Blvd Toronto Ontario .... TEL (416)463-3063

Photo/Design Associates Inc
409 Front St E Toronto Ontario .... TEL (416)368-1031

Pickering, Carl
33 Amroth Ave Toronto Ontario .... TEL (416)690-4629

Pilcher, Steve Illustration
67 Mowat Ave #137 Toronto Ontario .... TEL (416)537-9999

Plante, Ron
77 Davisville Ave #1515 Toronto Ontario .... TEL (416)487-9596

Pocket Press
467 Speers Rd #14 Oakville Ontario .... TEL (416)844-1893

Potts, Linda
10A Victoria Pk Ave Toronto Ontario .... TEL (416)698-2512

Prior, Ed Illustrator
3 Kitsilano Cres Richmond Hill Ontario .... TEL (416)884-9380

Pudsey, Kevin
342 Bryant Cres Burlington Ontario .... TEL (416)634-9803

Pullar, Gord
173 London St S Hamilton Ontario .... TEL (416)547-3343

Pykerman, Jeff
10 Huntley St #605 Toronto Ontario .... TEL (416)923-8776

Quinlan, Stephen Illustration Ltd
43 Eglinton Ave E #903 Toronto Ontario .... TEL (416)485-8277

Ranson, David
60 Bloor St W #901 Toronto Ontario .... TEL (416)928-1356

Reactor/Andreas Zaretzki
51 Camden St Toronto Ontario .... TEL (416)362-1913

Reactor/Bill Russell
51 Camden St Toronto Ontario .... TEL (416)362-1913

Reactor/Blair Drawson
51 Camden St Toronto Ontario .... TEL (416)362-1913

Reactor/Bob Fortier
51 Camden St Toronto Ontario .... TEL (416)362-1913

Reactor/Clancy Gibson
51 Camden St Toronto Ontario .... TEL (416)362-1913

Reactor/Gail Geltner
51 Camden St Toronto Ontario .... TEL (416)362-1913

Reactor/Henrik Drescher
51 Camden St Toronto Ontario .... TEL (416)362-1913

Reactor/James Marsh
51 Camden St Toronto Ontario .... TEL (416)362-1913

Reactor/Jamie Bennett
51 Camden St Toronto Ontario .... TEL (416)362-1913

Reactor/Jeff Jackson
51 Camden St Toronto Ontario .... TEL (416)362-1913

Reactor/Jerzy Kolacz
51 Camden St Toronto Ontario .... TEL (416)362-1913

Reactor/Joseph Salina
51 Camden St Toronto Ontario .... TEL (416)362-1913

Reactor/Kent Smith
51 Camden St Toronto Ontario .... TEL (416)362-1913

Reactor/Larry Eisenstein
51 Camden St Toronto Ontario .... TEL (416)362-1913

Reactor/Margaret Hathaway
51 Camden St Toronto Ontario .... TEL (416)362-1913

Reactor/Maurice Vellekoop
51 Camden St Toronto Ontairo .... TEL (416)362-1913

Reactor/Paula Munck
51 Camden St Toronto Ontario .... TEL (416)362-1913

Reactor/Rene Zamic
51 Camden St Toronto Ontario .... TEL (416)362-1913

Reactor/Ross MacDonald
51 Camden St Toronto Ontario .... TEL (416)362-1913

Reactor/Shelly Browning
51 Camden St Toronto Ontario .... TEL (416)362-1913

Reactor/Simon Ng
51 Camden St Toronto Ontario .... TEL (416)362-1913

Reactor/Steven Guarnaccia
51 Camden St Toronto Ontario .... TEL (416)362-1913

Reactor/Thomas Hunt
51 Camden St Toronto Ontario .... TEL (416)362-1913

Reactor/Tomio Nitto
51 Camden St Toronto Ontario .... TEL (416)362-1913

Reece, Kemp Illustrator
32 Agate Rd Ajax Ontario .... TEL (416)428-7289

Render Group Inc., The
961 Eglinton Ave #204 Toronto Ontario .... TEL (416)424-2101

Reno Art Works/Jill Chen
75 Oriole Gardens #204 Toronto Ontario .... TEL (416)928-0480

Reno Art Works/Joe Biafore
75 Oriole Gardens #204 Toronto Ontario .... TEL (416)928-0480

Reno Art Works/Kam Yu
75 Oriole Gardens #204 Toronto Ontario .... TEL (416)928-0480

Reno Art Works/Nicholas Vitacco
75 Oriole Gardens #204 Toronto Ontario .... TEL (416)928-0480

Reno Art Works/Thom Sevalrud
75 Oriole Gardens #204 Toronto Ontario .... TEL (416)928-0480

Reno Art Works/Tracy Walker
75 Oriole Gardens #204 Toronto Ontario .... TEL (416)928-0480

Reno Art Works/Vince Mancuso
75 Oriole Gardens #204 Toronto Ontario .... TEL (416)928-0480

Reno Art Works/Wallace Edwards
75 Oriole Gardens #204 Toronto Ontario .... TEL (416)928-0480

Rieger, Theodor
495 Davenport Rd Toronto Ontario .... TEL (416)920-7633

Robinson, Barry Illustration
345 Adelaide St W #501 Toronto Ontario .... TEL (416)977-0142

Robinson, Marshall
25 Sunrise Ave #707 Toronto Ontario .... TEL (416)285-4936

Robitaille, Chris
99 Queen St E 5th Fl Toronto Ontario .... TEL (416)864-0811

Rock Connection
44 Prince Andrew Place Don Mills Ontario .... TEL (416)391-0298

Rogers, Adam Illustrator
25 Liberty St #304 Toronto Ontario .... TEL (416)534-5198

Rother, Christina
376 Ashdale Ave Toronto Ontario .... TEL (416)465-7799

Roussy, Alma
20 Winona Dr Toronto Ontario .... TEL (416)653-5709

Rowe, Elizabeth
141 Courcelette Rd Toronto Ontario .... TEL (416)691-6121

Rubess, Balvis
260 Brunswick Ave Toronto Ontario .... TEL (416)927-7071

Ruhl, Greg Illustration
63A Yorkville Ave Toronto Ontario .... TEL (416)928-1997

Ruszkai, Gabor
107 Simpson Ave Toronto Ontario .... TEL (416)462-9207

Ryan Paul Art & Ingenuity
198 Walnut Ave #10 Toronto Ontario .... TEL (416)864-9669

Ryan, Terry/Wolff Art & Design
67 Mowat Ave #353 Toronto Ontario .... TEL (416)531-2480

S/C/F James Hill
232 Parliament St Toronto Ontario .... TEL (416)368-4999

S/C/F Tom Taylor
232 Parliament St Toronto Ontario .... TEL (416)368-4999

S/C/F Gary Richardson
232 Parliament St Toronto Ontario .... TEL (416)368-4999

S/C/F K.C. Rasmussen
232 Parliament St Toronto Ontario .... TEL (416)368-4999

S/C/F Katherine Helmer
232 Parliament St Toronto Ontario .... TEL (416)368-4999

S/C/F Willi Mitschka
232 Parliament St Toronto Ontario .... TEL (416)368-4999

Sanna, Valentino
82 Roncesvalles Ave #2 Toronto Ontario .... TEL (416)538-0232

Sardinha, Anthony
16 Sparta Rd Toronto Ontario .... TEL (416)249-0285

Sauve, Gordon Illustration
8 St. Thomas St #44 Toronto Ontario .... TEL (416)977-1453

Scene Canada
299 Main St N Markham Ontario .... TEL (416)294-8786

Schmidt, Ludo
1788 Pagehurst Ave Mississauga Ontario .... TEL (416)624-1679

Schreiber, Rick
38 Fifth St Toronto Ontario .... TEL (416)255-2923

Senin, Loreta
43 Winlock Park Willowdale Ontario .... TEL (416)221-1753

Sepahdari, Rezr
2451 Bridletowne Circle #14 Scarborough Ontario .... TEL (416)494-9479

Sepp, Peeter
92 Wells Hill Ave Toronto Ontario .... TEL (416)533-8934

Sevalrud, Thom
173 Queen St E #3 Toronto Ontario .... TEL (416)361-6320

Sevier, Gerry & Associates
122 Laird Dr #200 Toronto Ontario .... TEL (416)696-2366

Sharpshooter Art Studio
524 Queen St E Toronto Ontario .... TEL (416)860-0300

Sharpshooter/Anita Kunz
524 Queen St E Toronto Ontario .... TEL (416)860-0300

Sharpshooter/Barbara Klunder
524 Queen St E Toronto Ontario .... TEL (416)860-0300

Sharpshooter/Bill Boyko
524 Queen St E Toronto Ontario .... TEL (416)860-0300

Sharpshooter/Christine Bunn
524 Queen St E Toronto Ontario .... TEL (416)860-0300

Sharpshooter/Doug Martin
524 Queen St E Toronto Ontario .... TEL (416)860-0300

Sharpshooter/Francois Chartier
524 Queen St E Toronto Ontario .... TEL (416)860-0300

Sharpshooter/Gordon Sauve
524 Queen St E Toronto Ontario .... TEL (416)860-0300

Sharpshooter/Jacobson/Fernandez
524 Queen St E Toronto Ontario .... TEL (416)860-0300

Sharpshooter/Jean Christian Knaff
524 Queen St E Toronto Ontario .... TEL (416)860-0300

Sharpshooter/San Murata
524 Queen St E Toronto Ontario .... TEL (416)860-0300

Sharpshooter/Teric Liu
524 Queen St E Toronto Ontario .... TEL (416)860-0300

Sharpshooter/Wendy Wortsman
524 Queen St E Toronto Ontario .... TEL (416)860-0300

Shaw, David & Associates Ltd
2586A Yonge St #2 Toronto Ontario .... TEL (416)487-2019

Sherriff, Dean Illustration
17 Bradbrook Rd Toronto Ontario .... TEL (416)253-0677

Sherwood, Stewart
625 Yonge St #303 Toronto Ontario .... TEL (416)925-8528

Shoffner, Terry Illustrator Inc
11 Irwin Ave Toronto Ontario .... TEL (416)967-6717

Sinclair, Valerie
17 Bellwoods Pl #5 Toronto Ontario .... TEL (416)594-3400

Sisco, Sam Illustration
8 Sixth St Etobicoke Ontario .... TEL (416)251-5938

Smart Works/Steve MacEachern
109 Westmount Ave Toronto Ontario .... TEL (416)658-0053

Smith, Jerrard
901 Bathurst St Toronto Ontario .... TEL (416)537-2763

Smolak, Ted
33 Springhurst Ave Toronto Ontario .... TEL (416)596-3101

Snider, Jackie Illustration
RR# 7, Highway 30 Brighton Ontario .... TEL (613)475-4551

Snider, Stephen
RR# 7, Highway 30 Brighton Ontario .... TEL (613)475-4551

Sorozan, Marc
86 Parliament St #405 Toronto Ontario .... TEL (416)365-0184

Southern, William Studio
77 Marion St Toronto Ontario .... TEL (416)533-7229

Spotz
13 Hanley St Toronto Ontario .... TEL (416)762-5638

Spurll, Barbara Illustration & Caricature
366 Adelaide St E #431 Toronto Ontario .... TEL (416)594-6594

Stein, Laurie
80 Salisbury Ave Toronto Ontario .... TEL (416)961-3796

Steube, June
225 Indian Rd Toronto Ontario .... TEL (416)766-6725

Stiff, Norm
3368 Ingram Rd Mississauga Ontario .... TEL (416)569-9264

Strugnell, Lee Illustration Inc
25 Defries St Toronto Ontario .... TEL (416)863-6555

Stuart, John
401 Richmond St W #220 Toronto Ontario .... TEL (416)599-4304

Stuck, Marion
7251 Copenhagen Rd #62 Mississauga Ontario .... TEL (416)567-1493

Studio 446 Inc
446 Hillsdale Ave E Toronto Ontario .... TEL (416)487-1808

Studio Graphex/Dan Fell
468 Queen St E #102 Toronto Ontario .... TEL (416)867-9344

Studio Graphex/Ian Watts
468 Queen St E #102 Toronto Ontario .... TEL (416)867-9344

Suddick, Bill Cartoonist/Illustrator
20 Highcroft Rd Toronto Ontario .... TEL (416)469-0843

Summers, Mark
684 Dynes Rd #7 Burlington Ontario .... TEL (416)681-0907

Suzuki, Bob
67 Mowat Ave #339 Toronto Ontario .... TEL (416)588-0758

Tatchell, Annette
1980 Victoria Park Ave #1 Scarborough Ontario .... TEL (416)445-5383

Taylor, Aeon
3 Hildenboro Sq Agincourt Ontario .... TEL (416)756-1822

Technical Publications Services Ltd
11 Barrie Blvd St Thomas Ontario .... TEL (519)631-9490

Terry, Wayne Studio Ltd
12 Roxborough St W Toronto Ontario .... TEL (416)924-4008

the depARTment
1 Kenview Blvd Brampton Ontario .... TEL (416)792-1981

Thompson, Douglas J.
81 Carondale Cres Scarborough Ontario .... TEL (416)497-2424

Thompson, J.D.
81 Carondale Cres Scarborough Ontario .... TEL (416)497-2424

Three in a Box/Marcel Durocher
80 Spadina Ave #505 Toronto Ontario .... TEL (416)367-2446

Three in a Box/Maureen Paxton
80 Spadina Ave #505 Toronto Ontario .... TEL (416)367-2446

Three in a Box/Murray Kimber
80 Spadina Ave #505 Toronto Ontario .... TEL (416)367-2446

Three in a Box/Olena Kassian
80 Spadina Ave #505 Toronto Ontario .... TEL (416)367-2446

Three in a Box/Richard Hockney
80 Spadina Ave #505 Toronto Ontario .... TEL (416)367-2446

Ticar, Chris
12 Hawthorne Crt Belfountain Ontario .... TEL (519)927-5028

Timare, Tibor
2 Ridelle Ave #408 Toronto Ontario .... TEL (416)783-5604

Timms, Randy
309 Cordova Rd #205 Oshawa Ontario .... TEL (416)433-1337

Tindale, Watt Studio Inc
680 Queen Quay W #225 Toronto Ontario .... TEL (416)593-8762

Tonkin, Murray
61 Hannaford St Toronto Ontario .... TEL (416)699-8656

Torpedo! Design
18 Delroy Dr Toronto Ontario .... TEL (416)252-4259

Toth, Steven
258 Stanley Ave Hamilton Ontario .... TEL (416)529-3367

Tughan, James
50 Queen St Georgetown Ontario .... TEL (416)877-2683

Tyson, Sara
4 Selwood Ave Toronto Ontario .... TEL (416)694-8851

Union Studios
96 Spadina Ave 9th Fl Toronto Ontario .... TEL (416)365-9965

Uplis Limited
237 Clinton St Toronto Ontario .... TEL (416)536-8600

Vaculik, Angela
1221 Dundix Rd #104 Mississauga Ontario .... TEL (416)279-8586

Vakharia, Anees
478 Margueretta St Toronto Ontario .... TEL (416)588-9355

Van Der Linde, Henry
1333 Daimler Rd Mississauga Ontario .... TEL (416)822-9930

Van Gelder, Stephen
113 Walpole Ave Toronto Ontario .... TEL (416)462-9344

Van Kampen, Vlasta
206 Glenview Ave Toronto Ontario .... TEL (416)483-2678

Van Mil Studio Ltd
90 Nolan Crt Markham Ontario .... TEL (416)479-8674

Visser, Karen
1179A King St W #307 Toronto Ontario .... TEL (416)588-7093

Vivid Design Group
145 Wharncliffe Rd S London Ontario .... TEL (519)432-8212

Voo Doo Airforce/Gerald McLaughlin
717 Finley Ave #9-10 Ajax Ontario .... TEL (416)686-7554

Vowles, Bob
141 Cameron Ave Toronto Ontario .... TEL (416)223-2475

Walker, Graeme Illustrator
29 Wiggens Court Scarborough Ontario .... TEL (416)298-2008

Walker, James
54 Forest Park Cres Thornhill Ontario .... TEL (416)881-7560

Waller, Leslie Illustration
422 Dundas St Toronto Ontario .... TEL (416)944-1255

Wallis Studios
600 King St W Toronto Ontario .... TEL (416)862-1444

Ward, David
RR #1 Claremont Ontario .... TEL (416)649-2527

Watkinson, Terry (Medical)
285 Harbord St Toronto Ontario .... TEL (416)531-5395

Weiss, Chuck
44 Summertime Crt Brampton Ontario .... TEL (416)846-5146

Weissmann, Joe - Illustrator
331 Eglinton Ave E Toronto Ontario .... TEL (416)486-1122

Weisz, Anne
77 Ridge Hill Dr Toronto Ontario .... TEL (416)782-2604

Whiteboard Studio
90 Winges Rd #22 Woodbridge Ontario .... TEL (416)850-3582

Whitemore, Wendy
884 Sweetwater Cres Mississauga Ontario .... TEL (416)274-0345

Whitteker, Pam (Editorial)
72 Dessie St Brampton Ontario .... TEL (416)796-8238

Wiens, Carl H.
2350 Queen St E #1 Toronto Ontario .... TEL (416)699-1670

Wilson, Janet
81 Lamb Ave Toronto Ontario .... TEL (416)469-1879

Wingfelder, Wendy
Site 8, Box C Comp 7 Shanty Bay Ontario .... TEL (705)721-9584

Winters, Lorne
6131 Fullerton Cres Mississauga Ontario .... TEL (416)824-4743

Wong, Phyliss
6 Esterbrooke #70 Willowdale Ontario .... TEL (416)497-1647

Wood, Muriel Hughes
102 Wells Hill Ave Toronto Ontario .... TEL (416)533-0943

Workman, Chris
363 Sorauren Ave #403 Toronto Ontario .... TEL (416)462-4600

Wortsman, Wendy
684 Bathurst St #2 Toronto Ontario .... TEL (416)530-4047

Yardley Productions Inc
69 Liberty St. Toronto Ontario .... TEL (416)588-8695

Young, Marsha
19 Greenwood Rd Stouffville Ontario .... TEL (416)640-1504

Zaretzki, Andreas
219 Dufferin St #205B Toronto Ontario .... TEL (416)531-6000

Zarowny, Todd
25 St Nicolas St #333 Toronto Ontario .... TEL (416)962-9197

Zeltner, Tim
203 Ellsworth Ave Toronto Ontario .... TEL (416)653-2065

Zwolak, Paul
2466 Dundas St W #210 Toronto Ontario .... TEL (416)531-6253

ILLUSTRATORS — OTTAWA

Aartvark Creative Design & Photography
65 Bank St #200 Ottawa Ontario .... TEL (613)232-5133

Anfousse, Ginette
P.O. Box 703 Val David Québec .... TEL (819)322-2298

Artpix Incorporated
7 Jansen Rd Nepean Ontario .... TEL (613)820-5151

Bayne Herrera Graphic Commun. Ltd
1-155A MacLaren Ottawa Ontario .... TEL (613)233-5773

Colorad Limited
1749 St. Laurent Blvd Ottawa Ontario .... TEL (613)523-4000

Dallison, Ken
RR#3 Indian River Ontario .... TEL (705)295-4351

Farrar, David
39 Robertson Rd #503 Nepean Ontario .... TEL (613)596-0946

Hall, Janus Associates
701 - 280 Albert St Ottawa Ontario .... TEL (613)233-2682

Hardy, Pierre
PO Box 1095, Stn B Hull Québec .... TEL (819)595-2073

L & M Illustration Inc
1117 Burgundy Lane Orleans Ontario .... TEL (613)837-7654

MacMillan, Don
Box 574 Wakefield Quebec .... TEL (613)459-3529

MacPhail, Malcolm
334 Olmstead Sr #3 Vanier Ontario .... TEL (613)745-5370

Manchester, Betty
7 Jansen Rd Nepean Ontario .... TEL (613)820-5151

Mathais, Louis
10 Huntview Private Ottawa Ontario .... TEL (613)737-4544

McCarney & Mann Ltd
263 MacLaren St, Penthouse Orleans Ontario .... TEL (613)238-1211

Murdo Morrison Illustration Ltd
943 Blythdale Rd Ottawa Ontario .... TEL (613)725-1417

Optical Art Studio
380 Richmond Rd Ottawa Ontario .... TEL (613)728-2107

Robertson, Peter (Editorial)
623 Blair Rd Ottawa Ontario .... TEL (613)746-5985

Sanborn, Linda
120 Andrew St #3 Ottawa Ontario .... TEL (613)230-1738

Stanley, Robert Illustration
Woodlawn Ontario .... TEL (613)832-3465

Vivian, Jeanine
790 Springland Dr #522 Ottawa Ontario .... TEL (613)523-3785

Weber, Gordon Illustrations
6 Nanook Cres Kanata Ontario .... TEL (613)592-8826

ARCHITECTURAL ILLUSTRATORS

Architectural Renderings
2025 Sheppard Ave E Willowdale Ontario .... TEL (416)496-0635

Au-Yeung Designs
27 Greenbriar Rd #1 Willowdale Ontario .... TEL (416)229-2545

Connolly, Stuart
RR#1 Gormley Ontario .... TEL (416)727-8886

Cooper, Karen
25 Sherwood Ave Toronto Ontario .... TEL (416)480-1770

Creative Group Design Ltd
300B 17th Ave SW Calgary Alberta .... TEL (403)263-8100

Di Marco Design
600 Bay St Toronto Ontario .... TEL (416)977-0172

Dovaston, Terry
51 Broadview Ave Mississauga Ontario .... TEL (416)278-1401

G.A. Design
31 Silverton Ave Downsview Ontario .... TEL (416)638-4933

G.B. Turner Graphic Design Inc
115 De Grassi St Toronto Ontario .... TEL (416)466-0661

Grice, Gordon Architect Illustrator
878 Queen St W Toronto Ontario .... TEL (416)536-9191

Ingram, Garfield
878 Queen St W 2nd Fl Toronto Ontario .... TEL (416)531-4699

Jacobs, Craig Architectural Illust
727 Queens Ave London Ontario .... TEL (519)667-0882

Keogh Rendering
10 Grenoble Dr #1419 Don Mills Ontario .... TEL (416)423-2412

L&M Illustration Inc
1117 Burgundy Lane Orleans Ontario .... TEL (613)837-7654

McCarthy, Bernard - Illustration
1010 Vistula Dr Pickering Ontario .... TEL (416)839-5892

Milhouse, Cam
P.O. Box 157, Stn C Toronto Ontario .... TEL (416)534-3632

Morello Design & Co
61 Marlborough Ave Toronto Ontario .... TEL (416)963-4315

Multimedia Design Group Inc
450 MacLaren St Ottawa Ontario .... TEL (613)233-6201

Nasmith, Ted
37 Randolph Rd Toronto Ontario .... TEL (416)423-2124

Nice, Ken
878 Queen St W 2nd Fl Toronto Ontario .... TEL (416)588-7186

Powell, David/Heart Render Inc
236 Avenue Rd Toronto Ontario .... TEL (416)964-1545

Pryce Presentation Media Inc
1879 Gerrard St E Toronto Ontario .... TEL (416)463-6762

Ross, William/Morello Design
61 Marlborough Ave Toronto Ontario .... TEL (416)963-4315

Smolak, Ted
33 Springhurst Ave Toronto Ontario .... TEL (416)596-3114

Studio Arts Centre
15 Polson Toronto Ontario .... TEL (416)462-0026

Sullivan Studios
51 Bulwer St Toronto Ontario .... TEL (416)593-0543

The Render Group
961 Eglinton Ave E #204 Toronto Ontario .... TEL (416)960-0028

Versteeg Designs Ltd
600 Markham St Toronto Ontario .... TEL (416)537-9641

Yoshizawa, Yuji-Illustration
14 Glendower Circuit Scarborough Ontario .... TEL (416)754-4674

Zoras Design
414 Moore Ave Toronto Ontario .... TEL (416)429-4364

ASSOCIATIONS

Academy of Canadian Cinema
653 Yonge St 2nd Fl Toronto Ontario .... TEL (416)967-0315

Advertising Advisory Board
350 Bloor St E #402 Toronto Ontario .... TEL (416)961-6311

Art Directors Club, The
945 Mt Pleasant Rd Toronto Ontario .... TEL (416)493-1400

Association of Cdn Advertisers
180 Bloor St W #803 Toronto Ontario .... TEL (416)964-3805

Association of Chartered Industrial Designers
168 Bedford Rd 2nd Fl Toronto Ontario .... TEL (416)928-3069

Association of TV Prod/Directors
2 College St #306 Toronto Ontario .... TEL (416)927-1500

Canadian Advertising Foundation
350 Bloor St E #402 Toronto Ontario .... TEL (416)961-0131

CAPIC
400 Eastern Ave Toronto Ontario .... TEL (416)462-3677

Institute of Canadian Advertising
30 Soudan Ave 2nd Fl Toronto Ontario .... TEL (416)482-1396

National Advertising Benevolent Society of Canada
2 Bloor St W #1200 Toronto Ontario .... TEL (416)962-0446

National Audio Visual Association
77 Mowat Ave #209 Toronto Ontario .... TEL (416)535-9799

Radio Bureau of Canada
146 Yorkville Ave Toronto Ontario .... TEL (416)922-5757

DESIGNERS

Beradinelli Design Ltd
16 Brook St Halifax Nova Scotia .... TEL (902)477-7706

Communication Design Group Ltd
1725 Barrington St Halifax Nova Scotia .... TEL (902)425-6937

Focal Advertising & Marketing
6300 Lady Hammond Rd #700 Halifax Nova Scotia .... TEL (902)453-6000

Image Design Advertising Studio Inc
1550 Bedford Hwy #210 Sun Twr Bedford Nova Scotia .... TEL (902)835-3559

Multi-Concept
92 Convoy Halifax Nova Scotia .... TEL (902)457-1122

Orville Pulsifer & Associates Ltd
PO Box 1765 Truro Nova Scotia .... TEL (902)895-2243

Kiers Production Services Inc
761 Union St Fredericton New Brunswick .... TEL (506)450-2133

Pyrmid Airbrushing Graphics
28 Angelview Crt Fredrickton New Brunswick .... TEL (506)455-1806

PHOTOGRAPHERS

Coldwell Photography
2635 Clifton St Halifax Nova Scotia .... TEL (902)420-0501

Creagen, Michael Photography
PO Box 995, Stn M Halifax Nova Scotia .... TEL (902)455-3498

First Light Communications
PO Box 106 Seabright Tantallon Nova Scotia .... TEL (902)429-2076

Fisher, Blaine Photography
1533 Barrington St Halifax Nova Scotia .... TEL (902)420-9304

Fitzgerald, Owen
423 Charlotte St Sydney Nova Scotia .... TEL (902)564-2321

Georgakakos, George Photography
5230 Blowers St Box 621 Halifax Nova Scotia .... TEL (902)455-8484

Kauppi, Pekka Photography
Vantage Point #1 Seabright Nova Scotia .... TEL (902)450-5002

Lee, Albert Photography
20 Fairbanks St Dartmouth Nova Scotia .... TEL (902)464-1509

Middleton, David Photography
5134 Bishop St #3 Halifax Nova Scotia .... TEL (902)425-6202

Moore, Marvin Photography
5240 Blowers St Halifax Nova Scotia .... TEL (902)420-1559

Murchinson, Alex Photography
1533 Barrington St 2nd Fl Halifax Nova Scotia .... TEL (902)420-9304

Nichols, David Photography
6265 Quinpool Rd Halifax Nova Scotia .... TEL (902)423-4567

Prisma Productions
6265 Quinpool Rd #302 Halifax Nova Scotia .... TEL (902)423-4567

Reardon, Chris
Box 3303 Halifax Nova Scotia .... TEL (902)425-5032

Robinson/Campbell & Associates Ltd
960 Barrington St Halifax Nova Scotia .... TEL (902)425-2614

Seebright
Box 106 Tantallon Nova Scotia .... TEL (902)429-2076

Sun Dancer Air Shows Ltd
P.O. Box 1542 Halifax Nova Scotia .... TEL (416)925-4323

Zwerling, Stephen Photography Ltd
1593 Market St Halifax Nova Scotia .... TEL (902)425-4600

Atlantic Studios Ltd
110 Coverdale Rd Riverview New Brunswick .... TEL (506)387-4199

Saunders, Michael Photo-Graphic Illustrator
P.O. Box 1178 Woodstock New Brunswick .... TEL (506)328-3161

PHOTO/VIDEO EQUIPMENT & SUPPLIES

Tucker Electonics Ltd
153 Pennywell Rd Box 13639 St John's Nfld. .... TEL (709)722-6557

DESIGNERS — WINNIPEG

Circle Design Incorporated
601-63 Albert St Winnipeg Manitoba .... TEL (204)943-3693

Grand Design
127 Chestnut St Winnipeg Manitoba .... TEL (204)786-5629

Graphicom Design
491 Mandalay #303 Winnipeg Manitoba .... TEL (204)694-8121

GW Graphics
4-1599 Dugald Rd Winnipeg Manitoba .... TEL (204)775-4794

Hailey Graphix
250 McDermot Ave Winnipeg Manitoba .... TEL (204)947-0997

Hicks Studios Inc
158 Wildwood Park Winnipeg Manitoba .... TEL (204)284-4752

L N Design
6 Knotsberry Bay Winnipeg Manitoba .... TEL (204)253-8994

Lavilla & Harrison
1135 Henderson Hwy #204 Winnipeg Manitoba .... TEL (204)669-1881

Montage Design
8 Donald St 3rd Fl Winnipeg Manitoba .... TEL (204)452-2221

Network Display
66 King St #320 Winnipeg Manitoba .... TEL (204)943-7552

Nova Design
1485 Portage Ave #200E Winnipeg Manitoba .... TEL (204)783-6890

Riddell, Bob Design
169 St Vital Rd Winnipeg Manitoba .... TEL (204)255-7745

Schmidt, Norman Design
PO Box 32 St Norbert Manitoba .... TEL (204)261-0448

Simoens, Leo Design
33 Filbert Cres Winnipeg Manitoba .... TEL (204)669-6453

DESIGNERS — EDMONTON

Alexander, Wm Associates Advertising
706-5241 Calgary Tr S Edmonton Alberta .... TEL (403)437-4708

Cassel, Donald
7919 132 Ave Edmonton Alberta .... TEL (403)475-2574

Chapman, Keith
15108 77 Ave Edmonton Alberta .... TEL (403)487-4036

David Advertising Illustration & Design Ltd
10130 103rd St #1600 Edmonton Alberta .... TEL (403)423-3537

Dimension One Graphics Ltd
10018 86th Ave Edmonton Alberta .... TEL (403)433-2788

GDL
10113 104 St #324 Edmonton Alberta .... TEL (403)423-7028

Graphics Creative Art Studio Inc
202 10357 109 St Edmonton Alberta .... TEL (403)423-0673

Group West Graphics Ltd
11444 97th St Edmonton Alberta .... TEL (403)477-8244

Huff, William Advertising Ltd
58 Airport Rd Edmonton Alberta .... TEL (403)454-4536

Martin, Gabriel A.
12534-125 St Edmonton Alberta .... TEL (403)451-4630

Thumbprints
17303 106A Ave Edmonton Alberta .... TEL (403)483-1214

William Demchuk Design
5241 Calgary Trail S #502 Edmonton Alberta .... TEL (403)437-4708

DESIGNERS — CALGARY

Ad Venture Studio Inc
144-4th Ave SW #540 Calgary Alberta .... TEL (403)265-2020

Adams, Mark Design
239 10th Ave SE #302 Calgary Alberta .... TEL (403)237-0422

Briggs Design Studio Ltd
3211 Elbow Dr SW Calgary Alberta .... TEL (403)234-6372

Chanisa Agency
Box 727 Stn T Calgary Alberta .... TEL (403)248-0717

Karim, Yasmin Graphic Designer
982 Ranchview Cres NW Calgary Alberta .... TEL (403)239-1145

KARO Design
926-5th Ave SW #500 Calgary Alberta .... TEL (403)266-4094

Macpherson, E. Enterprises Ltd
366-7330 Fisher St SE Calgary Alberta .... TEL (403)252-5521

Taylor and Browning Design Associates
10th Avenue S.W. #221 Calgary Alberta .... TEL (403)233-8 423

Vigneault, Nelson Design
2943-19 St NE Calgary Alberta .... TEL (403)250-3357

DESIGNERS — VANCOUVER

AD Team Marketing Inc
3127 Grandview Hwy Vancouver B.C. .... TEL (604)439-7898

Alex Studio Ltd
155 Water St #3 Vancouver B.C. .... TEL (604)688-2221

Artec Datahouse Inc
225 Canada Ave #202 Duncan B.C. .... TEL (604)748-1444

Beyond Graphics
1130 Richter St Kelowna B.C. .... TEL (604)861-5005

Brymar Enterprises Ltd
9434 117A Street Delta B.C. .... TEL (604)581-9461

Cleland Kent Western Ltd
2285 Clark Drive Vancouver B.C. .... TEL (604)877-1141

Cochrane & Cassidy Design
12760 Bathgate Way #2 Richmond B.C. .... TEL (604)276-0838

Coombs Consulting Ltd
3077 Granville St #202 Vancouver B.C. .... TEL (604)733-9014

Corporate Concepts (Van) Productions Ltd
1281 West Georgia #100 Vancouver B.C. .... TEL (604)685-6201

Creative Promotions Group
133 West 17th St North Vancouver B.C. .... TEL (604)988-5258

Design & Graphics
1535 Fulton Ave W Vancouver B.C. .... TEL (604)926-4161

Design Works, The
2327 Yew St Vancouver B.C. .... TEL (604)734-0791

Designer's Edge Studio Limited, The
302-134 Abbott St Vancouver B.C. .... TEL (604)669-5245

Dharma Design & Consultation Ltd
1020 Mainland St #160 Vancouver B.C. .... TEL (604)687-7701

Dochstader, Daniel Enterprises
200 - 416 West Pender St Vancouver B.C. .... TEL (604)731-8425

Dunne, Murray F.
442 Hadden Dr West Vancouver B.C. .... TEL (604)922-4896

Gilbert, John Martin
4797 Highway West Vancouver B.C. .... TEL (604)731-8425

Graphic Resource Group, The
1237 Howe St Vancouver B.C. .... TEL (604)669-2287

Harrison-Green Marketing & Communication Inc
1199 West Pender St #101 Vancouver B.C. .... TEL (604)669-5262

Harron, Brent
1234 Barclay St #907 Vancouver B.C. .... TEL (604)689-1238

Karo Design Resources Inc
747 Bute St Vancouver B.C. .... TEL (604)688-9975

Logomotive Graphics
11642 - 82nd Ave Delta B.C. .... TEL (604)591-1437

Nagy, Dennis
40 Powell St #401 Vancouver B.C. .... TEL (604)685-2641

Newland, Marv
1168 Hamilton St #203 Vancouver B.C. .... TEL (604)681-2716

Nouwens, Arnold Graphic Arts
109 West 3rd Ave Vancouver B.C. .... TEL (604)876-3133

O'Mara & Ryan Ltd
1807 Maritime Mews #206 Vancouver B.C. .... TEL (604)681-4431

Orca Design
Six Gaoler's Mews Vancouver B.C. .... TEL (604)681-2884

Pacific Artist Studio
337 West Pender St Vancouver B.C. .... TEL (604)685-9932

Pacific Illustrations
1619 Store St #202 Victoria B.C. .... TEL (604)386-2551

Pacific Rim Design & Direction Inc.
720 E 27th Ave Vancouver B.C. .... TEL (604)879-6689

Reinhard Derreth Graphics Ltd
1147B Homer St Vancouver B.C. .... TEL (604)681-0714

Schade, Ullrich Assoc. Ltd.
1445 West Georgia St Vancouver B.C. .... TEL (604)669-1180

Siren Design Studios
1551 Johnston St #26 Vancouver B.C. .... TEL (604)662-8630

Solomon, Ivan Creative Thinkers
1220 West 6th St #101 Vancouver B.C. .... TEL (604)736-9796

Willms, Russ
2099 - 126 St White Rock B.C. .... TEL (604)731-8425

Zenith Graphics Ltd
898 Richards St Vancouver B.C. .... TEL (604)682-4521

ELECTRONICS GRAPHICS & SERVICES — VANCOUVER

Changing Images Productions Ltd
845 Cambrie St #800 Vancouver B.C. .... TEL (604)681-4391

Graphic Resource Group
1237 Howe St Vancouver B.C. .... TEL (604)669-2287

Tetrad Computer Applications Ltd
1445 W Georgia St Vancouver B.C. .... TEL (604)685-2295

EXHIBIT & DISPLAY — EDMONTON

By Design Ltd.
200-10361 82 Ave Edmonton Alberta .... TEL (403)439-5015

Derrick Exhibit & Trade Show Services Ltd
4757 93rd Ave NW Edmonton Alberta .... TEL (403)465-0192

Scene Shop, The
9510 105 Ave Edmonton Alberta .... TEL (403)424-4897

EXHIBIT & DISPLAY — CALGARY

Graphic Creations Ltd
1255 45 Ave NE #4 Calgary Alberta .... TEL (403)250-7120

Ideacon Display Products Inc
6037 6th St SE Calgary Alberta .... TEL (403)255-3637

L&M Signs Ltd
C9-6215 3rd St SE Calgary Alberta .... TEL (403)259-5688

Westwind Design
3608 MacLeod Trail S Calgary Alberta .... TEL (403)243-2337

EXHIBIT & DISPLAY — VANCOUVER

Aldrich/Pears Associates
1573 E Pender St Vancouver B.C. .... TEL (604)253-1125

All Set Design Ltd
1395 Grandview Highway Vancouver B.C. .... TEL (604)255-8282

Colorific Photo Labs
195 W 7th Ave Vancouver B.C. .... TEL (604)879-1511

Conventions Unlimited
7442 Fraser Park Dr Burnaby B.C. .... TEL (604)437-8355

Derrick Exhibits
1776 Broadway St #125 Port Coquitlam B.C. .... TEL (604)942-9255

Horizon Exhibits Inc
5438-176 St #105 Surrey B.C. .... TEL (604)576-2841

Mansueto Display Associates Ltd
430 Industrial Ave North Vancouver B.C. .... TEL (604)254-9321

Outline Display Canada Ltd.
3551 Viking Way #109 Richmond B.C. .... TEL (604)276-2366

Pentact Group
73 Water St 3rd Fl Vancouver B.C. .... TEL (604)682-6565

Seaboard Advertising
4295 Dawson St. Burnaby B.C. .... TEL (604)291-1229

Spectralite 70 Ltd.
11760 Voyageur Way #110 Richmond B.C. .... TEL (604)270-7564

Vancouver Plexiform
1236 Seymour St Vancouver B.C. .... TEL (604)688-3827

Western Display Service Ltd.
6791 Elmbridge Way #102 Richmond B.C. .... TEL (604)278-4641

PHOTOGRAPHERS — WINNIPEG

Barr, Bruce Photogaphy
396 Sherbrook St Winnipeg Manitoba .... TEL (204)783-1882

Flatland Productions
103 Helmsdale Avenue Winnipeg Manitoba .... TEL (204)667-3170

G.B. Graphics
250 Saulteaux Cres Winnipeg Manitoba .... TEL (204)885-7733

Hawthorne/Revere Marketing
415 Seven Oaks Ave Winnipeg Manitoba .... TEL (204)586-2284

Image Makers, The
Box 172 Transcona Winnipeg Manitoba .... TEL (204)224-5305

In Focus/Wes Pascoe
1360 Sargent Ave Winnipeg Manitoba .... TEL (204)783-4275

Kalen, Henry Limited
745 Wall St Winnipeg Manitoba .... TEL (204)774-3521

Lauder, Carey J. Photography
43 Picardy Pl Winnipeg Manitoba .... TEL (204)772-8837

Martens, Paul Photographer Inc
Box 231, 39 Hanover Rd Kleefeld Manitoba .... TEL (204)377-4443

Richards Studio/R. Gwizdak
690 St. Joseph St #306 Winnipeg Manitoba .... TEL (204)231-1416

Sytnyk, Brian Photography
221 McDermot Ave #20 Winnipeg Manitoba .... TEL (204)947-2388

Thorpe Photography
481 Dominion St #302 Winnipeg Manitoba .... TEL (204)772-6311

Tinker, Robert
140 The Glen Winnipeg Manitoba .... TEL (204)237-1306

PHOTOGRAPHERS — REGINA

Moulding, Keith Photography
3004 College Ave Regina Saskatchewan .... TEL (306)352-0220

Walker Photogaphics Ltd
1933 8th Ave #395 Regina Saskatchewan .... TEL (306)352-3707

PHOTOGRAPHERS — EDMONTON

B Bastell Studio
10330-104 St 3rd Fl Edmonton Alberta .... TEL (403)423-2494

Biggar, Ian W. Photography
11615-78 Ave Edmonton Alberta .... TEL (403)436-2340

Blue Moon Words & Pictures
635 Milbourne Rd E Edmonton Alberta .... TEL (403)463-1777

Bolsius, Marc Photography
10618-105 Ave Edmonton Alberta .... TEL (403)426-1607

Brown, Dwayne
12534-125 St Edmonton Alberta .... TEL (403)451-4630

C.W. Hill Photography Ltd
14503 Stoney Plain Rd Edmonton Alberta .... TEL (403)453-3333

Darklight Studios
17344-107th Ave Edmonton Alberta .... TEL (403)486-3966

Dates, Fred
8709-156 St Edmonton Alberta .... TEL (403)486-5680

Dyberg Studios
7347-104 St Edmonton Alberta .... TEL (403)431-0683

Hammond, Don/Ranson Photography
26 Airport Rd Edmonton Alberta .... TEL (403)454-9674

Henderson Photography
182 Gariepy Cres Edmonton Alberta .... TEL (403)483-8049

IND/COMM Photographics
3703-32nd St Edmonton Alberta .... TEL (403)440-0113

Katz, Fred Photography
7347-104 St Edmonton Alberta .... TEL (403)431-0494

Lotus Studio
10453-84 Ave Edmonton Alberta .... TEL (403)431-0447

McKeown Graphic Design Ltd
440-10113 104 St Edmonton Alberta .... TEL (403)426-4031

Middle Earth Gallery Ltd, The
10107-89th St Edmonton Alberta .... TEL (403)421-9239

New Visions Photography Ltd
11715H-108 Ave Edmonton Alberta .... TEL (403)454-7786

Pape, Rick/Edmonton Journal
10006-101 St Adv Dept Edmonton Alberta .... TEL (403)429-5200

Post, Victor Photography
8 Perron St St. Albert Alberta .... TEL (403)459-5239

Prosofsky, Merle Photography Ltd
106-8905 51st Ave Edmonton Alberta .... TEL (403)468-5585

Puckrin's Production House Ltd
12644-126 St Edmonton Alberta .... TEL (403)451-3660

Pydde, Darrell Photographs
5108-50 Ave #203 Wetaskiwin Alberta .... TEL (403)352-8260

Ranson Photographers Ltd
26 Airport Rd Edmonton Alberta .... TEL (403)454-9674

Robertson, James Photography
3703-32nd St Edmonton Alberta .... TEL (403)440-0113

Sundance Photo Graphics Ltd
5205-39B Ave Edmonton Alberta .... TEL (403)463-3301

Top Art Photographics Ltd
11304-125 St Edmonton Alberta .... TEL (403)452-3324

Wagner, Les
10119-82 Ave Edmonton Alberta .... TEL (403)439-5851

Wiebe Photogaphy
14754-48th Ave Edmonton Alberta .... TEL (403)435-4496

PHOTOGRAPHERS — CALGARY

Accent Photography Ltd
201-10601 Southport Rd SW Calgary Alberta .... TEL (403)271-4120

Angus of Calgary Photography Ltd
4911-17th Ave SW Calgary Alberta .... TEL (403)246-0888

Bako/Becq Inc
3047-4th St SW Calgary Alberta .... TEL (403)243-9789

Bilodeau/Preston Ltd
1615 10th Ave SW #100 Calgary Alberta .... TEL (604)245-1804

Campbell, Gary Photography
1316 1st St SW Calgary Alberta .... TEL (403)237-5656

Cotton Wood Consultants
615 Deer Croft Way SE Calgary Alberta .... TEL (403)271-1408

Dufresne, Leah Photography
309,603-11 Ave SW Calgary Alberta .... TEL (403)262-2628

Fisher, Larry Photography
4928 Rumblewood Rd NE Calgary Alberta .... TEL (403)241-1224

Fusion Studios
PO Box 634 Banff Alberta .... TEL (403)762-3450

Haase, Peter Photographics Ltd
2300 Oakmoor Dr SW #106 Calgary Alberta .... TEL (403)238-3008

Harder, Brian Commercial Photography Ltd
240 11th Ave SW #400 Calgary Alberta .... TEL (403)263-0803

Image House, The
3304 Centre St N Calgary Alberta .... TEL (403)276-7021

Images of Nature
RR# 2 Camrose Alberta .... TEL (403)672-7307

Johnson, Frank
5621 11 St NE #105 Calgary Alberta .... TEL (403)275-5874

Kan, Garry
PO Box 1980 Stn M Calgary Alberta .... TEL (403)250-6882

Kokotovich, Ric
1316-1st St SW Calgary Alberta .... TEL (403)237-5656

Landes Photographic Design
1906-30th Ave SW Calgary Alberta .... TEL (403)245-3057

Leon, Peter Photography Inc
3500-27th St NE #9 Calgary Alberta .... TEL (403)291-9198

MacDougal, Larry Photography
Box 2135 Stn M Calgary Alberta .... TEL (403)245-0531

Marsh, Bill Photography
Box 2533 Banff Alberta .... TEL (403)762-3209

Morrow, Patrick Photographer
Box 2278 Canmore Alberta .... TEL (403)678-2901

Muller Photography
429-2nd Ave W Box 1576 Cardston Alberta .... TEL (403)653-4646

Nasser, Amyn
Box 30263, Stn B Calgary Alberta .... TEL (403)264-7964

Ooms, Roy Photography
715-4A St NE Calgary Alberta .... TEL (403)276-4321

Oresnik, John
Box 8896, Stn F Calgary Alberta .... TEL (403)265-1879

Photographic Dimensions of Calgary
71 Chisholm Cres NW Calgary Alberta .... TEL (403)289-8251

Pictures Taken By Norbert Ltd
3917-17 Ave SE Calgary Alberta .... TEL (403)272-4900

PNE Photographic Services
2719 Cedarbrae Dr SW Calgary Alberta .... TEL (403)281-1091

Salus, John Photographer
417 Riverfront Ave SE Calgary Alberta .... TEL (403)263-6090

Say Cheez
617-14th Ave Hwy 14 Wainwright Alberta .... TEL (403)842-3299

Stallknecht, Kim Photography
1001-17th Ave SE Calgary Alberta .... TEL (403)237-7436

Studio Kemper Photography Ltd
3535 Beaver Rd NW Calgary Alberta .... TEL (403)282-7465

The Kelly Group
443-25th Ave NE Calgary Alberta .... TEL (403)232-6141

Thomas, Chris Photography
722-11th Ave SW Calgary Alberta .... TEL (403)263-4680

Tomlinson, Ian Photography
1148A-43rd St SW Calgary Alberta .... TEL (403)233-2575

Turner, Jim Photography
P O Box 3780, Stn B Calgary Alberta .... TEL (403)224-4465

Vitaris, Mark
PO Box 3052, Stn B Calgary Alberta .... TEL (403)289-1612

Wallis, Cliff Photography
615 Deer Croft Way SE Calgary Alberta .... TEL (403)271-1408

Watanabe, Roger
152 Castleridge Dr NE Calgary Alberta .... TEL (403)293-1748

Weber, Walter Photography
PO Box 6008, Stn A Calgary Alberta .... TEL (403)259-4042

Winter Vision Ltd
117 Mountain Ave Box 2069 Banff Alberta .... TEL (403)762-2006

Yunker, Gerard Photography Inc
1902-11 Street SE Calgary Alberta .... TEL (403)269-8345

PHOTOGRAPHERS — VANCOUVER

AAA Image Makers
2420 Number Eight Rd Richmond B.C. .... TEL (604)273-1334

Action Film Services Ltd
537 West Georgia St Vancouver B.C. .... TEL (604)687-2528

Action Reprographics Ltd
2166 West Fourth Ave Vancouver B.C. .... TEL (604)731-6313

Allen, Tom Photography
7565 Burgess St Burnaby B.C. .... TEL (604)522-5513

Ampro Photo Workshops Ltd
636 E Broadway Vancouver B.C. .... TEL (604)876-5501

Andre, Jacques Photography
PO Box 33812, Stn D Vancouver B.C. .... TEL (604)682-8187

Animotion Inc
5429 Douglas St W Vancouver B.C. .... TEL (604)921-6646

Artona Studios Ltd
2111 W 16th Vancouver B.C. .... TEL (604)736-7281

Baswick, Delores Photographics Ltd
68 Water St #304 Vancouver B.C. .... TEL (604)688-0636

Bertrand, Ray Photographer
209-340 E 14th Ave Vancouver B.C. .... TEL (604)873-9186

Bestway Photo
15453 - 85 Ave Surrey B.C. .... TEL (604)526-3394

Blacklaws, Rick
302 West 2nd Ave Vanvouver B.C. .... TEL (604)873-9378

Blake, Robert Photography
462 East Pender St Vancouver B.C. .... TEL (604)254-5305

Bounsall, Tony Photography
177 Joseph St Victoria B.C. .... TEL (604)383-1814

Brons, Doug Photography
1304 Seymour St Vancouver B.C. .... TEL (604)682-8982

Brooks, Barry
1221 Cotton Dr Vancouver B.C. .... TEL (604)253-4450

Brooks, Roger and Associates
316 East 1st Ave #200 Vancouver B.C. .... TEL (604)872-2717

Buchan, Douglas Photography
314 W Pender St Vancouver B.C. .... TEL (604)687-1933

Cameron, Chris Photography
2023 Whyte Ave Vancouver B.C. .... TEL (604)736-6188

Canadian Marathon Photos Inc
101-1252 Burrard St Vancouver B.C. .... TEL (604)685-0414

CAPIC Vancouver Chapter
21 East 5th Ave Vancouver B.C. .... TEL (604)872-1248

Charach, Hartley Photographer
2257 West 6th Ave Vancouver B.C. .... TEL (604)737-1595

Cheadle, Chris Photography
PO Box 2573 Sidney B.C. .... TEL (604)655-4676

Chin, Albert Photography
1150 Homer St Vancouver B.C. .... TEL (604)685-2000

Clarke, Bob Photographer
15 East Third Ave Vancouver B.C. .... TEL (604)290-2412

Cline, Daryl Kahn Photography
4540 West 3rd Ave Vancouver B.C. .... TEL (604)228-9182

Collins, Bill Photography
225 Mowat St #205 New Westminster B.C. .... TEL (604)525-6056

Commercial Illustrators Ltd
910 Beach Ave Vancouver B.C. .... TEL (604)684-8467

Cooper, David Photography
1150 Homer St 2nd Fl Vancouver B.C. .... TEL (604)685-8715

Cooper, Ken Productions
Box 142, Stn A Vancouver B.C. .... TEL (604)681-2522

Currie, Steven Photographer
2783 West 5th Ave Vancouver B.C. .... TEL (604)736-4644

d'Estrube Photography
604 Yates St Victoria B.C. .... TEL (604)384-4511

Dafoe, John Photography
1809 Martime Mews Vancouver B.C. .... TEL (604)669-8995

Dancs, Andras Photography
518 Beatty St #603 Vancouver B.C. .... TEL (604)684-6760

Datene, Will Photographer
3368 East 2nd Ave Vancouver B.C. .... TEL (604)253-1594

Dean, Heather Photography
566 Cardero #24 Vancouver B.C. .... TEL (604)684-1425

Dee, Stuart Photography
1104 Homer St Vancouver B.C. .... TEL (604)681-8604

Dezso, Victor Photography
2741 Skeena St #5 Vancouver B.C .... TEL (604)430-0026

Durant, Ross
316 East 1st Ave #200 Vancouver B.C. .... TEL (604)872-2717

Eagle, Alistair Photography
402 West Pender St Vancouver B.C. .... TEL (604)688-8867

Emerald Sea Photo Limited
11551 Pelican Crt Richmond B.C. .... TEL (604)274-9432

Erikson, Glen E. Photographics
3825 Arbutus St Vancouver B.C. .... TEL (604)736-4656

Etkin, Rick Photographs Ltd
21 East 5th Ave Vancouver B.C. .... TEL (604)875-0535

F22 Commercial Photography
#212-9654 192nd St Surrey B.C. .... TEL (604)888-2264

Fedorak Photo
28 W Nicola Kamloops BC .... TEL (604)372-1255

First Image Productions Ltd
2780 Granville St #206 Vancouver B.C. .... TEL (604)736-5955

Fisher, Gordon J.
302-134 Abbott St Vancouver B.C. .... TEL (604)669-5245

Freedman, Eric Photography
518 Beatty St Vancouver B.C. .... TEL (604)683-2544

Fry, Howard Photography
309 West Cordova St #26 Vancouver B.C. .... TEL (604)684-7545

Fulker, John Associates
1755-29th St West Vancouver B.C. .... TEL (604)922-6857

G.M. Studios
59 West 7th Ave Vancouver B.C. .... TEL (604)872-8277

Gascon, Michel Photography
PO Box 15647, MPO Vancouver B.C. .... TEL (604)685-1185

Gauvin, Brian
4260 John St Vancouver B.C. .... TEL (604)876-5433

Gemini Photo
1551 Johnston St Gran. Island Vancouver B.C. .... TEL (604)688-7433

Giebelhaus, Brian P
PO Box 3565 Westminster B.C. .... TEL (604)525-7846

Gifford, Ed
27441 112th Ave Maple Ridge B.C. .... TEL (604)462-8612

Goldie, Colin
59 West 7th Ave Vancouver B.C. .... TEL (604)872-8277

Goldstein, Larry Photography
21 East 5th Ave Vancouver B.C. .... TEL (604)877-1117

Goodman Studios Ltd
4355 Gallant Ave North Vancouver B.C. .... TEL (604)929-4533

Grant, Ted Photography Ltd
1817 Feltham Rd Victoria B.C. .... TEL (604)477-2156

Gray, David Photography
21 East 5th Ave Vancouver B.C. .... TEL (604)877-1550

Gregory, Doane Photography Ltd
335 West 11th Ave Vancouver B.C. .... TEL (604)879-0556

Habal, Jan
203-1020 Hamilton St Vancouver B.C. .... TEL (604)988-6970

Hagerman, Donna
397 West 5th Ave Vancouver B.C. .... TEL (604)877-1755

Hamilton, Marianne Photography
385 Ginger Dr #306C NewWestminister B.C. .... TEL (604)522-8187

Harvey, Al
PO Box 34245 Vancouver B.C. .... TEL (604)738-7878

Harvey, Tim
505 Hamilton St 2nd Fl Vancouver B.C. .... TEL (604)687-2227

Hattenberger, Patrick
2000 Ontario St Vancouver B.C. .... TEL (604)872-6002

Hayhurst, Vincent Advertising Photography
16432-24th Ave Surrey B.C. .... TEL (604)538-1523

Haylett, Chris Photography
1052 Homer St Vancouver B.C. .... TEL (604)688-7500

Helcermanas-Benge, Chris
6588 Wellington Ave West Vancouver B.C. .... TEL (604)644-2014

Helgren, Chris
1133 E 16th Ave Vancouver B.C. .... TEL (604)686-0488

Hersee, Philip Photography Inc
155 Water St, Gastown Vancouver B.C. .... TEL (604)687-2921

Higinbotham, Pat/Studio 54
54 W Hastings St Vancouver B.C. .... TEL (604)684-7642

Hill, Kharen Photography Inc
PO Box 34476, Station D Vancouver B.C. .... TEL (604)685-5545

Holmes, Ron Photogarpher
804 E 15th Ave #4 Vancouver B.C. .... TEL (604)875-9903

Holuboff, Keith Photography
4262 Carnarvon St Vancouver B.C. .... TEL (604)731-6800

Honey, Ken Photography
518 West Hastings St Vancouver B.C. .... TEL (604)682-5323

Howard, Denise Photographer
102-125 W 18th St N Vancouver B.C. .... TEL (604)680-0509

Ilicic Productions
400 Smithe St #102 Vancouver B.C. .... TEL (604)683-5655

Image Minder
308-8575 Heather St Vancouver B.C. .... TEL (604)327-5520

Image West Photography
3050 Larkdowne Rd Victoria B.C. .... TEL (604)598-7527

Incident Photography Publishing
1650 Cedar Cres Vancouver B.C. .... TEL (604)731-6468

Infocus Photographic Services
12 Bastion Square Victoria B.C. .... TEL (604)386-1133

Jones, David Thomas Photography
327-309 W Cordova St N Vancouver B.C. .... TEL (604)688-9242

Kallberg, Kent
1138 Homer St Vancouver B.C. .... TEL (604)689-5115

Karpa, Robert
1510 W 1st Ave #403 Vancouver B.C. .... TEL (604)738-1612

Keevil, Jay David
890 Younette Dr West Vancouver B.C. .... TEL (604)681-8787

Kenji Photographic Design
1741 W 2nd Ave Vancouver B.C. .... TEL (604)734-5227

Kenny, John Douglas Photography Ltd
1134 Homer St #302 Vancouver B.C. .... TEL (604)683-2257

Kent Photographics Ltd
1138 Homer St Vancouver B.C. .... TEL (604)689-5115

Ketcheson, Blair
1506-2055 Pendrell St Vancouver B.C. .... TEL (604)731-8425

Kinch, Greg
7100 Champlain Cres #32 Vancouver B.C. .... TEL (604)644-5245

Klaver, Andrew Photography
PO Box 34181, Stn D Vancouver B.C. .... TEL (604)733-3959

Konting, Jim Photo Studio
1166 High Rd Kelowna B.C. .... TEL (604)861-9211

Kwong, Robert M. Photographer
220 East 4th St #23 North Vancouver B.C. .... TEL (604)987-6600

Lederer, Joseph Photography
1150 Homer St Vancouver B.C. .... TEL (604)687-2458

Little, Paul
2247 Folkestone Way #107 West Vancouver B.C. .... TEL (604)925-1959

Looking Good Photographic
1570 Fell Ave North Vancouver B.C. .... TEL (604)985-0915

Luey, Rod
59 W 7th Ave Vancouver B.C. .... TEL (604)872-8277

Lum, Raymond Photography
1810 Pine St Vancouver B.C. .... TEL (604)731-0131

Mainstreet Production Inc
205 Victoria Drive, 3rd Fl Vancouver B.C. .... TEL (604)669-0825

Martin-Morice, Philippe
309 West Cordova St #26 Vancouver B.C. .... TEL (604)684-7545

Mayer, Ken
59 West 7th Ave Vancouver B.C. .... TEL (604)872-8277

McLean, Barry Photography
11845 - 99A Ave Surrey B.C. .... TEL (604)584-0843

Melnychuk, Rob Photography
4023 West 16th Ave Vancouver B.C. .... TEL (604)228-1132

Miles, Raeff
505 Hamilton St 2nd Fl Vancouver B.C. .... TEL (604)687-2227

Montizambert Photography
102-400 Smithe St Vancouver B.C. .... TEL (604)687-7770

Morrison, Paul Photography
8632 Forest Ridge Box 162 Whistler B.C. .... TEL (604)932-6854

Mountain Moments Custom Photography
Box 165 Whistler B.C. .... TEL (604)932-3274

Murray, Derik Photography Inc
1128 Homer St Vancouver B.C. .... TEL (604)669-7468

Nagai, Kenji
1741 W 2nd Ave Vancouver B.C. .... TEL (604)734-5227

Neel, David Photography
PO Box 4154 Vancouver B.C. .... TEL (604)876-6833

Neufeldt, Geoff Photography
1235 Comox St #304 Vancouver B.C. .... TEL (604)681-7129

Nicholson, David Photography
3640 St Georges Ave North Vancouver B.C. .... TEL (604)925-1562

Normandin, Albert Photography
565 Shaw Ave Coquitlam B.C. .... TEL (604)461-0766

North Light Images Ltd
518 Beatty St #603 Vancouver B.C. .... TEL (604)684-6760

O'Brien-Bell, Catherine Photography
21 East 5th Ave Vancouver B.C. .... TEL (604)876-5483

Otte, Gary Photographers Ltd
21-1551 Johnston St Vancouver B.C. .... TEL (604)681-8421

Pacific Artists Studio
337 West Pender St Vancouver B.C. .... TEL (604)685-9932

Paris, Michael Photography
252 East 1st Ave Vancouver B.C. .... TEL (604)875-9401

Pedrero, Joaquin/Fotografica Studios
548 Cambie St #302 Vancouver B.C. .... TEL (604)685-0557

Pelling, Tim
355 West 17th Ave Vancouver B.C. .... TEL (604)872-8329

Pentact Group
73 Water St 3rd Fl Vancouver B.C. .... TEL (604)682-6565

Photex Studio Inc.
437 West Hastings St Vancouver B.C. .... TEL (604)687-4812

Poustka, Denis
1606 W 10th Ave Vancouver B.C. .... TEL (604)685-6874

Prism Colour Prints
970 Homer St Vancouver B.C. .... TEL (604)687-3593

Ramsey, Dale
14290-16th Ave White Rock B.C. .... TEL (604)536-1666

Rath, Leanna Photographics
Box 681 Whistler B.C. .... TEL (604)932-4264

Real Estate Board of Greater Vancouver
1101 West Broadway Vancouver B.C. .... TEL (604)736-4551

Redpath, Tony Photography
#340-440 West Hastings St Vancouver B.C. .... TEL (604)684-1380

Rich, Alice
810 West Broadway #178 Vancouver B.C. .... TEL (604)736-9664

Robertson Photography
560 Beatty St #202 Vancouver B.C. .... TEL (604)681-0011

Rogers, Jack Photography
Box 196 Port Coquitlam B.C. .... TEL (604)941-3491

Sanders, Dale Photography
4515 West 1st Ave Vancouver B.C. .... TEL (604)228-1280

Schallie, Gerald
P.O. Box 35247 Stn E Vancouver B.C. .... TEL (604)596-5864

Schulhof Photography
518 Beatty St #703 Vancouver B.C. .... TEL (604)683-4898

Scott, Robert J Productions
316 East 1st Ave Vancouver B.C. .... TEL (604)872-2766

Scott, Simon Associates
1627 W 2nd Ave Vancouver B.C. .... TEL (604)733-9797

Seguin, Denis/Fotoworks
102-160 West Hastings St Vancouver B.C. .... TEL (604)687-1153

Semeniuk, Robert Photography
P.O. Box 69327 Stn K Vancouver B.C. .... TEL (604)255-8336

Shackleton, Deborah Photographer
3290 Maple St Vancouver B.C. .... TEL (604)731-6754

Sheldan, M.D. Photography & Design
1304 Seymour St Vancouver B.C. .... TEL (604)684-1370

Sherlock, John Studio
225 Smithe St Vancouver B.C. .... TEL (604)683-2614

Sipma, Hans Photography
252 East 1st Ave Vancouver B.C. .... TEL (604)875-9401

Skotnicki, Roman M. Photographer
120 Columbia St North Vancouver B.C. .... TEL (604)683-6834

Smith, Brian Photography
Box 126 Whistler B.C. .... TEL (604)932-5131

Smith, Cynthia
1923 Parker St #202 Vancouver B.C. .... TEL (604)255-4101

Snape, Neil Photo
518 Beatty St #704 Vancouver B.C. .... TEL (604)683-4444

St. Arnaud, Ray Photography
Victoria B.C. .... TEL (604)595-2685

Steuart, David Photographer
402 W Pender St #211 Vancouver B.C. .... TEL (604)682-0011

Stevens, Naomi Photography
1627 W 2nd Ave Vancouver B.C. .... TEL (604)733-0211

Stockdale, Christopher B & Associates
200-1028 Hamilton St Vancouver B.C. .... TEL (604)685-2750

Storme Photography
397 West 5th Ave Vancouver B.C. .... TEL (604)877-1755

Sullivan, Carolyn Photography
5407 Killarney #1 Vancouver B.C. .... TEL (604)433-5113

Sutton, Lloyd Photography
1028 Hamilton St #200 Vancouver B.C. .... TEL (604)688-6993

Svensson Photographic Inc
1252 Burrard St #101 Vancouver B.C. .... TEL (604)685-8381

Tanner Photo
810 West Broadway #204 Vancouver B.C. .... TEL (604)667-1602

Tanner, Peter
3862 West 33rd Ave Vancouver B.C. .... TEL (604)667-1602

Timmermans, Peter
882 W 19th Ave Vancouver B.C. .... TEL (604)872-4941

Tregillas, Henry Photography Ltd
1111 Homer St Vancouver B.C. .... TEL (604)685-7278

Turnbull, Tom
3 - 630 E Broadway Vancouver B.C. .... TEL (604)939-4244

Vogt, Jurgen
936 East 28th Ave Vancouver B.C. .... TEL (604)876-5817

Walton, Dawn Photography
2055 York Ave #215 Vancouver B.C. .... TEL (604)733-0080

Ward, Stirling Photographic Design
1020 Hamilton St Vancouver B.C. .... TEL (604)687-3554

Warman, Margaret Rose
4533 Jerome Place North Vancouver B.C. .... TEL (604)987-7634

Waterhouse-Hayward, Alex
5909 Athlone St Vancouver B.C. .... TEL (604)669-6500

Weber Creative Group Ltd
1370 E Georgia Vancouver B.C. .... TEL (604)251-7450

Weddell, Jeff Photography
2729 West 13th Ave Vancouver B.C. .... TEL (604)943-5414

Weitzel, Jane Photography Ltd
402 West Pender St #211 Vancouver B.C. .... TEL (604)682-3000

Wildman Photography
106 West 1st St 3rd Fl North Vancouver B.C. .... TEL (604)988-2753

Wong, Kent Photography
5121 Crawford Pl Kamloops B.C. .... TEL (604)573-4593

Zavitz, Perry Photography
1885 Barclay St #407 Vancouver B.C. .... TEL (604)688-8775

Zenuk, Alan
P.O. Box 33896, Station D Vancouver B.C. .... TEL (604)733-8271

STOCK PHOTOGRAPHY

Canapress Photo Service
36 King St E 4th Fl Toronto Ontario .... TEL (416)364-0321

Creative Stock Agencies Inc
70 Scollard St #202 Toronto Ontario .... TEL (416)324-9800

First Light Associated Photographers
1 Atlantic Ave #204 Toronto Ontario .... TEL (416)532-6108

Focus Stock Photography Inc
950 Yonge St #409 Toronto Ontario .... TEL (416)968-6619

Image Bank Canada, The
40 Eglinton Ave E #307 Toronto Ontario .... TEL (416)322-8840

Image Finders Photo Agency Inc
134 Abbott St Vancouver B.C. .... TEL (604)688-9818

Mach 2 Stock Exchange, The
1409 Edmonton Trail NE #200 Calgary Alberta .... TEL (403)230-9363

Masterfile
415 Yonge St #200 Toronto Ontario .... TEL (416)977-7267

Miller/Comstock
180 Bloor St W #1102 Toronto Ontario .... TEL (416)925-4323

Mosiac Stock Photo Agency
836 Yonge St Toronto Ontario .... TEL (416)499-2936

Petkov, Marin Photographer
MPO Box 2431 Vancouver B.C. .... TEL (604)941-1190

Photo Artists Canada
620 Richmond St W #1 Toronto Ontario .... TEL (416)367-9770

Stock Market Inc, The
93 Parliament St #228 Toronto Ontario .... TEL (416)362-7767

Superstock - Four x Five
512 King St E #300 Toronto Ontario .... TEL (416)860-1518

Take Stock Inc
705,603-7th Ave SW Calgary Alberta .... TEL (403)233-7487

Valan Photos
490 Dulwich Ave St. Lambert Québec .... TEL (514)465-2557

Viewpoints West Photofile Ltd
1252 Burrard St #101 Vancouver B.C. .... TEL (604)685-8381

FILM/VIDEO/AV

Outlook Productions Ltd
1432 Erin St Winnipeg Manitoba .... TEL (204)774-0659

Winnipeg Audio-Visual Services
1432 Erin St Winnipeg Manitoba .... TEL (204)775-6662

Roska Photography
11235 Braniff Rd S W Calgary Alberta .... TEL (403)281-0232

Parklane (Video) Productions
10315 78 Ave Edmonton Alberta .... TEL (403)432-1174

Vicom Ltd
14713 116 Ave Edmonton Alberta .... TEL (403)452-4082

Video Pack Ltd
14805 119 Ave Edmonton Alberta .... TEL (403)451-4444

Alpha Cine Service
916 Davie St Vancouver B.C. .... TEL (604)688-7757

Avcom International
1401 Crown St North Vancouver B.C. .... TEL (604)986-1174

British Columbia Film Commission
770 Pacific Blvd S Vancouver B.C. .... TEL (604)660-2732

Changing Images Productions Ltd.
845 Cambie St # 800 Vancouver B.C. .... TEL (604)681-4391

Circle Productions Ltd.
1700 Cypress St Vancouver B.C. .... TEL (604)733-5727

Coast Cine Centre
1219 Richards St Vancouver B.C. .... TEL (604)689-8018

Corporate Concepts
808 West Hastings St #500 Vancouver B.C. .... TEL (604)685-6201

Creative House
1152 Mainland St #400 Vancouver B.C. .... TEL (604)688-5696

Gastown Poste & Transfer
50 West 2nd Ave Vancouver B.C. .... TEL (604)685-8143

Gilbert, John Martin
4797 Highway West Vancouver B.C. .... TEL (604)925-1049

Labour Market Services
P.O. Box 11145 W Georgia Vancouver B.C. .... TEL (604)666-8221

Motion Picture Association
207 West Hastings St #1101 Vancouver B.C. .... TEL (604)684-4712

Northwest Communications Ltd
839 Cambie St #201 Vancouver B.C. .... TEL (604)688-3444

Pacific Artists Studio
337 W Pender St Vancouver B.C. .... TEL (604)685-9932

Pentact Group
73 Water St 3rd Fl Vancouver B.C. .... TEL (604)682-6565

Poco Productions
#60 1507 W 12th Ave Vancouver B.C. .... TEL (604)736-7626

Polaris Entertainment
134 Abbott St 6th Fl Vancouver B.C. .... TEL (604)688-9561

Post-Haste Video
1177 W 8th Ave Vancouver B.C. .... TEL (604)734-7727

Producers' Workshop
1152 Mainland St #400 Vancouver B.C. .... TEL (604)681-9588

Q.E.D. Communications Ltd.
1249 Howe St Vancouver B.C. .... TEL (604)688-1257

Shane Lunny Productions Inc.
560 Beatty St #305 Vancouver B.C. .... TEL (604)669-0333

Stronco Audio Visual
960 Howe Vancouver B.C. .... TEL (604)685-7723

Target Canada Productions
1710 West 2nd Ave Vancouver B.C. .... TEL (604)734-9122

Tourmaline Entertainment
MPO Box 3641 Vancouver B.C. .... TEL (604)683-5079

Triad Communications Ltd
2751 Oxford St Vancouver B.C. .... TEL (604)253-3990

Vancouver Cinecom Associates Ltd
1227 Richards St Vancouver B.C. .... TEL (604)683-2351

Vicom Ltd
1309 W Pender St Vancouver B.C. .... TEL (604)662-8298

Vidatron Communicaitons Inc.
100-1020 Mainland St Vancouver B.C. .... TEL (604)681-9308

Western Professional Film Laboratories Ltd
1325 Boundary Rd Vancouver B.C. .... TEL (604)299-1439

Yale Town Productions Inc
304-990 Homer St Vancouver B.C. .... TEL (604)669-3543

PHOTO/VIDEO EQUIPMENT & SUPPLIES — EDMONTON

Janna Agencies
7508-82 Avenue Edmonton Alberta .... TEL (403)465-4104

McBain Camera Ltd
10805 107 Ave Edmonton Alberta .... TEL (403)420-0404

Precision Camera Service Ltd
7625 99 St Edmonton Alberta .... TEL (403)439-1638

PHOTO/VIDEO EQUIPMENT & SUPPLIES — VANCOUVER

Commercial Electronics Ltd
1335 Burrard St Vancouver B.C. .... TEL (604)669-5525

Norlynn AV Services
Box 86548 North Vancouver B.C. .... TEL (604)988-3441

Wharton, Ecliffe
Box 972 26153-72nd Ave Aldergrove B.C. .... TEL (604)530-5275

PHOTO LABORATORIES — EDMONTON

Carousel Photographics Ltd
10525 Jasper Ave Edmonton Alberta .... TEL (403)424-7161

Middle Earth Gallery Ltd
10107 89 St Edmonton Alberta .... TEL (403)421-9239

Northwest Color Laboratories Ltd
10245 95th St Edmonton Alberta .... TEL (403)422-6163

PHOTO LABORATORIES — CALGARY

Riley's Reproductions
621-8 Ave SW Calgary Alberta .... TEL (403)266-6051

PHOTO LABORATORIES — VANCOUVER

Abbot & Tincombe Photo Services Ltd
2028 W 4th Ave Vancouver B.C. .... TEL (604)736-0171

ABC Photocolour Products Ltd
1618 West 4th Ave Vancouver B.C. .... TEL (604)736-7017

Action Film Services Ltd
537 Georgia St Vancouver B.C. .... TEL (416)687-2528

Ampro Photo Workshops Ltd
636 E Broadway Vancouver B.C. .... TEL (604)876-5501

Colorific
195 West 7th Ave Vancouver B.C. .... TEL (604)879-1511

Commercial Illustrators
910 Beach Ave Vancouver B.C. .... TEL (604)684-8467

G. King Photo-Colour Ltd
472 W 15th Ave Vancouver B.C. .... TEL (604)873-9329

Key Colour Photo Lab Ltd
117 E 2nd Ave Vancouver B.C. .... TEL (604)873-4023

Prism Colour Prints
920 Homer St Vancouver B.C. .... TEL (604)687-3593

Professional Colour Prints Ltd
1760 W 2nd Ave Vancouver B.C. .... TEL (604)731-6311

Quad Colour
61 West 7th Avenue Vancouver B.C. .... TEL (604)872-5958

Smith Photo Prints
1251a Homer St Vancouver B.C. .... TEL (604)688-5667

Spectra Colour Services Ltd
1620 W 5th Ave Vancouver B.C. .... TEL (604)738-6112

Spotty Dog Photo Lab
1066 Seymour St Vancouver B.C. .... TEL (604)685-4815

Tricolor Prolab (1979) Ltd
1100 Lansdowne St #J Coquitlam B.C. .... TEL (604)464-3035

Western Professional Film Lab
1325 Boundary Rd Vancouver B.C. .... TEL (604)299-1439

ILLUSTRATORS — WINNIPEG

Alan Pakarnyk
225 Symington Rd Winnipeg Manitoba .... TEL (204)222-6153

Cal Harrison
551 Neil Ave Winnipeg Manitoba .... TEL (204)669-1881

Cause & Effect Communication Arts
1254 Lorette Ave, 2nd Fl Winnipeg Manitoba .... TEL (204)452-9010

Flatland Productions
103 Helmsdale Ave. Winnipeg Manitoba .... TEL (204)667-3170

Hawthorne/Revere Marketing
415 Seven Oaks Ave Winnipeg Manitoba .... TEL (204)586-2284

Lilac Studio Illustration & Design
61 Gertie St, 2nd Fl Winnipeg Manitoba .... TEL (204)943-2210

Lori Robson
1254 Lorette Ave, Main Fl Winnipeg Manitoba .... TEL (204)475-9694

Mullin Design & Illustration
52-221 McDermot Ave Winnipeg Manitoba .... TEL (204)943-9932

Pastucha, Ron
336 McMeans Ave W Winnipeg Manitoba .... TEL (204)222-3178

Quilliams, David Advertising
449 Campbell St Winnipeg Manitoba .... TEL (204)488-3632

Stampnick, Ken
11 Presidents Crt Winnipeg Manitoba .... TEL (204)224-2464

Tek-Nikl Illustration
99 Roslyn Rd #5C Winnipeg Manitoba .... TEL (204)475-1358

Tim Van Gorp
17 Berkshire Bay Winnipeg Manitoba .... TEL (204)233-9500

Tutura, John
395 River Ave #19 Winnipeg Manitoba .... TEL (204)475-6053

W.B Johnston Art & Illustration
572 Mountain Ave Winnipeg Manitoba .... TEL (204)582-1686

ILLUSTRATORS — EDMONTON

Blommaert, Gerard
8765-51st Ave 2nd Fl Edmonton Alberta .... TEL (403)468-7240

Bookends Designworks West
6408 35 Ave Edmonton Alberta .... TEL (403)463-7364

Burkholder, Richard
4834 106th St Edmonton Alberta .... TEL (403)434-0732

Busby, Verne
10350 122 St #1602 Edmonton Alberta .... TEL (403)488-8226

Chen, Shih-Chien
2839 35 St Edmonton Alberta .... TEL (403)462-8617

Chez, Mark/Firehouse Graphics
10010-107a Ave Edmonton Alberta .... TEL (403)493-8153

Cook, Payne & Associates Inc
1600 Royal LePage Bldg Edmonton Alberta .... TEL (403)429-9911

GB Campbell & Associates
6527 111 St Edmonton Alberta .... TEL (403)435-8356

Gerard Graphics Ltd
8765 51st Ave 2nd Fl Edmonton Alberta .... TEL (403)468-7240

Hallis-Graphics Ltd
17352 107 Ave Edmonton Alberta .... TEL (403)484-5538

Hines, Kathryn
9828 87th Ave Edmonton Alberta .... TEL (403)439-4076

Kobylka, Keith
3532 105A St Edmonton Alberta .... TEL (403)436-5778

Michaelchuck, Rod
11331 99 Ave Edmonton Alberta .... TEL (403)488-3009

Myhre, Don
7000 113 St Edmonton Alberta .... TEL (403)432-0267

Ponech, Dave
101158 103 St Edmonton Alberta .... TEL (403)427-2031

Richards, Bill
1105-10140 113 St Edmonton Alberta .... TEL (403)423-1035

Saxby Payne & Cook Inc
10130 103rd St #1600 Edmonton Alberta .... TEL (403)429-9911

Thumbprint
17303 106a Ave Edmonton Alberta .... TEL (403)483-1214

ILLUSTRATORS — CALGARY

Bersea, Dianne
2013-1st Ave NW Calgary Alberta .... TEL (403)283-5740

Dabrowska, Alina
822-3130 66 Ave SW Calgary Alberta .... TEL (403)249-7008

DaSilva/Bill Ross
239-10 Ave SE #300 Calgary Alberta .... TEL (403)269-8575

DaSilva/Jan Sovak
239-10 Ave SE #300 Calgary Alberta .... TEL (403)269-8575

DaSilva/Jonathon Bowser
239-10 Ave SE #300 Calgary Alberta .... TEL (403)269-8575

DaSilva/Ron Hawker
239-10 Ave SE #300 Calgary Alberta .... TEL (403)269-8575

DaSilva/Ron Leishman
239-10 Ave SE #300 Calgary Alberta .... TEL (403)269-8575

Dotto, Gerry
32 Groveland Rd Sherwood Park Alberta .... TEL (403)467-8527

Gherkin Studios
805-8th Ave SW #905 Calgary Alberta .... TEL (403)263-4193

KARO/Elaine Prodor
926-5th Ave #500 Calgary Alberta .... TEL (403)266-4094

KARO/Michael Dangelmaier
926-5th Ave #500 Calgary Alberta .... TEL (403)266-4094

LaFontaine, Max
RR#1 Site 2 Box 19 Millarville Alberta .... TEL (403)931-3393

Lee, Hock-Tiam
522-10 Ave NE Calgary Alberta .... TEL (403)277-4204

Lisowski, Lornce
144-4th Ave #540 Calgary Alberta .... TEL (403)265-2020

Lydiatt, Geoff
PO Box 975 Canmore Alberta .... TEL (403)678-6290

Ong-Lee, Hui-Cheng
#304, 639-14th Ave SW Calgary Alberta .... TEL (403)245-5200

Ross, Bill
11005 Sacramento Dr SW Calgary Alberta .... TEL (403)255-6483

Sleeca Creative Inc
240-11th Ave SW #588 Calgary Alberta .... TEL (403)245-3822

Smith, Gail & Associates
1842-14 St S W Calgary Alberta .... TEL (403)245-4761

Sovak, Jan Illustration
1440 Acadia Dr SE Calgary Alberta .... TEL (403)269-8575

Storeshaw, Robert Illustration
PO Box 2989 Stn M Calgary Alberta .... TEL (403)292-4547

Van Ginkel, Paul
40 Edgemont Estates Rd NW Calgary Alberta .... TEL (403)241-0516

Watanabe, Roger
152 Castleridge Dr NE Calgary Alberta .... TEL (403)235-7520

Watermark Studios
#500, 1207-11th Ave SW Calgary Alberta .... TEL (403)228-7949

Woolgar, Susan
901-50 St E Edson Alberta .... TEL (403)723-3423

ILLUSTRATORS — VANCOUVER

Alex Studio Ltd
3-155 Water St Vancouver B.C. .... TEL (604)688-2221

Baillie, Alex
3530 Finch Pl Vancouver B.C. .... TEL (604)437-7318

Bantock, Nick Illustration
416 West Pender St #214 Vancouver B.C. .... TEL (604)731-8425

Bishop, Peter
1607 West 2nd Ave Vancouver B.C. .... TEL (604)734-8818

Burgess, Jeff Illustration
416 West Pender St #200 Vancouver B.C. .... TEL (604)731-8425

Caldwell, Heather
416 West Pender St #202 Vancouver B.C. .... TEL (604)685-9154

Chaplin, Carl/Great Pacific Northwest Art Co
1695 West 7th Ave Vancouver B.C. .... TEL (604)736-1399

Cleland-Kent Western Ltd.
2285 Clark Dr Vancouver B.C. .... TEL (604)877-1141

Crymble, Frank
2190 Bellview #304 West Vancouver B.C. .... TEL (604)922-4836

Dunne, Murray F.
442 Hadden Dr West Vancouver B.C. .... TEL (604)922-4892

Dwillies, Paul Ltd
217-811 Beach Ave Vancouver B.C. .... TEL (604)683-1728

Eisner, Ken
604 Yates St Victoria B.C. .... TEL (604)389-1244

Gilbert, John Martin
4797 Highway West Vancouver B.C. .... TEL (604)731-8425

Harron, Brent
334 West Cordova Vancouver B.C. .... TEL (604)689-1238

Heine, Mark David
1983 Whyte Ave Vancouver B.C. .... TEL (604)737-7615

Henrich, Soren Designs
1739 Haultain St Victoria B.C. .... TEL (604)370-2653

Karim, Yasmin
5401 Dominion St Burnaby B.C. .... TEL (604)298-0013

Kirkaldy, Evelyn Design & Illustration
973 E 29th Ave Vancouver B.C. .... TEL (604)875-0951

Kotter, Stefan Illustrator
310 - 1211 Cameron St New Westminster B.C. .... TEL (604)526-6169

Kraus, Deborah Illustration
31914 Royal Crescent Clearbrook B.C. .... TEL (604)854-1812

Lawrence, Liz Design Inc
555 West Hastings St #700 Vancouver B.C. .... TEL (604)681-4759

Leonard Rooney
702 - 518 Beatty St Burnaby B.C. .... TEL (604)684-9525

Logomotive Graphics
11642 - 82nd Ave Delta B.C. .... TEL (604)591-1437

Lynch, Brent Graphics Inc
870 West 7th Ave #64 Vancouver B.C. .... TEL (604)875-1917

Masterscript Illustrators
PO Box 2063 New Westminster B.C. .... TEL (604)522-3899

Milne, Jonathan/Papersculptureworks
1102 Homer St #206 Vancouver B.C. .... TEL (604)684-7184

Montoliu, Raphael
8521 Timber Court Burnaby B.C. .... TEL (604)421-0632

Naiman, Linda & Associates Inc
8453 Duff St Vancouver B.C. .... TEL (604)327-1565

Newland, Marv
1168 Hamilton St #203 Vancouver B.C. .... TEL (604)681-2716

Nouwens, Arnold Graphic Arts
109 W 3rd Ave Vancouver B.C. .... TEL (604)876-3133

Pacfic Illustrations
202-1619 Store St Victoria B.C. .... TEL (604)386-2551

Pacific Artists Studios
337 West Pender St Vancouver B.C. .... TEL (604)685-9932

Phillips, Kelly
405 East 4th St North Vancouver B.C. .... TEL (604)689-5335

Photo/Graphics
1052 Homer St Vancouver B.C. .... TEL (604)984-9932

Poch, Jim Illustrator
420 West 22nd Ave Vancouver B.C. .... TEL (604)879-9062

Pon, Amy J. Illustration
823 Union St Vancouver B.C. .... TEL (604)254-4161

Price, Heather
1955 Wylie Ave Vancouver B.C. .... TEL (604)877-0446

Rep Art/Brent Lynch
2491 West 22nd Ave Vancouver B.C. .... TEL (604)731-8425

Rep Art/Heather Price
2491 West 22nd Ave Vancouver B.C. .... TEL (604)731-8425

Rep Art/Jeff Burgess
2491 West 22nd Ave Vancouver B.C. .... TEL (604)731-8425

Rep Art/Mark Heine
2491 West 22nd Ave Vancouver B.C. .... TEL (604)731-8425

Rep Art/Russ Willms
2491 West 22nd Ave Vancouver B.C. .... TEL (604)731-8425

Rimmer, Jim
1182 E Hastings St Vancouver B.C. .... TEL (604)731-8425

Silcock, Marlene
15109 Marine Dr White Rock B.C. .... TEL (604)531-0411

Solomon, Ivan Creative Thinker
101-1220 W 6th Ave Vancouver B.C. .... TEL (604)736-9796

Stockmann, William C.
1460 Barclay St #505 Vancouver B.C. .... TEL (604)682-2526

Thomsen, Ernie
Box 518 Gibsons B.C. .... TEL (604)731-8425

Total Graphics
1607 W 2nd Ave Vancouver B.C. .... TEL (604)734-8818

Turner, Patrick A. Illustration
1050 Harwood St Vancouver B.C. .... TEL (604)688-4244

Tylman, Richard Illustration
303 - 1150 Jervis St Vancouver B.C. .... TEL (604)731-8425

Vanderleek, Kevin
14488-105A Ave Surrey B.C. .... TEL (604)584-6876

Watermarks
202 - 416 West Pender St Vancouver B.C. .... TEL (604)731-8425

Webber, Dave The Artist
23-415 W Cordova St Vancouver B.C. .... TEL (604)685-6027

Willms, Russ
2099 - 126 St White Rock B.C. .... TEL (604)731-8425

Williams, Pamela/Anodos Studios
RR #1 Pender Island B.C. .... TEL (604)629-6705

Zenith Graphics Ltd
898 Richards St Vancouver B.C. .... TEL (604)682-4521

GRAPHISTES/DESIGNERS

Anchor Advertising
5512 Chemin St-François, St-Laurent, Québec .... TEL (514) 333-0093

Angers, Claude
10 rue Ontario o. #506, Montréal, Québec .... TEL (514) 843-3219

Ara No'va Design
239, rue Notre Dame o. 4e étage, Montréal .... TEL (514) 849-2375

Art Communication Design Inc
946 av. Victoria #1, St-Lambert, Québec .... TEL (514) 466-7247

Axion Design
1638c rue Sherbrooke o., Montréal, Québec .... TEL (514) 935-5409

Bèlanger, Legault Designers Ltèe
360, rue Notre Dame o. #400, Montréal, Québec .... TEL (514) 284-2323

Banz'ai Communications Inc
6300 av. de Parc, Montréal, Québec .... TEL (514) 277-5339

Beauchamp, Bernard
6510, 38e av. #5, Montréal, Québec .... TEL (514) 729-4526

Beaudry, Bernard
78, rue Breton St-Constant, C.P. 1388, Québec .... TEL (514) 638-2922

Beaulieu, Gilles Graphiste
6757, 12e av., Montréal, Québec .... TEL (514) 374-9761

Belier Communications
113 Côte de la Montagne, Québec, Québec .... TEL (418) 692-0011

Bellemare Rivard et Associés
430 rue Ste-Hélène #602, Montréal, Québec .... TEL (514) 849-6566

BGMS Design Inc
317, Place d'Youville, Montréal, Québec .... TEL (514) 288-4233

Blais, Claude
1364, rue Laurier est, Montréal, Québec .... TEL (514) 527-7597

Bleau, Duperrey, Giguère et Associés
35 Grande Allèe est, Québec, Québec .... TEL (418) 529-9361

Bleu Réflex
334, Terrasse St-Denis #503, Montréal, Québec .... TEL (514) 845-3005

BOS
3575, boul. St-Laurent #905, Montréal, Québec .... TEL (514) 848-0019

Bochud, Gérard
820, rue Ste-Hélène, Longueuil, Québec .... TEL (514) 679-0956

Boissoneault, Gagné Inc
253, rue St-Paul #203, Québec, Québec .... TEL (418) 692-2006

Bonneville, Paul et Associés
1030, rue St-Alexandre #410, Montréal, Québec .... TEL (514) 875-7188

Bossardt Design Ltée
52 Le Royer o., Vieux-Montréal, Québec .... TEL (514) 849-3776

Boum Graphique, Le
643 Notre Dame #202, Montréal, Québec .... TEL (514) 861-3448

Bourassa, Jacques Design Inc.
415, rue St-Gabriel #101, Montréal, Québec .... TEL (514) 861-1965

Bouvry, Bienvenu, Castonguay et Associés
360, rue St-François-Xavier #301, Montréal, Québec .... TEL (514) 282-9767

Brault et Bélair et Associés
51 St-Paul o., Montréal, Québec .... TEL (514) 287-7126

Braunova — Désmarteau, Aléna
6, rue Désmarteau, Boucherville, Québec .... TEL (514) 641-2354

Brouard, Francyne
1149, Marie Gaudard, Cap Rouge, Québec .... TEL (418) 658-8973

Brousseau, Pierre
247, rue de la Flore, Saint-Nicholas, Québec .... TEL (418) 835-4012

Bujold, Claudine
211, av. Stanstead, Ville Mont-Royal, Québec .... TEL (514) 342-1240

CABD Design/Claude Alex Beïque
45 Butternut, Aylmer, Québec .... TEL (819) 684-0953

Cabana Séguin Design Inc.
1420, rue Sherbrooke o. #600, Montréal, Québec .... TEL (514) 285-1311

Catalpa Design Inc./Langeder, Helmut
1260, rue University #103, Montréal, Québec .... TEL (514) 866-7484

Ceccon, Vasco
45, rue McNider, Outremont, Québec .... TEL (514) 277-5552

Centre Créatif de Montréal/Montreal Creative Centre
407, rue Dowd, Montréal, Québec .... TEL (514) 861-6323

Centre International de Design
85, rue St-Paul o., Montréal, Québec .... TEL (514) 842-4545

Chagnon, Marie-Josée
4316 St-Laurent #400, Montréal, Québec .... TEL (514) 842-5873

Charette, Jacques & Associates Ltd.
77, rue Laurier, Hull, Québec .... TEL (819) 771-0441

Charney, Israel
4354, rue de Bullion, Montréal, Québec .... TEL (514)842-6922

Charpentier, Garneau Communications Inc
275, rue St-Jacques #600, Montréal, Québec .... TEL (514) 848-9770

Charron Concepte
2360 av. de Lasalle #207, Montréal, Québec .... TEL (514) 254-7227

Christensen, Louise
1179 rue Jodin, Verdun, Québec .... TEL (514) 768-3879

CNEDG
19 rue Le Royer o.HH. Québec .... TEL (514) 499-0844

Communication Untel et Untel Inc
404 rue Ontario est, Montréal, Québec .... TEL (514) 845-6425

Communications Bleu Blanc Rouge
417, St-Nicolas #500, Montréal, Québec .... TEL (514) 288-7000

Communications DG4
738 av. Marin, Montréal, Québec .... TEL (514) 933-2420

Communications Soleil
4360, rue Iberville, Montréal, Québec .... TEL (514) 523-2163

Concept Visuel Voyant Inc
1589 Chemin St-Louis, Sillery, Québec .... TEL (418) 681-9622

Cossette, Claude
4070, rue Pierre-Gallet, Cap-Rouge, Québec .... TEL (418) 656-7285

Coulombe, Latreille & Assoc.
409, rue St. Nicolas #200, Montréal, Québec .... TEL (514) 845-5261

Coutu, André
1434, rue Ste-Catherine o. #415, Montréal, Québec .... TEL (514)866-4475

Couture, Guylaine
4860, Edouard Montpetit #16, Montréal, Québec .... TEL (514)735-7145

Couture, Tremblay Graphisme et Comm.
515 chemin Ste-Foy, Québec, Québec .... TEL (418) 681-7368

Créations Image Publicitaire
1130, rue Sherbrooke o. #1500, Montréal, Québec .... TEL (514) 842-7873

Crayon Design
415, rue Le Moyne #402, Vieux-Montréal, Québec .... TEL (514) 842-5938

Dallaire et Giguère Inc
70, rue de la Barre #118, Montréal, Québec .... TEL (514) 442-2702

Derôme Design
414, rue McGill #203, Montréal, Québec .... TEL (514) 398-0683

Design & Communications
4465, rue Sherbrooke o., Montréal, Québec .... TEL (514) 932-1428

Design Communications
533, rue Cherbourg #201, Longueuil, Québec .... TEL (516) 679-0240

Desjardins, Hubert et Associés
1222 rue Mackay #300, Montréal, Québec .... TEL (514) 934-4762

Desjarts Inc
2374 Bord du Lac, Ile Bizard, Québec .... TEL (514) 696-7532

Desnoyers, Michel
43, rue Labelle, L'Assomption, Québec .... TEL (514) 654-3705

Devost, Robert Design
565, de L'Argentière #10, Montréal, Québec .... TEL (514) 322-0303

Di Liello, Fernanda
6995 Gouin est, #1006, Montréal, Québec .... TEL (514) 326-3578

Dialogue-Communications
270, Chemin Ste-Foy, Québec, Québec .... TEL (418) 647-1114

Drab, Carole Conception Visuelle
7657 rue Drolet, Montréal, Québec .... TEL (514) 277-4961

Droscha, Karin
3555, av. Atwater #308, Montréal, Québec .... TEL (514) 935-5670

Duchesne, Odette
100, av. des Commandeurs, Lévis, Québec .... TEL (418) 835-4013

Dufour, Martin
2359, Duvernay #100, Montréal, Québec .... TEL (514) 939-2137

Dumont Gratton
477, St-François-Xavier #409, Montréal, Québec .... TEL (514) 842-8006

Etcovitch, Barbara
800 Pl. Victoria, Montréal, Québec .... TEL (514) 934-2311

Filion, Michel
1188, rue Sherbrooke o., Montréal, Québec .... TEL (514) 848-8130

Fleury, Pierre
417, rue St-Pierre #57, Montréal, Québec .... TEL (514) 844-6431

Folio Garetti
187, Ste-Catherine est, Montréal, Québec .... TEL (514) 844-6194

Forget, Claude
CP 6128, Succ. A, Montréal, Québec .... TEL (514) 343-7704

Fortier-Blouin, Francine
470 Meilleur, Sherbrooke, Québec .... TEL (819) 566-5340

Frenette, Denis
25 de Vaudreuil, Blainville, Québec .... TEL (514) 437-4028

Gad Shaanan Design Inc
2455 Chemin Manella #390, Ville Mount Royal, Québec ...... TEL (514) 735-9550

Gagnon Design
5126, av. du Parc #103, Montréal, Québec .... TEL (514) 273-9330

Galéa, Pierre
3724, av. Laval, Montréal, Québec .... TEL (514) 842-9363

Gauthier Designers
356, rue Le Moyne, Vieux-Montréal, Québec .... TEL (514) 844-1159

Gauthier, Pierre
7010, boul. des Villes Iles, St-François, Laval, Québec ...... TEL (514) 666-1781

Goodhue Design Communications
474, rue McGill, Vieux-Montréal, Québec .... TEL (514) 866-7811

Gottschalk + Ash International
2050, rue Mansfield #900, Montréal, Québec .... TEL (514) 844-1995

Graetz, Andrew
1501, rue Barré, Montréal, Québec .... TEL (514) 989-9551

Grapevine Communications Inc
1851 Ste-Catherine o. #200, Montréal, Québec .... TEL (514) 939-6411

Graphème Communication-Design
1558 av. Docteur Penfield, Montréal, Québec .... TEL (514) 932-2617

Graphisme Lavalin
1100 boul. René Levesque o., Montréal, Québec .... TEL (514) 876-4455

Grauerholz, Angela
5662 Clarke, Montréal, Québec .... TEL (514) 270-3107

Gravel, Marie-Josée
426 Victoria #303, St-Laurent, Québec .... TEL (514) 466-8859

Grenier, Denis
16, rue Metcalfe, Sherbrooke, Québec .... TEL (819) 566-5340

Groupe Everest
81 rue Sherbrooke o., Montréal, Québec .... TEL (514) 842-1433

GSM Design Inc./Marquart, Laurent
317, Place d'Youville, Montréal, Québec .... TEL (514) 288-4233

Gutman, Jack & Associés Inc.
760, rue St-Paul o. #2, Montréal, Québec .... TEL (514) 875-7535

Hébert, Catherine
53 Duke #230, Montréal, Québec .... TEL (514) 874-1589

Hablutzel & Yung Inc
2159, rue MacKay #300, Montréal, Québec .... TEL (514) 288-4318

Hackett Boyer
5356 boul. St-Laurent, Montréal, Québec .... TEL (514) 272-6131

Harder, Rolf & Associés Inc.
1638c rue Sherbrooke o., Montréal, Québec .... TEL (514) 939-4018

High-Touch Communications
4480, Côte de Liesse #200, Montréal, Québec .... TEL (514) 739-2461

HJKM Design et Communication
430, rue McGill 3e étage, Montréal, Québec .... TEL (514) 393-9797

Huel, Georges & Associés Inc.
65, rue Sherbrooke est #206, Montréal, Québec .... TEL (514) 843-4953

Idéart Inc.
1525, rue Sherbrooke o. 3e étage, Montréal, Québec .... TEL (514) 933-9291

Illustration Design Short & Sweet
4420, Levesque est #209, Laval, Québec .... TEL (514) 664-3348

Images, Revues et Corrigés
4247, rue St Dominique 3e étage, Montréal, Québec ...... TEL (514) 982-6022

Jacobs, Adrian
4657, av. Melrose, Montréal, Québec .... TEL (514) 484-5463

Jalbert, Daniel/Jars Design
10 rue Ontario o. #903, Montréal, Québec .... TEL (514) 844-0530

Jensen, Carmen
3439, av. Oxford, Montréal, Québec .... TEL (514) 481-7143

JKJ/Studio Jasmin Keeman Jameison Inc.
1410, rue Guy #20, Montréal, Québec .... TEL (514) 937-2865

JLM Design
3906, rue Clark, Montréal, Québec .... TEL (514) 843-5055

Kelly Lavoie Design
244 Saint-Jacques o. #700, Montréal, Québec .... TEL (514) 286-9025

Knecht, Marcel et Associés Inc
360 St-Jacques o. #1910, Montréal, Québec .... TEL (514) 842-1131

L'Allier, Denis
2351 Duvernay #200, Montréal, Québec .... TEL (514) 937-4585

L'Heureux, Hélène, Gottschalk + Ash
2050, rue Mansfield #900, Montréal, Québec .... TEL (514) 844-1995

Léger, Francine
45, rue McNider, Outremont, Québec .... TEL (514) 277-5552

Il y a des signes
qui ne trompent pas

Ne laissez pas

le hasard guider

votre choix

d'un graphiste.

Être membre

de la SGQ,

c'est un signe

de professionnalisme.

**Société
des Graphistes
du Québec inc.**

Pour recevoir un exemplaire du répertoire de nos membres: 514.397.0537.

THE BEST OF GRAPHIC DESIGN FOR THE BEST IN GRAPHIC DESIGN

NATIONAL COUNCIL OF GRAPHIC DESIGN FIRMS

■ ARA NO'VO DESIGN ■ AXION DESIGN INC. ■ BLEAU, DUPERREY, GIGUERE & ASSOCIÉS INC. ■ BOSSARDT DESIGN LTÉE ■ BOUVRY BIENVENU CASTONGUAY ET ASSOCIÉS INC. ■ CABANA, SÉGUIN DESIGN INC. ■ CHARPENTIER GARNEAU INC. COMMUNICATIONS ■ COUTURE TREMBLAY GRAPHISME ET COMMUNICATION ■ CRAYON DESIGN ET COMMUNICATION ■ GOODHUE DESIGN COMMUNICATION INC. ■ GOTTSCHALK + ASH INTERNATIONAL ■ GRAPHEME COMMUNICATION-DESIGN ■ GSM DESIGN ■ LAJEUNESSE & ASSOCIÉS PUBLICITÉ INC. ■ MARKETEL PUBLIM INC. ■ MATTEAU PARENT ■ NOLIN LAROSÉE DESIGN COMMUNICATIONS INC. ■ PARALLELE DESIGN INC. ■ SOCIÉTÉ DE COMMUNICATIONS GRAPHIQUES SOCOM INC. ■ STUDIO BI INC. ■ VASCO DESIGN INTERNATIONAL INC. ■ VERGE LEBEL COMMUNICATIONS INC.

NATIONAL COUNCIL OF GRAPHIC DESIGN FIRMS

La Societe des Graphistes du Québec Inc
Place Bonaventure, CP 1122, Montréal, Québec .... TEL (514)397-0537

Lafaille, Denis
5578 Hadley, Montréal, Québec .... TEL (514) 768-2369

Lajeunesse et Associés
1440, rue Ste-Catherine o. #200, Montréal, Québec ...... TEL (514) 393-8223

Lalonde Pedriks Budd Design
1254, rue Mackay 2e étage, Montréal, Québec .... TEL (514) 939-1582

Lammarre, Christiane Graphisme
1258, rue Rabelais, Repentigny, Québec .... TEL (514) 654-9186

Langevin, Turcotte Inc.
28 rue St-Paul est #53, Montréal, Québec .... TEL (514) 875-1012

Lascaux Communications Graphiques
1121, rue Ste-Catherine o. #502, Montréal, Québec .... TEL (514) 982-6991

Le Groupe DKY
440, rue St-Pierre, Montréal, Québec .... TEL (514) 499-1133

Le groupe Hugron et Associés Inc
3556 boul. St-Laurent #200, Montréal, Québec .... TEL (514) 849-4133

Le Mot Dessiné
5890, av. Monkland #401, Montréal, Québec .... TEL (514) 485-1800

Lebel, Guy
1039, av. des érables, Québec, Québec .... TEL (418) 529-0158

Leclair, Jean
7811 boul. Louis-H Lafontaine #204, Ville d'Anjou, Québec ... TEL (514)355-1813

Legault, Diane
75, boul. Dorchester o., Montréal, Québec .... TEL (514) 289-3061

Legoupil Communication
424, rue Guy #200, Montréal, Québec .... TEL (514) 939-3379

Lemieux, Jean-René
1, cité Bellevue #509, Québec, Québec .... TEL (418) 527-6740

Lennox-Riopel, Anne-Marie
440, av. Merton, St-Lambert, Québec .... TEL (514) 671-4880

Les Communications Ovation
1525, rue Sherbrooke o. #300, Montréal, Québec .... TEL (514) 937-7509

Les Entreprises Jacrel Ltée
294, boul. Desmarchais, Verdun, Québec .... TEL (514) 766-2714

Les Studios Graphidée
28, rue St-Paul est #52, Montréal, Québec .... TEL (514) 875-2075

Lugo Design
6550, rue Cartier #2, Montréal, Québec .... TEL (514) 467-0856

Lumbago
2116 Gauthier, Montréal, Québec .... TEL (514) 521-3992

Lymburger - Associés
6955, boul. St-Michel #100, Montréal, Québec .... TEL (514) 376-0481

Meloche, Robert
1255, carré Phillips #777, Montréal, Québec .... TEL (514) 878-1001

Major, Michel
417, St-Pierre #701, Montréal, Québec .... TEL (514) 842-3052

Mallet, Michel
30, rue Louise #1, Longueuil, Québec .... TEL (514) 448-1215

Mallette, Richard Concepteur Inc.
118, rue de Port, Montréal, Québec .... TEL (514) 844-3263

Marchand, Jacques/Tactique Design
336, rue Lafontaine, Rivières du Loup, Québec .... TEL (418) 867-3640

Marketel Publim
871 Chemin St-Louis, Québec, Québec .... TEL (418) 683-4931

Marlowe Communications Inc.
4626 rue Ste-Catherine o., Westmount, Québec .... TEL (514) 935-4462

Matteau Parent
1390, Ch Ste-Foy, Ste-Foy, Québec .... TEL (418) 682-0925

Metz, Frédéric
Universite du Montréal, CP 8888-Succ A, Montréal, Qué. .. TEL (514) 987-3921

Michaud, Suzanne Design
222 Cours Dominion #30, Montréal, Québec .... TEL (514) 939-0537

Millet, Jean
1199, rue Bleury 11e étage, Montréal, Québec .... TEL (514) 873-7545

Mongeau, Alain
344, rue Gilford, Montréal, Québec .... TEL (514) 987-4193

Mongeau, Bacon, Chen & Associés Inc
320, Notre Dame est, Montréal, Québec .... TEL (514) 397-0755

Mounier, Florent
2120 rue Sherbrooke est #605, Montréal, Québec .... TEL (514) 522-1254

Nolin, Larosée et Associés Inc.
1176, rue Bishop #300, Montréal, Québec .... TEL (514) 861-1331

Pépin, Pierre Designer
752, rue Nérée Trembly #4, Ste-Foy, Québec .... TEL (418) 656-1544

Paprocki & Associés Inc.
2157, L.O. David, Montréal, Québec .... TEL (514) 593-5598

Parallel Design
2750 Ch Ste-Foy #229, Ste-Foy, Québec .... TEL (418) 657-6702

Parent, Luc Designer
3988-A Berri, Montréal, Québec .... TEL (514) 499-0786

Phaneuf, Michel
90, rue Ste-Anne #205, Ste-Anne-de-Bellevue, Québec .... TEL (514) 457-3452

Pigeon, Thomas Design Group, The
1000, rue Wellington, Montréal, Québec .... TEL (514) 875-6844

Pilotte, Normand
10728, boul. Olympia, Montréal, Québec .... TEL (514) 388-5260

PinArts Graphiques
1750, rue Desjardins, Drummondville, Québec .... TEL (819) 478-7185

Primeau Dupras Communication Graphique
3575, boul. St-Laurent #501, Montréal, Québec .... TEL (514) 987-1399

Prisma Graphique
222 rue Dominion #40, Montréal, Québec .... TEL (514) 933-9957

Proulx, Gaetan
334, Terasse St-Denis #503, Montréal, Québec .... TEL (514) 845-3005

Rabagliati, Michel
3575, boul. St-Laurent #533, Montréal, Québec .... TEL (514) 284-0161

Rabbat, Ramez Visual Communications Inc
355, rue Guy, 2e étage, Montréal, Québec .... TEL (514) 933-5200

Robert, Gilles et Associés Design
353, St-Nicolas #105, Montréal, Québec .... TEL (514) 845-6830

Roch, Ernst
C.P. 1056, Succ. B, Montréal, Québec .... TEL (514) 933-5950

Rosenbaum, Paul
4093, av. de l'Esplanade, Montréal, Québec .... TEL (514) 845-1075

Roy Design
87 McCulloch, Montréal, Québec .... TEL (514) 495-4717

Roy, André
C.P. 6600, Québec, Québec .... TEL (418) 682-5154

Rudophi, Paola Design
CP 66, Westmount, Québec .... TEL (514) 937-8788

Savard, Francine
417, rue St-Pierre #57, Montréal, Québec .... TEL (514) 844-6431

Schell, Wolf Design & Assoc. Inc.
1220, MacKay, Montréal, Québec .... TEL (514) 935-7098

Signis
305, rue de l'Hôtel de Ville, Chicoutimi, Québec .... TEL (418) 545-0488

Simard Communications Marketing
144c av. Principale, Rouyn, Québec .... TEL (819) 797-0537

Simard, Hamel Communications Ltée
474, rue St-Alexis, Montréal, Québec .... TEL (514) 287-9811

Simard, Yves Design Inc
378, Laurier, Granby, Québec .... TEL (514) 287-9219

Slachta, Paul
350 LeMoyne, Montréal, Québec .... TEL (514) 849-0260

SOCOM
222, rue Dominion #30, Montréal, Québec .... TEL (514) 939-0480

Standish Design
85, Belvedere North, Sherbrooke, Québec .... TEL (819) 822-0515

Stilus Design Inc
1435, rue Bleury #520, Montréal, Québec .... TEL (514) 842-7873

Studio 2 + 2 Inc.
376 av. Victoria #222, Westmount, Quebec .... TEL (514) 489-7211

Studio 70
1370, rue de Touraine, Ste-Julie, Québec .... TEL (514) 649-9395

Studio Ascension
81, rue Sherbrooke o., Montréal, Québec .... TEL (514) 842-8869

Studio BI Inc.
353, rue St-Nicolas #105, Montréal, Québec .... TEL (514) 845-1271

Studio Bograf
180, rue Ste-Catherine est 6 étage, Montréal, Québec .... TEL (514) 871-1424

Studio Catalpa Inc.
1260, rue Université #103, Montréal, Québec .... TEL (514) 866-7484

Studio Claude Raymond
7575, Rte. Transcanadienne, St-Laurent, Québec .... TEL (514) 745-3117

Studio de la Montagne Communication Visuelle Inc
2105 de la Montagne #300, Montréal, Québec .... TEL (514) 288-7414

Studio Graphème Inc.
455, av. Grande Allée est, Québec, Québec .... TEL (418) 647-2730

Studio La Klé
515, Chaline, St-Lazare, Québec .... TEL (514) 455-3300

Studio Olsson
1790, boul. Gouin est, Laval, Québec .... TEL (514) 382-8822

Studio St-Louis Inc.
2100, rue Guy #200, Montréal, Québec .... TEL (514) 989-5555

Studio Versatile Ltée
1041, rue Berri, Montréal, Québec .... TEL (514) 842-8908

Sutherland, David
1650, boul. de Maisonneuve o. #300, Montréal, Québec .... TEL (514) 931-2400

Tandem Design
415, Le Moyne #302, Montréal, Québec .... TEL (514) 284-3570

Tessier, Martin
10, 748 Brunet, Montréal, Québec .... TEL (514) 383-7812

TNT
4908 Sherbrooke o., Montréal, Québec .... TEL (514) 483-2744

Tracé Créative
4515, Clark #100, Montréal, Québec .... TEL (514) 844-2110

Trudeau, Dominic
4814, Henri-Julien, Montréal, Québec .... TEL (514) 437-4585

Verge, Lebel Guy & Associés
1039, av. des érables, Québec, Québec .... TEL (418) 529-0158

Visionnaires
1104 Greene Ave, Westmount, Québec .... TEL (514) 931-6133

Williams, Larry & Associates
350 LeMoyne, Montréal, Québec .... TEL (514) 849-0260

Zed Graphics Communications Inc
2110 Bonin, Montréal, Québec .... TEL (514) 331-2419

DESIGNERS INDUSTRIELS — INDUSTRIAL DESIGNERS

Archambault, Marc-Antoine
8743, rue René-Labelle, Montréal, Québec .... TEL (514) 383-1550

Armand, Francine
6360, rue Duquesne, Montréal, Québec .... TEL (514) 872-1464

Asselin, Michel Designers
3620, av. Laval, Montréal, Québec .... TEL (514) 499-1149

Aubé, Martin
1114, Pl. des Cormiers #3, Valcourt, Québec .... TEL (514) 532-2211

Barriault, Robert
575, Pl. Nicolet, St-Bruno, Québec .... TEL (514) 383-3747

Beauregard, Michel
2615, rue des Pintates, Ste-Rose, Laval, Québec .... TEL (514) 252-4970

Bernard Bertrand et Associés Inc
625, de Lasalle #370, Montréal, Québec .... TEL (514) 259-4510

Bernier, Denis
6150, av. du Boisé #B4, Montréal, Québec .... TEL (514) 277-6436

Blanchet, André
1027, rue d'Angoulême, Chicoutimi, Québec .... TEL (418) 545-1481

Bolduc, Bernard
84, Philippe Goulet, Repentigny, Québec .... TEL (514) 654-8203

Borri, Carlos
1505, Bois de Boulogne, Chicoutimi, Québec .... TEL (418) 696-0388

Boulva, Paul
221, rue Lockhart, Ville Mt-Royal, Québec .... TEL (514) 646-6377

Bourassa, Jean
181, rue Denison o. #402, Granby, Québec .... TEL (514) 772-2495

Breton, Pierre-André
3273, boul. Gouin Est #1, Montréal, Québec .... TEL (514) 931-8289

Brosseau, Jacques
1298, Chemin du Fleuve, St-Romuald, Québec .... TEL (418) 659-6600

Carpintero, Carlos Fernando
19, Le Royer #304, Montréal, Québec .... TEL (514) 842-9208

Casavant, Richard-Alain Designers
779, rue du Patrimoine RR 1, Prévost, Québec .... TEL (514) 224-4908

Casgrain, Manon
677, rue Reynolds, Granby, Québec .... TEL (514) 372-9910

Castilloux, Marc
423, rue Duvernay, Longueuil, Québec .... TEL (514) 463-1372

CDI Designers Inc
2014, boul. Charest o. #105, Ste-Foy, Québec .... TEL (418) 682-2273

Charlebois, Yves
8322, De Reims, Montréal, Québec .... TEL (514) 437-2555

Clic Design
6540, rue de Lanaudière, Montréal, Québec .... TEL (514) 273-8338

Cloutier, Maurice
3550, Jeanne-Mance #E3105, Montréal, Québec .... TEL (514) 284-2323

Continuum Design
1303, av. Greene #111, Westmount, Québec .... TEL (514) 939-2300

Coutu, Jacques
2231, rue Quesnel, Montréal, Québec .... TEL (514) 987-7757

Dallaire, Michel Designers
2151 A, rue de la Montagne, Montréal, Québec .... TEL (514) 282-9262

Daoust, Jacques
RR 3, Cowansville, Québec .... TEL (514) 263-5975

De Winter, Koen M. M.
534, Rockhill Cres, Beaconsfield, Québec .... TEL (514) 694-9111

Design Associates Inc
4180, av. Marlowe, Montréal, Québec .... TEL (514) 486-6325

Design et Communication
4465, rue Sherbrooke o., Montréal, Québec .... TEL (514) 932-1428

Designer Douglas Ball Inc
88, rue St-Anne, St-Anne-de-Bellevue, Québec .... TEL (514) 457-9861

Desrosiers, André Designers Ind
152 Brunswick, Pointe Claire, Québec .... TEL (514) 694-5573

Dubois, André et Associés Designers
1550, Docteur Penfield #1405, Montréal, Québec .... TEL (514) 935-9303

Dubuc, Alain
126, rue de Cadillac, Châteauguay, Québec .... TEL (514) 668-0710

Eberhard Von Huene & Associates
346, rue Aime Vincent, Vaudreuil, Québec .... TEL (514) 424-0186

Enta Designs Inc
1080 St-Mathieu #201, Montréal, Québec .... TEL (514) 932-9845

Expo Design International
2160, de la Province, Longueuil, Québec .... TEL (514) 442-4087

Favreau, Marcel Designers
226, Berlioz #405, Ile des Soeurs, Québec .... TEL (514) 263-1455

Finkel, Henry Industrial
PO Box 505, Westmount, Québec .... TEL (514) 935-7749

Floralium Design
100, boul. des Prairies #801A, Laval, Québec .... TEL (514) 629-4727

Fournier, Isabelle
8615, rue Lucien Plante, Montréal, Québec .... TEL (514) 254-5521

Foy, Jérôme
4590, boul. Pie IX #9, Montréal, Québec .... TEL (514) 931-8209

Genois, Denis
8475, rue Christophe-Colomb, Montréal, Québec ...... TEL (514) 383-1550

Geoffrion, Richard
1336, rue Logan, Montréal, Québec .... TEL (514) 523-9986

GID Design
2205 Leon Hamel, Québec, Québec .... TEL (418) 682-0346

Girard, Marcel
1600, rue Athlone, Ville Mont-Royal, Québec .... TEL (514) 697-6912

Gosselin, Brian
CP 8116, Montréal, Québec .... TEL (514) 871-6677

Groupe D.E.S. Inc
460, St-Paul est #206, Montréal, Québec .... TEL (514) 844-8507

GSM/Morley Smith
1400, rue Pomba, St-Laurent, Québec .... TEL (514) 337-3041

Innovation Design
12514, Chemin du Moulin, St-Canut, Mirabel, Québec .... TEL (514) 431-7893

Interaction/Design
3450, rue Aylmer #101, Montréal, Québec .... TEL (514)288-1983

Jeannotte, André J. W. et Associés
4480, Promenade Paton #302, Chomedey, Laval, Québec ... TEL (514) 284-2282

Katz Design Inc
4710, rue St-Ambroise #225, Montréal, Québec .... TEL (514) 939-1697

Lévesque, Guy Designer Ltée
310 Ontario est, Montréal, Québec .... TEL (514) 288-1983

Labbé Designers et Associés Inc
6401, av. Coolbrook, Montréal, Québec .... TEL (514) 735-8163

Lafleur, Jacques
26 Jacques Racicot, Boucherville, Québec .... TEL (514)737-9883

Lalande, Philippe Designers
370, rue Guy #211, Montréal, Québec .... TEL (514) 932-8582

Lamarche, Claude
145, av. Lake, Dorval, Québec .... TEL (514) 631-2856

Lanier, Addison
215, boul. St-Laurent #42, Montréal, Québec .... TEL (514) 393-3172

Lapointe, Denys
53, Belvedere N #204, Sherbrooke, Québec .... TEL (819) 565-3593

Lapointe, Y.A. Designer
1275, Chemin Roy, St-Elie d'Orford, Québec .... TEL (819) 566-1338

Laroche, Robert
411, rue de Lanoue, Ile-des-Soeurs, Québec .... TEL (514) 631-2120

Laurent, André
6355, 44e Ave #2, Montréal, Québec .... TEL (514) 640-4382

Laverdure, Jean
600, boul. Frederick Phillips, St-Laurent, Québec ..... TEL (514) 744-8200

Mailhot, Laurent
9, boul L'Ange Gardien, L'Assomption, Québec .... TEL (514) 589-3300

Mauffette, Claude Design Industriel
4710, rue Ste-Ambroise #220, Montréal, Québec .... TEL (514) 939-2494

Mongeau, François
193, rue Pierre-Foretier, Ile Bizard, Québec .... TEL (514) 638-2264

Morelli, Michel
6891, rue Chambord, Montréal, Québec .... TEL (514) 435-1971

Morin Lessard McInnis Inc
1840, rue Sherbrooke o., Montréal, Québec .... TEL (514) 935-5409

Morin, André Designer
400, Route 2-20, Pointe Claire, Québec .... TEL (514) 694-6048

Myssil Design
50, Pl Crémazie o., #306, Montréal, Québec .... TEL (514) 389-3370

Myssil Design/Sylvain Charette
50, Pl Crémazie o., #306, Montréal, Québec .... TEL (514) 389-3370

Myssyl Design/Michel Couture
50, Pl Crémazie o., #306, Montréal, Québec .... TEL (514) 389-3370

Neove Design Inc
315, rue St-Laurent o., Longueuil, Québec .... TEL (514) 670-0547

OVIFO Design Inc
10645, Grande-Allée, Québec, Québec .... TEL (418) 931-8209

Payer, Jacques
8475, rue Christophe-Colomb, Montréal, Québec ...... TEL (514) 383-1550

Phénix, Serge
832, rue Heartland, Montréal, Québec .... TEL (514) 731-0439

Pinchiero, Victor
CP 6128, Succursale A, Montréal, Québec .... TEL (514) 343-7556

Primeau, Mario
6260 Mariveau #204, St-Léonard, Québec .... TEL (514) 325-1600

Rondeau, Pierre
1, de la Montagne, Valcourt, Québec .... TEL (514) 532-2211

Shaanan, Gad Design Inc
2455, Chemin Manella #390, Ville Mount Royal, Québec ..... TEL (514) 735-9550

Shalinsky, Bernard
685, av. Meloche, Dorval, Québec .... TEL (514) 636-6682

Shardon Design
7, Ronald Dr, Montréal, Québec .... TEL (514) 489-2197

Sodeplan Inc
1180, rue Drummond #770, Montréal, Québec .... TEL (514) 871-8833

Styl-Concept Inc
11841, rue de Tracy, Montréal, Québec .... TEL (514) 745-3707

Subert, Vladimir
996, rue MacNaughton, Montréal, Québec .... TEL (514) 731-5134

Taillefer, Guy
8940, boul. Lacordaire, St-Léonard, Québec .... TEL (514) 744-8200

Vachon, Luc
120, rue Signay, Nicolet, Québec .... TEL (819) 293-6606

Vignau, Pierre
911 Jean Talon est #205, Montréal, Québec .... TEL (514) 271-7101

Wendrich, Robert
740, boul. Pine Beach, Dorval, Québec .... TEL (514) 633-8610

DESIGN D'INTERIEUR/ CORPORATIF — CORPORATE INTERIOR DESIGN

Champalimaud, Alexandra & Associés Inc
1420, rue Sherbrooke O. #401, Montréal, Québec .... TEL (514) 845-9532

Charron, Pierre
218, rue St-Paul o. 3e plancher, Montréal, Québec .... TEL (514) 849-3205

Chouinard, Denis
200, av. des Commandeurs, Montréal, Québec .... TEL (418) 835-2744

Dubois, André et Ass. Designers Inc
1550, av. Docteur Penfield #1405, Montréal, Québec .... TEL (514) 935-9503

Groupe Design Forrest
625, boul. René Lévesque #1525, Montréal, Québec .... TEL (514) 875-8507

GSM Design Inc
317 Place d'Youville, Montréal, Québec .... TEL (514) 288-4233

IN DESIGN/Conrath, Gary
451, St-Sulpice #K-3, Montréal, Québec .... TEL (514) 287-9716

Innova Design
1030, St-Alexandre #900, Montréal, Québec .... TEL (514) 875-5655

Le Groupe Robert Vachon Design Inc
360, St-François-Xavier #500, Montréal, Québec .... TEL (514) 843-3505

Leopold Architectural Design Inc
1180, rue Drummond #600, Montréal, Québec .... TEL (514) 393-1636

Marshall/Moore/Goyette Design Inc
2000 Mansfield #1505, Centre Manuvie, Montréal, Québec TEL (514) 843-3344

McClintock, Patricia L.
4040, Chemin Trafalgar, Montréal, Québec .... TEL (514) 932-1860

Moureaux Hauspy Design Inc
2140, St-Mathieu, Montréal, Québec .... TEL (514) 935-4321

Ove Design/Claude Bérube
465, rue St-Jean #001, Montréal, Québec .... TEL (514) 844-8421

Pluri Design Canada Inc
438, rue St-Pierre #202, Montréal, Québec .... TEL (514) 845-3233

Sodeplan
1180, rue Drummond #770, Montréal, Québec .... TEL (514) 871-8833

INFOGRAPHIE/ELECTRONICS — GRAPHICS & SERVICES

André Perry Vidéo
1501, Barré, Montréal, Québec .... TEL (514) 932-3500

Bourassa, Jacques Photo Design
415, rue St-Gabriel #101, Vieux-Montréal, Québec .... TEL (514) 861-1965

Dessie Inc.
463, rue Ste-Catherine o. #260, Montréal, Québec .... TEL (514) 842-2571

Dignum Infographie
1905, rue William, Montréal, Québec .... TEL (514) 931-4221

Grafnetix (Systèmes) Inc.
777 rue de la Commune, Montréal, Québec .... TEL (514) 861-3389

Héotech Communications
373, Pl d'Youville #505, Montréal, Québec .... TEL (514) 845-3315

Montréal Creative Center/Centre Créatif de Montréal
395, rue Dowd, Montréal, Québec .... TEL (514) 861-6323

Onzieme Ciel
2120, rue Sherbrooke Est #1105, Montréal, Québec .... TEL (514) 522-1254

Poly-Production
1583, boul. St-Laurent, Montréal, Québec .... TEL (514) 288-4823

Prisma Graphique
222, rue Dominion #40, Montréal, Québec .... TEL (514) 933-9957

Projections Audio-Visuel Ltée
1422, rue Notre-Dame o., Montréal, Québec .... TEL (514) 935-3958

Studio Arizona/JLM Design
3906, rue Clark, Montréal, Québec .... TEL (514) 843-5055

Studio du Havre Inc.
2295 St-Marc #305, Montréal, Québec .... TEL (514) 932-1012

REDACTEURS (FRANCAIS) — WRITERS (FRENCH)

Abbeloos, Charles J. (Adaptex)
5585, rue Verdi, Brossard, Québec .... TEL (514) 672-5697

Aird Lemieux et Associés
317, Pl. d'Youville, Montréal, Québec .... TEL (514) 844-8307

Boileau, Chantal
169, Napoléon, Montréal, Québec .... TEL (514) 499-1306

Carrier, Mark
748, av. Greene, Montréal, Québec .... TEL (514) 932-1074

Communications Idéo Inc
414, rue St Pierre #701, Montréal, Québec .... TEL (514) 842-1755

Couture, François
5311, rue Sherbrooke O. #1319, Montréal, Québec .... TEL (514) 487-6767

de Cotret, Pierre-René
2198 Regent, Montréal, Québec .... TEL (514) 526-6780

Demers, Denyse
6000 Pl. Northcrest, Montréal, Québec .... TEL (514) 342-4382

Forces Créatives
417, rue St-Pierre #701, Montréal, Québec .... TEL (514) 849-0526

Fugére, Claude
4481, av. de l'Esplanade #1, Montréal, Québec .... TEL (514) 727-5109

Interface
117, de Vincy, Benières, Québec .... TEL (418) 836-1395

Line Arsenault
1, Grande Allée est #6, Québec, Québec .... TEL (418) 524-9939

Montpetit, Charles
4282C, rue Fullum, Montréal, Québec .... TEL (514) 525-4565

Nadeau, Jean
196, rue St-Paul, Québec, Québec .... TEL (418) 694-0418

Penabad-Casas, Thomas
PO Box 52, Stn Place Du Parc, Montréal, Québec .... TEL (514) 272-8180

Simonnot, Frédéric
7675, 22e avenue, Montréal, Québec .... TEL (514) 495-4459

Trottier, Benoît
82 Notre Dame o. #200, Montréal, Québec .... TEL (514) 499-2820

REDACTEURS (ANGLAIS) — WRITERS (ENGLISH)

Clark, Jennifer
3644, av. de Musée #41, Montréal, Québec .... TEL (514) 844-9083

Crayon Design
415, rue Le Moyne #402, Vieux Montréal, Québec .... TEL (514) 842-5938

Feingold, Byrna
3250, av. Forest Hill #1809, Montréal, Québec .... TEL (514) 739-7883

DESIGN D'EXPOSITION — EXHIBIT & DISPLAY

Avant-Garde Display Ltée
1303, rue William #200, Montréal, Québec .... TEL (514) 931-3399

Expo 4 Inc.
2300, rue Victoria, Lachine, Québec .... TEL (514) 637-4625

Expo Graphics & Displays
65, rue Adrien Roberts #6, Hull, Québec .... TEL (819) 770-5167

Exposervice Standards Ltée
C.P. 1120, Place Bonaventure, Montréal, Québec .... TEL (514) 395-2450

Exposystemes Canada
3469, boul. Industriel, Chomedy-Laval, Québec .... TEL (514) 662-6066

Expovision Inc.
1520 55th Avenue, Lachine, Québec .... TEL (514) 631-2800

Idée Environnement Inc
218, rue St-Paul o., Montréal, Québec .... TEL (514) 849-3205

La Boîte du Pinceau d'Arlequin
1919 rue William, Montréal, Québec .... TEL (514) 939-1919

Les Concepts Polystand Inc.
4020, rue St-Ambroise #150, Montréal, Québec .... TEL (514) 931-5211

Les Etalages Archex Ltée
9200 Henri-Bourassa o., St-Laurent, Québec .... TEL (514) 334-1012

Muséo Techni
1428, av. Overdale, Montréal, Québec .... TEL (514) 876-1192

Productions d'Hier à Demain Inc.
1600, Notre Dame o. #210, Montréal, Québec .... TEL (514) 934-0101

Skyline Displays Canada
1999, boul. Champlain, Chambly, Québec .... TEL (514) 658-8795

Skyline Displays Mirex
73, rue Chaput, Joliette, Québec .... TEL (514) 756-0346

Skyline Displays Montréal
10 Edison, Montréal, Québec .... TEL (514) 393-9033

Skyline Displays Pringles
CP 1266, Nicolet, Québec .... TEL (819) 293-5927

Studio Summit Inc
1959, Notre-Dame-de-Fatima, Laval, Québec .... TEL (514) 669-7129

PHOTOGRAPHES — PHOTOGRAPHERS

Air Photo Productions
6520, Clanranald, Montréal, Québec .... TEL (514) 527-1184

Alix & Gagné Inc
4060 boul. St-Laurent #307, Montréal, Québec .... TEL (514) 987-9525

Allard, François
RR#1, Dunham, Québec .... TEL (514) 295-2505

Amyot, André Photographe
636 Giffard, Longueuil, Québec .... TEL (514) 679-2314

Arpin, Pierre, Photographe
1063 rue St-Alexandre #200, Montréal, Québec .... TEL (514) 876-1730

Arsenault, Pierre
5221, boul. St-Laurent #300, Montréal, Québec .... TEL (514) 274-2738

Aventure Studio
1029 Beaver Hall Hill #500, Montréal, Québec .... TEL (514) 874-0097

Bélanger, Diane
4710, rue St-Ambroise #317, Montréal, Québec .... TEL (514) 939-1910

Barbeau, Serge
1881 St-André #300, Montréal, Québec .... TEL (514) 525-3569

Barriere, Yves
10, Ontario o. #901, Montréal, Québec .... TEL (514) 842-6962

Batchelor, Michael
1030, rue St-Alexandre #901, Montréal, Québec .... TEL (514) 861-1094

Baumgartner, Peter Photographie Inc
1905, rue William, Montréal, Québec .... TEL (514) 989-1484

Beauchemin, Serge
1245, rue Redpath Cres, Montréal, Québec .... TEL (514) 287-9322

Beaulieu, Yves
4060, boul. St-Laurent #108, Montréal, Québec .... TEL (514) 843-7788

Beauregard, Bruno
1030, rue St-Alexandre #903, Montréal, Québec .... TEL (514) 397-0565

Bedard, Pierre
8475, Christophe Colombe, Montréal, Québec .... TEL (514) 383-1550

Belber, Gerald/Chroma Communication
5120, av. de Courtrai #14, Montréal, Québec .... TEL (514) 340-1234

Belleau, Steve Photographe
11842 Brunet, Montréal, Québec .... TEL (514) 326-7132

Beniak, Roland
1660, rue Eiffel, Boucherville, Québec .... TEL (514) 449-4449

Berubé, Jean-François
4314, rue Fabre, Montréal, Québec .... TEL (514) 526-5618

Bognar, Tibor
8182, rue St-Hubert, Montréal, Québec .... TEL (514) 387-1646

Bohn, Bernard
4060, boul. St-Laurent #409, Montréal, Québec .... TEL (514) 287-1589

Bourque, Evie-Lucie
85, Rose de Lima, Montréal, Québec .... TEL (514) 933-0222

Bouthillette, Jose Photographe
16 Charles de Longueuil, Ste-Julie, Québec .... TEL (514) 876-2830

Brodeur, Denis
8945, Mauriac, St-Léonard, Québec .... TEL (514) 321-7677

Bruel, Jean-Yves Inc.
400, rue McGill #2, Montréal, Québec .... TEL (514) 398-9595

Brunelle, Francois Photo Design Inc.
307, rue Ste-Catherine o. #310, Montréal, Québec .... TEL (514) 288-6612

Burch, Bob
2153 rue Wellington, Montréal, Québec .... TEL (514) 933-5846

Bureau, Claude & Associés Inc.
454, rue Marconi, Ste-Foy, Québec .... TEL (418) 683-4114

Callahan/Tsunokawa Inc.
417, rue St-Pierre #224, Montréal, Québec .... TEL (514) 849-8404

Cantin, Louis
4815, Esplanade, Montréal, Québec .... TEL (514) 274-9650

Carruthers, Allan
3511, rue Hutchison #1, Montréal, Québec .... TEL (514)288-4333

Casavant, Paul
160 Shannon, Montréal, Québec .... TEL (514) 874-1588

Caty, André Photographe
1029 Beaver Hall #502, Montréal, Québec .... TEL (514) 298-0457

Charbonneau, Pierre
4335 Harvard, Montréal, Québec .... TEL (514) 481-2645

Charland, Pierre
995, rue Wellington #240, Montréal, Québec .... TEL (514) 861-9327

Charlebois, Claude
1077, rue Bégin, Ville St-Laurent, Québec .... TEL (514) 334-5162

Charlebois, David Claude
3940, Cote des Neiges, C55, Montréal, Québec .... TEL (514) 989-9082

Charles, Elizabeth
4828, boul. Maisonneuve o., Montréal, Québec .... TEL (514)866-6588

Chen, Roderick
1420, rue Notre-Dame o., Montréal, Québec .... TEL (514) 931-2203

Clarke, Oliver
445, St-Pierre #303, Montréal, Québec .... TEL (514) 849-0369

Clement, Serge
4060, boul. St-Laurent #705, Montréal, Québec .... TEL (514) 842-1646

Cloutier, Michel Photographe
4030, St-Ambroise #344, Montréal, Québec .... TEL (514) 939-9774

Colavecchio, Dominic
722 Milot, St-Hubert, Québec .... TEL (514) 678-2392

Collie, Peter, Photographie
406 St-Eloi #1, Montréal, Québec .... TEL (514) 849-4042

Communication Paquet & Associés
1250 2e rue Parc Industriel, Ste-Marie de Beauce, Québec TEL (418) 387-5858

Cornellier, André
222 rue Dominion #15, Montréal, Québec .... TEL (514) 933-4000

Cornu, Alain
3704, av. Laval, Montréal, Québec .... TEL (514) 845-5888

Craig, Patrick Photographe
461 St-Sulpice #300, Montréal, Québec .... TEL (514) 285-4621

Cramer, Marc
4318 A boul. St-Laurent, Montréal, Québec .... TEL (514) 289-9305

Crayon Design
415, rue Le Moyne #402, Vieux-Montréal, Québec .... TEL (514) 842-5938

Creations Jacques Beaudoin
4710, rue St-Ambroise #109, Montréal, Québec .... TEL (514) 939-2839

Crevier, Pierre
5465, av. Bordeaux, Montréal, Québec .... TEL (514) 523-8702

Darby, Mike
3964 Hotel de Ville, Montréal, Québec .... TEL (514) 842-5765

De Carufel, René
5691, Waverley, Montréal, Québec .... TEL (514) 935-6808

De Grosbois, Louise/G.R.A.A.V. Inc
1600 de Lorimier, Montréal, Québec .... TEL (514) 521-1984

Delbuguet, René
1299, rue Guy, Montréal, Québec .... TEL (514) 932-1630

Denault, Pierre/Flip Image
4060, St-Laurent #206, Montréal, Québec .... TEL (514) 843-7239

Denis, Claude
307, Ste-Catherine o. #730, Montréal, Québec .... TEL (514) 845-1823

Desaulniers, François
970, McEachern #402, Montréal, Québec .... TEL (514) 271-5797

Desjardins, François Photographie Inc
CP 1421, Sherbrooke, Québec .... TEL (819) 823-8409

Di Nezza, John Photographe
465, St-Alexandre #3, Longueuil, Québec .... TEL (514) 677-7538

Donohue, Joseph
5263 Dalou, Montréal, Québec .... TEL (514) 481-3884

Doyon, André
4060, boul. St-Laurent #105, Montréal, Québec .... TEL (514) 845-4670

Drolet, Marc
449, rue Ste-Hélène #400, Montréal, Québec .... TEL (514) 843-8274

Drummond, Michael
40 Anwerth Rd, Westmount, Québec .... TEL (514) 933-5205

Dubé, Yvan
595 Montcalm, Longueuil, Québec .... TEL (514) 646-3946

Dubreuil, Michel
307 rue Ste-Catherine o. #200, Montréal, Québec .... TEL (514) 843-6791

Ducharme, Louis
17, rue St-Jacques #209, Québec, Québec .... TEL (418) 692-4343

Duclos, Gilbert Photo
1030, St-Alexandre #400, Montréal, Québec .... TEL (514) 879-9480

Duey, Adrien
1030, rue St-Alexandre #812, Montréal, Québec .... TEL (514) 879-1848

Dury, Pierre
6595, 12e avenue, Montréal, Québec .... TEL (514) 374-9841

Dutesco, Robert
995, rue Wellington #230, Montréal, Québec .... TEL (514) 866-0726

Dutil, Georges
3954 St-Hubert #3, Montréal, Québec .... TEL (514) 848-0014

Edgar, Robin/Location Photography
899 de l'Eglise, Verdun, Québec .... TEL (514) 762-0785

Edge, Dennis
235, rue Peel, Montréal, Québec .... TEL (514) 871-1936

Eigenmann, Jean-Daniel
1583 boul. St-Laurent, Montréal, Québec .... TEL (514) 288-4823

Errel Productions
1872, rue Notre Dame o., Montréal, Québec .... TEL (514) 932-3102

Filion, Michel
1030 St-Alexandre #903, Montréal, Québec .... TEL (514) 397-0565

Fisher, Bob
14406, av. Madison, Pierrefond, Québec .... TEL (514) 620-4040

Foldes, Peter
17226 Chemin Ste Marie, Kirkland, Québec .... TEL (514) 694-4017

Fotowerke International
4064, boul. St-Laurent, Montréal, Québec .... TEL (514) 288-6693

Fournier, Richard
125 de Verchères, Ville Ste-Cathe, Québec .... TEL (514) 632-4922

Gagné, Michel-Réflexion
1255 Carre Phillips #1000, Montréal, Québec .... TEL (514) 876-1620

Gagnon, Sylvain
390 Rielle #105, Montréal, Québec .... TEL (514) 768-9792

Gendron, Denis
5215, Berri #100, Montréal, Québec .... TEL (514) 277-8686

Germain, Yvan
6031, Christophe Colomb, Montréal, Québec .... TEL (514) 495-1152

Gibson, Malcolm
704, rue Notre Dame o. #402, Montréal, Québec .... TEL (514) 871-0005

Gontran, Michel Photo
173, rue Peel, Montréal, Québec .... TEL (514) 861-0300

Gordon, Bruce W.
3671, rue Drolet, Montréal, Québec .... TEL (514) 499-0749

Graetz Productions Photographiques
425, rue Guy, Montréal, Québec .... TEL (514) 989-9551

Gratton, Jean-François
3666, rue St-Laurent #200, Montréal, Québec .... TEL (514) 849-0451

Gregoire, Normand Photographe
10, Ontario o. #504, Montréal, Québec .... TEL (514) 845-7939

Gros D'Aillon, Pierre
30, rue Notre Dame o. #300, Montréal, Québec .... TEL (514) 844-6059

Guevremont, Robert Photographic
1085, St-Alexandre #502, Montréal, Québec .... TEL (514) 393-1056

Halmaï, Pierre
3510, boul. St-Laurent #405, Montréal, Québec .... TEL (514) 842-0775

Hammond, Linda Dawn
3816, boul. St-Laurent #405, Montréal, Québec .... TEL (514) 849-0849

Harris, Barry Studio
4030, St-Ambroise #450, Montréal, Québec .... TEL (514) 933-6545

Hindian, Carlo
1751, rue Richardson #3410, Montréal, Québec .... TEL (514) 939-2988

Homer, Stephen
4710, rue St-Ambroise #317, Montréal, Québec .... TEL (514) 939-1725

Hotte, André
445, rue St-Pierre #204, Vieux Montréal, Québec .... TEL (514) 287-1820

Hungerbuhler, Carl
1583 St-Laurent, Montréal, Québec .... TEL (514) 288-2549

Image Média/Dalpont, André
6344, rue St-Hubert, Montréal, Québec .... TEL (514) 271-4433

Images, Revues et Corrigés
4247, rue St Dominique 3e étage, Montréal, Québec .... TEL (514) 982-6022

Joly, Emmanuel
4060, boul. St-Laurent #103, Montréal, Québec .... TEL (514) 499-1764

Kirsch, Lawrence
P.O. Box 143, N.D.G., Montréal, Québec .... TEL (514) 486-6887

Komaromi, Devesh/Mediamatrix
1413, av. Argyle, Montréal, Québec .... TEL (514) 395-8684

Kristian, Frank
2002, rue MacKay, Montréal, Québec .... TEL (514) 932-3520

Labelle, Lise Photographe
4282 A av. Delorimier, Montréal, Québec .... TEL (514) 939-1168

Labelle, Paul
307, rue Ste-Catherine o. #200, Montréal, Québec .... TEL (514) 845-5523

Lachapelle, Marc
424, rue Longueuil, Longueuil, Québec .... TEL (514) 651-0211

Lajeunesse, Eric
329 Louis-Hebert, Granby, Québec .... TEL (514) 375-2726

Langevin, Suzanne
5880, Waverly, Montréal, Québec .... TEL (514) 495-1209

Langlois, Claude-Simon/Les Productions Milnox Inc.
822 de l'Epée, Montréal, Québec .... TEL (514) 279-1352

Laporta, Robert
1872 Notre Dame o., Montréal, Québec .... TEL (514) 932-3102

Laramée-Morel Communications AV
4850 St-Ambroise #108, Montréal, Québec .... TEL (514) 933-5575

Lauzon, Gilles
275, rue St-Jacques #19, Montréal, Québec .... TEL (514) 281-9872

Lavigne, Pierre
4060, boul. St-Laurent #103, Montréal, Québec .... TEL (514) 288-1209

Lavigueur, Guy/Productions Punch Inc
1463, rue Prefontaine, Montréal, Québec .... TEL (514) 598-5100

Le Clair, François Photographe Enr
10, rue Ontario o. #901, Montréal, Québec .... TEL (514) 843-3340

Leduc, Huguette Photographe
825, av. Dollard, Outremont, Québec .... TEL (514) 279-7675

Lefebvre, Yves Photographe
6001, Jeanne Mance, Montréal, Québec .... TEL (514) 270-4372

LeMoyne, Roger
1827, av. Lincoln, Montréal, Québec .... TEL (514) 935-5534

Lemieux, Jean
4232 rue Delaney, Pierrefonds, Québec .... TEL (514) 421-7454

Lemoyne, Roger
1827 av. Lincoln, Montréal, Québec .... TEL (514) 935-5534

Lepine, Francis
275A Rang L'Annonciation, Oka, Québec .... TEL (514) 479-1749

Lepper, Derek
27 Aurora Pt-Claire, Montréal, Québec .... TEL (514) 694-6168

Les Paparazzi, Photographe
1447 de Bleury 2e étage, Montréal, Québec .... TEL (514) 843-6041

Les Photographes Kedl Ltée
336, rue du Roi, Québec, Québec .... TEL (418) 522-8437

Les Productions D'Hier à Demain Inc
1600 Notre-Dame o. #210, Montréal, Québec .... TEL (514) 934-0101

Lessard, Carl
4060 rue St-Laurent #103, Montréal, Québec .... TEL (514) 499-0683

Levine, Ron Photography
1619, rue William #202, Montréal, Québec .... TEL (514) 932-8069

Longpré, Jean
3510, boul. St-Laurent, Montréal, Québec .... TEL (514) 282-1052

Lussier, Louis
2315, rue Olivier-Robert, Montréal, Québec .... TEL (514) 526-2531

Maisonneuve, Ronald
415, rue St-Gabriel, #103, Montréal, Québec .... TEL (514) 871-2811

Major, Louis-Michel
1030 rue St-Alexandre #414, Montréal, Québec .... TEL (514-879-1271

Malka, Daniel
4475, rue St-Laurent #202, Montréal, Québec .... TEL (514) 844-6353

Marcos, Michael Photography
5207, Mariette Ave, Montréal, Québec .... TEL (514) 482-4836

Martin, Dennis
4062, boul. St-Laurent, Montréal, Québec .... TEL (514) 845-1807

Martinière, Pascal
4710, rue St-Ambroise #323, Montréal, Québec .... TEL (514) 939-1718

Massé, Patrice
1881, rue St-André #301, Montréal, Québec .... TEL (514) 521-9598

Mastrovito, Perry-Réflexion
1255, Carré Phillips, Montréal, Québec .... TEL (514) 876-1620

Mat, Jac
4710, rue St-Ambroise #343, Montréal, Québec .... TEL (514) 939-1982

McCarthy, Paul/Au Puits de Lumiere Inc
3738, rue St-Dominique 3e étage, Montréal, Québec .... TEL (514) 849-8526

McGaraughty, Gerry
42, av. de Pins o. #2, Montréal, Québec .... TEL (514) 982-6935

McNeil, Pierre
550, place de Montagne #150, Boucherville, Québec .... TEL (514) 655-4310

Mediati, Bruno
CP 5754, Succ. B, Montréal, Québec .... TEL (514) 492-4905

Michaud, Claude Photography
1652 Panet, Montréal, Québec .... TEL (514) 522-9231

Mongeau, Bacon, Chen & Associés Inc.
320, rue Notre-Dame est, Montréal, Québec .... TEL (514) 397-0755

Mongeau, Pierre Louis
995, rue Wellington #213, Montréal, Québec .... TEL (514) 871-3962

Montebello, Marc Photographe
CP 684, Succ NDG, Montréal, Québec .... TEL (514) 488-6848

Moores, Glen
124, rue McGill #300, Montréal, Québec .... TEL (514) 397-1846

Morcos, Michael Magued Photography
5207, Mariette, Montréal, Québec .... TEL (514) 482-4836

Morel, Sylvain
4850 St-Ambroise #108, Montréal, Québec .... TEL (514) 933-5575

Morin, Clément/Photo C.M.
4710 rue St-Ambroise #222, Montréal, Québec .... TEL (514) 939-2346

Morin, Henry, Photographie Inc.
7, Ronald Dr, Montréal, Québec .... TEL (514) 485-0737

Morin, Jean
7865 St-Denis, Montréal, Québec .... TEL (514) 356-0273

O'Hara, John
1155 rue Wellington, Montréal, Québec .... TEL (514) 932-6803

O'Neill, Sean
1261 Shearer #8222, Montréal, Québec .... TEL (514) 939-3791

OSE Huit 10
4030, rue St-Ambroise #429, Montréal, Québec .... TEL (514) 939-0810

Ostiguy, Brigitte Photographe
360, boul. Charest est #201, Québec, Québec .... TEL (418) 649-0080

Ouellet, Guy/Phot'oeil
570 St-Clement #305, Montréal, Québec .... TEL (514) 256-5560

Panneton, André
4060, boul. St-Laurent, #103, Montréal, Québec .... TEL (514) 843-5424

Paquin, Yves
307, rue Ste-Catherine o. #610, Montréal, Québec .... TEL (514) 844-2902

Parks, Richard
307, rue Ste-Catherine o. #650, Montréal, Québec .... TEL (514) 843-6426

Passaseo, Joseph
7586, Ste-Hubert, Montréal, Québec .... TEL (514) 270-3242

Payment, Guy
372, rue Ste-Catherine o. #115, Montréal, Québec .... TEL (514) 866-3173

Pellat, Philip
5625, av. du Parc #2, Montréal, Québec .... TEL (514) 274-2481

Pelletier, Robert
1077, rue Bégin, St-Laurent, Québec .... TEL (514) 339-9830

Perez, Michel
4850, St-Ambroise #108, Montréal, Québec .... TEL (514) 499-1305

Perrault, Pierre
C.P. 104, Succ. M, Montréal, Québec .... TEL (514) 525-2040

Petit, Bernard
4060, boul. St-Laurent #102, Montréal, Québec .... TEL (514) 844-6817

Philion, Dominique
125 Elmire #316, Montréal, Québec .... TEL (514) 844-2477

Philion-Parizeau
338 est St-Antoine, Montréal, Québec .... TEL (514) 393-8934

Photographes Kedl Ltée
336, rue du Roi, Québec, Québec .... TEL (418) 529-0621

Photographie Industrielle Ltée
8533 9e avenue, St-Michel, Québec .... TEL (514) 725-9808

Photohaus
193 Maplecrest, Rosemere, Québec .... TEL (514) 433-1600

Photolab Yves Thomas
6338 av. Victoria #17, Montréal, Québec .... TEL (514) 739-1929

Photosphere Inc.
747A Guy, Montréal, Québec .... TEL (514) 932-4271

Pilon, Michel
141, rue Shannon, Montréal, Québec .... TEL (514) 861-6169

Pinsonneault, H. Sylvain
142 St-Denis, St-Lambert, Québec .... TEL (514) 465-7118

Plouffe, Richard
445, 4 ieme Ave, Deux Montagnes, Québec .... TEL (514) 473-8046

Poirier, Michel
4005, pl. Etourneau, Terrebonne, Québec .... TEL (514) 433-3129

Poissant, Richard
970, McEachran #402, Outremont, Québec .... TEL (514) 271-5979

Poly-Production
1583, boul. St-Laurent, Montréal, Québec .... TEL (514) 288-4823

Poulin, Daniel
1331, rue Ste-Catherine est, Montréal, Québec .... TEL (514) 526-2824

Pouliot, Bernard
CP 1625 Succ Pl d'Armes, Montréal, Québec .... TEL (514) 983-1474

Production Jean Blais Inc
745, rue Guy #300, Montréal, Québec .... TEL (514) 937-2634

Production Punch Inc/Guy Lavigueur
1463, rue Prefontaine, Montréal, Québec .... TEL (514) 598-5100

Productions d'Hier à Demain Inc.
1600, Notre Dame o. #210, Montréal, Québec .... TEL (514) 934-0101

Proulx, Russell
335, rue St Paul o. #2, Montréal, Québec .... TEL (514) 287-1038

Prud'Homme, Louis
4060 boul. St-Laurent #305, Montréal, Québec .... TEL (514) 289-8711

Raymond, Jean-Marc/Visu-1 Inc.
1751, rue Richardson #4125, Montréal, Québec .... TEL (514) 931-0085

Raymond, Maryse
141, rue Anne #301, Montréal, Québec .... TEL (514) 861-2212

Richard, Monic
443, rue St-Vincent #300, Vieux Montréal, Québec .... TEL (514) 866-2237

Robitaille, Luc Photo Inc
995, rue Wellington #218, Montréal, Québec .... TEL (514) 861-3322

Rochon, Pierre
4060, boul. St-Laurent #305, Montréal, Québec .... TEL (514) 495-1441

Savoie, Gilles
1421 Montcalm, Montréal, Québec .... TEL (514) 526-4649

Sirois, Alain
3510, boul. St-Laurent #314, Montréal, Québec .... TEL (514) 849-8464

Slobodian, Michael
1447, rue Bleury 3e étage, Montréal, Québec .... TEL (514) 844-1007

Sparrow Photos Ltd
Box 143, NDG, Montréal, Québec .... TEL (514) 486-6887

St-Laurent, James
4530 Clark #401, Montréal, Québec .... TEL (514) 845-3300

Studio 70
1370, rue de Touraine, Ste-Julie, Québec .... TEL (514) 649-9395

Studio Arizona
3906, rue Clark, Montréal, Québec .... TEL (514) 843-5055

Studio Dan Lavoie
461, rue St-Sulpice, 4e étage, Montréal, Québec .... TEL (514) 281-6296

Studio Don Graetz
420, rue St-Martin, Montréal, Québec .... TEL (514) 933-8868

Studio Michel Laloux Inc
418, rue St-Sulpice, Montréal, Québec .... TEL (514) 287-9583

Studio Photo Raymond Martinot
410, rue de Vaudreuil, Montréal, Québec .... TEL (514) 876-1725

Terpanjian, Paul Photography
760, rue St-Paul o., Montréal, Québec .... TEL (514) 866-1338

Tessier, Guy
1061, rue St-Alexandre #404, Montréal, Québec .... TEL (514) 866-0998

The Braun Agency
1600 Notre-Dame o. #309, Montréal, Québec .... TEL (514) 939-3389

Therrien, André
468, rue Walnut, St-Lambert, Québec .... TEL (514) 465-7657

Thomas, Leon
1030, rue St-Alexandre #901, Montréal, Québec .... TEL (514) 393-1540

Tilt Inc.
231, rue St-Paul o., Montréal, Québec .... TEL (514) 844-0294

Tomovich, Velly P.
790, rue Outremont #10, Montréal, Québec .... TEL (514) 279-3604

Travers, David Photography Inc.
980, rue St-Paul o. #208, Montréal, Québec .... TEL (514) 861-9107

Tremblay, Jean
1070, rue de Bleury #620, Montréal, Québec .... TEL (514) 866-0639

Tremblay, Richard Max
4547, av. Delorimier, Montréal, Québec .... TEL (514) 524-5148

Trudeau, Lyne Enr
CP Box 1752, Place d'Armes Succ, Montréal, Québec .... TEL (514) 937-4023

Tsunokawa, Mas
417 rue St-Pierre #224, Montréal, Québec .... TEL (514) 849-8404

Turgeon Giard, Linda
5592, Marie-Victorin, Contrecoeur, Québec .... TEL (514) 587-5570

Vézina, Alain
5791, av. Royal Boischatel, Beauport, Québec .... TEL (418) 822-1234

Vaccaro, Domenic
1261 Shearer #1800, Montréal, Québec .... TEL (514) 931-5658

Vachon, Jean
95, rue Prince, Montréal, Québec .... TEL (514) 395-2227

Valiquet, Carl Photographe
745, rue Guy #201, Montréal, Québec .... TEL (514) 932-8817

Van Dusen, Ray Photography
2062, Belgrave Ave, Montréal, Québec .... TEL (514) 486-5054

Verrall, Paul
601 Strathmore Blvd, Dorval, Québec .... TEL (514) 397-9091

Visual Aspects
1872, rue Notre Dame o., Montréal, Québec .... TEL (514) 989-1642

WAHZO!
410 St-François-Xavier #2, Montréal, Québec .... TEL (514) 849-0739

Weiner, Danny
6210, av. Clanranald, Montréal, Québec .... TEL (514) 733-8719

Wenk, Jonathan
42, av. Pine o. #5, Montréal, Québec .... TEL (514) 842-4589

Williams, Larry & Associates
350, LeMoyne, Montréal, Québec .... TEL (514) 849-0260

Wojcicki, Michael
1990, rue William #201, Montréal, Québec .... TEL (514) 939-2571

Wolfstein, Ed
CP 1444 Pl Bonaventure, Montréal, Québec .... TEL (514) 487-9346

Zabbal, Pierre
4710, rue St-Ambroise #351, Montréal, Québec .... TEL (514) 939-2086

Zimbel, George S.
1538, rue Sherbrooke o. #813, Montréal, Québec .... TEL (514) 931-6387

Zone Productions
3575, boul. St-Laurent #711, Montréal, Québec .... TEL (514) 842-1187

PHOTOTHEQUES — STOCK PHOTOGRAPHY

Alpha Diffusion
797, av. Champagneur, Outremont, Québec .... TEL (514) 273-4322

Canapress Photo Service
36 King St E 4th Fl Toronto Ontario .... TEL (416)364-0321

Cinémanima Inc.
56, rue St-Pierre #306, Québec, Québec .... TEL (418) 692-0352

Creative Stock Agencies Inc
70 Scollard St #202 Toronto Ontario .... TEL (416)324-9800

Edgar, Robin/Photo
899 de l'Eglise, Verdun, Québec .... TEL (514) 762-0785

First Light Associated Photographers
1 Atlantic Ave #204 Toronto Ontario .... TEL (416)532-6108

Focus Stock Photography Inc
950 Yonge St #409 Toronto Ontario .... TEL (416)968-6619

Four by Five Inc
512 King St E #300 Toronto Ontario .... TEL (416)860-1518

Image Bank Canada, The
40 Eglinton Ave E #307 Toronto Ontario .... TEL (416)322-8840

Image Finders Photo Agency Inc
134 Abbott St Vancouver B.C. .... TEL (604)688-9818

Mach 2 Stock Exchange, The
1409 Edmonton Trail NE #200 Calgary Alberta .... TEL (403)230-9363

Masterfile
415 Yonge St #200 Toronto Ontario .... TEL (416)977-7267

Miller/Comstock
180 Bloor St W #1102 Toronto Ontario .... TEL (416)925-4323

Mosiac Stock Photo Agency
836 Yonge St Toronto Ontario .... TEL (416)499-2936

Petkov, Marin Photographer
MPO Box 2431 Vancouver B.C. .... TEL (604)941-1190

Photo Artists Canada
620 Richmond St W #1 Toronto Ontario .... TEL (416)367-9770

Publiphoto Inc.
797, av. Champagneur, Outremont, Québec .... TEL (514) 273-4322

Réflexion Photothèque
1255, Carré Phillips #1000, Montréal, Québec .... TEL (514) 876-1620

Stock Market Inc, The
93 Parliament St #228 Toronto Ontario .... TEL (416)362-7767

Superstock - Four x Five
512 King St E #300 Toronto Ontario .... TEL (416)860-1518

Superstock/Quatre par Cinq
417, rue St-Pierre #800, Montréal, Québec .... TEL (514) 849-2181

Take Stock Inc
705,603-7th Ave SW Calgary Alberta .... TEL (403)233-7487

Valan Photos
490 Dulwich Ave, St. Lambert, Québec .... TEL (514)465-2557

Viewpoints West Photofile Ltd
1252 Burrard St #101 Vancouver B.C. .... TEL (604)685-8381

PHOTO-LOCATION DE STUDIO — PHOTO: STUDIO RENTAL

Baumgartner, Peter Photographie Inc
1905, rue William, Montréal, Québec .... TEL (514) 989-1484

Studio Arizona
3906, rue Clark, Montréal, Québec .... TEL (514) 843-5055

Vachon, Jean
95, rue Prince, Montréal, Québec .... TEL (514) 395-2227

Valiquet, Carl Photographe
745, rue Guy #201, Montréal, Québec .... TEL (514) 932-8817

RETOUCHE — RETOUCHING

A&L Graphic Emulsion Stripping Inc.
364, rue St-Paul o., Montréal, Québec .... TEL (514) 845-0974

Crayon Design
415, rue Le Moyne #402, Vieux-Montréal, Québec .... TEL (514) 842-5938

Dorris, Carole
8420, rue Henri-Julien, Montréal, Québec .... TEL (514) 384-4769

Etcovitch, Barbara
800 Pl. Victoria, Montréal, Québec .... TEL (514) 934-2311

Galéa, Pierre
3724 av. Laval, Montréal, Québec .... TEL (514) 842-9363

Holloway, Geoffrey & Graham
1255, Phillip Square #909, Montréal, Québec .... TEL (514) 397-1545

Jean Lebrun
2136, rue Dollard, Longueuil, Québec .... TEL (514) 679-9255

Juteau, Yolande
2054 Jeanne-Mance, Montréal, Québec .... TEL (514) 289-8525

Lacas, Jean-Paul (J.P. Art Inc.)
1118, rue Ste-Catherine o. #211, Montréal, Québec .... TEL (514) 861-5601

Martin, Jean-Louis
4060, boul. St-Laurent #310, Montréal, Québec .... TEL (514) 845-8502

Miscione, Nick Retouchers
424, rue Guy #110, Montréal, Québec .... TEL (514) 939-2136

Monté, Robert
1421, rue Bishop #304, Montréal, Québec .... TEL (514) 849-6421

Montréal Creative Centre/Centre Créatif de Montréal
407, rue Dowd, Montréal, Québec .... TEL (514) 861-6323

ILLUSTRATEURS — ILLUSTRATORS

Achard, Marcel
3433, rue Peel #1, Montréal, Québec .... TEL (514) 842-9332

Ahern, Jean-Yves
4621 Christophe-Colombe, Montréal, Québec .... TEL (514) 521-0494

Anfousse, Ginette
C.P. 703, Val David, Québec .... TEL (819) 322-2298

Arcouette, Evelyne
687, rue Lacasse, Montréal, Québec .... TEL (514) 931-7425

Armanville, Jean-Pierre
3090 Linton #11, Montréal, Québec .... TEL (514) 733-4262

Arts Graphiques Pierre Chalifoux
1254 rue Mackay 3e étage, Montréal, Québec .... TEL (514) 934-0043

Azzuolo, Elia
7185, Louis-Hémon, Montréal, Québec .... TEL (514) 729-1741

Back, Francis
4706, rue Marquette, Montréal, Québec .... TEL (514) 527-9536

Banville, Martin
555, Moreau, Montréal, Québec .... TEL (514) 598-1417

Barrette, Doris
9380, Dubuisson, Montréal, Québec .... TEL (514) 352-8353

Beauchemin Marie-France
4651, rue Sallabery, Carignan, Québec .... TEL (514) 447-4956

Beaudet, Sophie
420 des Bouleaux est #1, Québec, Québec .... TEL (418) 624-3346

Beaudoin, Frederick
3089 A, Bossuet, Montréal, Québec .... TEL (514) 257-0204

Beaulac, Mario
3642, Adam, Montréal, Québec .... TEL (514) 523-7201

Beauregard, Christianne
428, rue Metcalfe, Westmount, Québec .... TEL (514) 934-0982

Bédard, Guy
136, rue St-Georges, Henryville, Québec .... TEL (514) 299-2010

Béha, Philippe
5193, rue Cartier, Montréal, Québec .... TEL (514) 843-3219

Bélair, François
3620, Lorne Crescent #805, Montréal, Québec .... TEL (514) 849-7195

Bélanger, Debbie
4310, av. Laval, Montréal, Québec .... TEL (514) 399-3879

Bélanger, Yves
4847, des Erables, Montréal, Québec .... TEL (514) 523-1786

Bélanger-Dubé, Marie
7957, de Gaspé, Montréal, Québec .... TEL (514) 384-3139

Bélisle, Jean-François
379, rue Bernard o. #5, Montréal, Québec .... TEL (514) 276-8024

Bello, Jean
6893, rue Chabot, Montréal, Québec .... TEL (514) 721-5932

Bénard, Christian
334, Terrasse St-Denis #503, Montréal, Québec .... TEL (514) 845-3005

Benhaim, Maxime
1030, rue St-Alexandre #205, Montréal, Québec .... TEL (514) 861-2080

Benoît, Ivan
4620, rue Barclay #1, Montréal, Québec .... TEL (514) 733-3607

Benoit, Jean-Marie
2280, rue Orléans, Montréal, Québec .... TEL (514) 259-7107

Berkson, Nina
400, rue Dowd #300, Montréal, Québec .... TEL (514) 878-2359

Berry, Tom
1434, rue Ste-Catherine o. #103, Montréal, Québec .... TEL (514) 861-7044

Berthelot, Huguette
4806, St-Denis, Montréal, Québec .... TEL (514) 849-7926

Bertin, Marie
196, rue Léonard, Rimouski, Québec .... TEL (418) 722-7953

Bigras, Robert
1075 Vanier, St-Laurent, Québec .... TEL (514) 747-1248

Bisson, Michel
4546 Messier, Montréal, Québec .... TEL (514) 596-0143

Blandino, Carmello
9435, boul. Gouin est, Montréal, Québec .... TEL (514) 648-3584

Bleu Réflex
334, Terrasse St-Denis #503, Montréal, Québec .... TEL (514) 845-3005

Boisjoly, Marthe
4665, boul. Gouin est, #3, Montréal, Québec .... TEL (514) 321-8719

Boisvert, André
4060 boul. St-Laurent #309, Montréal, Québec .... TEL (514) 844-0935

Boivin, Jacques
4531, de Bordeaux, Montréal, Québec .... TEL (514) 525-7014

Borduas, Lorraine
1455, René-Lévesque est, #303, Montréal, Québec .... TEL (514) 597-6056

Bouchard, Alain
155, rue Querbes, Outremont, Québec .... TEL (514) 272-3519

Bouchard, Jocelyne
1451, boul. St-Joseph est, Montréal, Québec .... TEL (514) 527-8424

Bouchard, Philippe
2080 rue Amherst #5, Montréal, Québec .... TEL (514) 598-7878

Boudreau, Hélène
6152 Hutchison, Montréal, Québec .... TEL (514) 495-2156

Bourbonnière, Sylvie
949, Gilford, Montréal, Québec .... TEL (514) 525-2934

Bousquet, Suzanne
CP 1876 Place d'Armes, Montréal, Québec .... TEL (514) 738-7191

Brassard, France
4730, Mentana, Montréal, Québec .... TEL (514) 529-6183

Brault, Micheline
455 des Bouleaux, L'Acadie, Québec .... TEL (514) 347-6056

Brochard, Philippe
3643, St-Laurent #301, Montréal, Québec .... TEL (514) 987-7668

Brochu, Andrée
3400, place Joseph N. Drapeau #301, Montréal, Québec ..... TEL (514) 526-6764

Brooks, Anne-Marie
2050, Claremont #14, Montréal, Québec .... TEL (514) 487-9377

Brunet, Charles
9341, rue Berri, Montréal, Québec .... TEL (514) 382-5660

Bujold, Claudine
211, av. Stanstead, Ville Mont-Royal, Québec .... TEL (514) 342-1240

Butt, Evelyn
5402, St-Dominique, Montréal, Québec .... TEL (514) 272-5539

Cammarata, Aldo
145 6e Avenue, Terrebonne, Québec .... TEL (514) 621-4692

Cantin, Charles
809, Cartier, Québec, Québec .... TEL (418) 524-1931

Cardinal, Alain
7837, St-Gérard, Montréal, Québec .... TEL (514) 279-5932

Castonguay, Daniel
4060, boul. St-Laurent #309, Montréal, Québec .... TEL (514) 843-4877

Catalpa Design Inc./Langeder, Helmut
1260, rue University #103, Montréal, Québec .... TEL (514) 866-7484

Caya, Silvie
6724, St-Denis, Montréal, Québec .... TEL (514) 495-2174

Cécil, René
1555, rue Malet, CP 273, Rock Forest, Québec .... TEL (819) 564-8061

Chabot, Joceline
4433, rue Bordeaux, Montréal, Québec .... TEL (514) 524-4970

Charney, Israel
4354, rue de Bullion, Montréal, Québec .... TEL (514) 842-6922

Chartier, François
3871 Henri-Julien, Montréal, Québec .... TEL (514) 842-7795

Chartrand, Martine
1575, rue Robert Charbonneau #104, Montréal, Québec ..... TEL (514) 339-1340

Chevrier, Andrée
4479, Delorimier, Montréal, Québec .... TEL (514) 523-6212

Chouinard, Marc
3235, rue des Aulnes #101, Québec, Québec .... TEL (418) 626-7660

Churchill, Jane
5334, rue de l'Esplanade, Montréal, Québec .... TEL (514) 279-0461

Claf Illustration Inc./Claude Lafrance
5340, Louis Joseph Doucet, Montréal, Québec .... TEL (514) 255-3919

Clairoux, Jacques
339, est CH. de la Rabastaliere, St-Bruno, Québec .... TEL (514) 653-7746

Claverie, Guy
7963, rue Foucher, Montréal, Québec .... TEL (514) 272-5494

Cloutier, Paul
6450, de Marseille #3, Montréal, Québec .... TEL (514) 254-2286

Clunes, Amaya
2258 Hampton, Montréal, Québec .... TEL (514) 489-6147

Conan, Rodolphe
4593, rue Ste-Catherine est, Montréal, Québec .... TEL (514) 254-6896

Corno, Johanne
10, rue Ontario o. #700, Montréal, Québec .... TEL (514) 270-3489

Corrigou, Alain
432, 4ieme rue, Québec, Québec .... TEL (418)647-2246

Cosentino, Carlo/Illustratech Inc.
1168, rue Ste-Catherine o. #207, Montréal, Québec .... TEL (514) 876-1442

Costela, Jean-Manuel
7114, St-Laurent, Montréal, Québec .... TEL (514) 270-9156

Côté, Chantal
1211 rue Gilford, Montréal, Québec .... TEL (514) 523-3688

Côté, Geneviéve
8577, René-Labelle, Montréal, Québec .... TEL (514) 382-9791

Côté, Manon
2280, rue d'Orléans, Montréal, Québec .... TEL (514) 259-7107

Côté, Martin
1030 St-Alexandre #709, Montréal, Québec .... TEL (514) 875-6723

Côté, Suzanne
4853, rue St-Urbain, Montréal, Québec .... TEL (514) 282-9367

Côté, Sylvie
1128, rue Daigneault, Acton Vale, Québec .... TEL (514) 546-3714

Cournoyer, Jacques
4258 Papineau, Montréal, Québec .... TEL (514) 527-5083

Cousineau, Normand
1235, rue Bernard o. #15, Outremont, Québec .... TEL (514) 273-9527

Craigmyle, Lynne/Illustration a L'Aerographe
CP 428, Montréal, Québec .... TEL (514) 843-1813

Crayon Design
415, rue Le Moyne #402, Vieux-Montréal, Québec .... TEL (514) 842-5938

Creative Action
164, Berlioz, Nuns Island, Québec .... TEL (514) 769-7092

Cullen, Johanne
5505 St-Laurent #4203 B, Montréal, Québec .... TEL (514) 274-8346

Cyr, Francine
7825, St-Dominique, Montréal, Québec .... TEL (514) 279-8573

Déry, Lorraine
2410, Chemin Ste-Foy, Ste-Foy, Québec .... TEL (418) 659-6620

Dagenais, Yvan
5938, Falco C.P. 2226, Rock Forest, Québec .... TEL (819) 864-9507

Daigle, Stéphan
5830, 9e Avenue, Montréal, Québec .... TEL (514) 374-7031

Dansereau, Gérard
2360, de la Salle #302, Montréal, Québec .... TEL (514) 255-0552

Dariusz, Pedryc
6345, rue Hamilton #3, Montréal, Québec .... TEL (514) 767-2131

Davidts, Robert
5578, Clark, Montréal, Québec .... TEL (514) 273-1999

De Blois, Danielle
9162, Henri-Julien, Montréal, Québec .... TEL (514) 387-4644

Demers, Michel
1273, av. Lajoie, Outremont, Québec .... TEL (514) 274-3448

Denis, Adeline
3955, rue Dupuis #9, Montréal, Québec .... TEL (514) 731-5218

Deronzier, Sylvie Illustratrice
4855, av. du Parc, Montréal, Québec .... TEL (514) 842-2388

Desbiens, Suzanne
3800, rue St-Kevin #2, Montréal, Québec .... TEL (514) 844-5880

Deschênes, Diane
4210, rue de Bullion, Montréal, Québec .... TEL (514) 849-5985

Desjardins, Charles/Tandem
4853, St-Laurent, Montréal, Québec .... TEL (514) 284-3570

Desputeaux, Hélène
80, rue Bourgeois, Beloeil, Québec .... TEL (514) 446-3496

Desrochers, Louise
5706, Marc Sauvalle, Montréal, Québec .... TEL (514) 767-9533

Desroches, Joanne
4173, rue Laval, Montréal, Québec .... TEL (514) 954-1650

Devlin, Michéle
235, av. Melville #1, Westmount, Québec .... TEL (514) 935-3988

Dias, Rui
131, Petit Lac Connelly, St-Hyppolyte, Québec .... TEL (514) 563-3444

Dombrowski, Josée
Rang Bois Franc Pierre Riche, St-Apollinaire, Québec ...... TEL (418) 692-2642

Doucet, Lise
4595, rue Drolet, Montréal, Québec .... TEL (514) 286-2660

Drab, Carolle
8296, de Châteaubriand, Montréal, Québec .... TEL (514) 381-1150

Dunningan, Huguette
120, Chemin du Sommet CP 353, Piedmont, Québec .... TEL (514) 227-6103

DuRepos, Ronald
1421, rue Bishop #203, Montréal, Québec .... TEL (514) 843-8056

Duranceau, Suzanne
4899, rue Sherbrooke o. #2&4, Montréal, Québec .... TEL (514) 484-6229

Durand, Pierre
3483, av. de l'hotel de Ville #1, Montréal, Québec .... TEL (514) 842-0583

Duval, Guylaine
175, rue Winder, Lennoxville, Québec .... TEL (819) 563-3195

Editions et Graphisme d'Avant Garde
777 de la Commune o. #103, Montréal, Québec .... TEL (514) 874-1529

Eibner, Frederic
775, Querbes, Outremont, Québec .... TEL (514) 272-4798

Eid, Jean-Paul
5262, Jeanne-Mance, Montréal, Québec .... TEL (514) 270-4708

Evans, Maurice
5214 rue des Erables, Montréal, Québec .... TEL (514) 526-0615

Faniel, Christiane
10967 Bruxelles, Montréal-Nord, Québec .... TEL (514) 325-1615

Faniel, Jean-Paul
6775, 20e avenue, Montréal, Québec .... TEL (514) 722-1585

Faniel, Lucie
5250, av. du Parc #16, Montréal, Québec .... TEL (514) 270-3222

Farei, Patrick
3479, Prud'homme, Montréal, Québec .... TEL (514) 878-1321

Faucher, Pierrette
977, ave Mainguy, Ste-Foy, Québec .... TEL (418) 659-2639

Filion, Rémi
10 787, boul. St-Laurent, Montréal, Québec .... TEL (514) 385-3521

Fillion, Francis
140, Lockwell #6, Québec, Québec .... TEL (514) 641-1594

Fleury, Pierre
417, rue St-Pierre #57, Montréal, Québec .... TEL (514) 844-6431

Forant, France
172, Notre-Dame, Repentigny, Québec .... TEL (514) 582-3044

Frischeteau, Gerard
2217, av. Oxford, Montréal, Québec .... TEL (514) 489-0887

Gaboury, Robert
24 Mont Royal o. #1003, Montréal, Québec .... TEL (514) 499-9644

Gadzala, Fred
200, Roy est, Montréal, Québec .... TEL (514) 842-1553

Gagné, Isabelle
1500, rue Provinciale, Québec, Québec .... TEL (418) 681-1899

Gagnon, Jean
5505 St-Laurent #4203, Montréal, Québec .... TEL (514) 279-8338

Gagnon, Michel
639, av. de l'Épée #14, Outremont, Québec .... TEL (514) 844-3911

Galéa, Pierre
3724 av. Laval, Montréal, Québec .... TEL (514) 842-9363

Galouchko, Annouchka
5830, 9e avenue, Rosemount, Québec .... TEL (514) 374-7031

Gardner, Jocelyn
6217, rue MacDonald, Montréal, Québec .... TEL (514) 735-8879

Garneau, Michel
6622, Casgrain, Montréal, Québec .... TEL (514) 272-2988

Gastonguay, Rémi
7613, St-Hubert, Montréal, Québec .... TEL (514) 276-0660

Gauthier, Luc
530, rue Maple, St-Lambert, Québec .... TEL (514) 671-6739

Gay, Marie-Louise
773, rue Davaar, Montréal, Québec .... TEL (514) 273-0368

Gendron, Raymond
3999 Mentana, Montréal, Québec .... TEL (514) 597-2812

Germain, Colette
7003, Cartier, Montréal, Québec .... TEL (514) 494-9542

Gervais, Maurice
390 de la Concorde #15, Montréal, Québec .... TEL (514) 688-1643

Godbout, Réal
9390, Millen, Montréal, Québec .... TEL (514) 385-9340

Godin, Eric
2014, rue Sherbrooke est, Montréal, Québec .... TEL (514) 525-8437

Goldstyn, Jacques
5795, Northmount, Montréal, Québec .... TEL (514) 735-7989

Gonzalez, Pedro
3642, Coloniale #2, Montréal, Québec .... TEL (514) 842-5262

Gosselin, Alain
5932 St-Urbain, Montréal, Québec .... TEL (514) 271-3170

Gosselin, Pierre
439, boul. Edouard VII, St-Jacques-Le-Mineur, Québec .... TEL (514) 347-3791

Gouin, Marguerite
554, rue William-David, Montréal, Québec .... TEL (514) 252-7931

Gouin, Suzanne
556, William-David, Montréal, Québec .... TEL (514) 252-0339

Grant, Steven
4230, Pierre de Coubertin #9, Montréal, Québec .... TEL (514) 256-9550

Grauerholz, Angela
3510, boul. St-Laurent #312, Montréal, Québec .... TEL (514) 288-3998

Greffard, Lise
3331, rue Maréchal #17, Montréal, Québec .... TEL (514) 385-1825

Grenier, Denis
16, rue Metcalfe, Sherbrooke, Québec .... TEL (819) 566-5340

Groleau, Michel
4113 A, Coloniale, Montréal, Québec .... TEL (514) 933-2555

Groz, Bernard
1360, rue Bernard ouest #11, Outremont, Québec .... TEL (514) 272-0491

Guay, Richard
4655, Jeanne d'Arc #3, Montréal, Québec .... TEL (514) 256-3421

Hébert, Michel
1374, rue Cardinal, St-Laurent, Québec .... TEL (514) 744-6589

Héroux, Diane
110, rue Bourget #4, Montréal, Québec .... TEL (514) 499-0561

Hainault-Loranger, Hélène
6970, 12e Avenue #2, Montréal, Québec .... TEL (514) 721-6389

Haworth, Michel
23, rue Black, Valleyfield, Québec .... TEL (514) 373-2689

Herrera, Diego
2312, Centre #35, Montréal, Québec .... TEL (514) 937-9098

Hone, Christine
599, de la Montage, Notre-Dame-du-Partage, Québec .... TEL (418) 867-2455

Houde, Pierre
4396, rue Brébeuf, Montréal, Québec .... TEL (514) 526-8255

Hudon, François
903 Mont Royal est, Montréal, Québec .... TEL (514) 598-1461

Hupfer, Christian
4373, rue Henri-Julien, Montréal, Québec .... TEL (514) 284-2255

Images, Revues et Corrigés
4247, rue St-Dominique 3e étage, Montréal, Québec .... TEL (514) 982-6022

Jarry, Pierre
8162 Henri-Julien, Montréal, Québec .... TEL (514) 387-4644

Jerome, Daniel
2495, rue Ardennes, Brossard, Québec .... TEL (514) 462-1762

JKJ-Studio Jasmin Keenan Jamieson Inc
1410, rue Guy #20, Montréal, Québec .... TEL (514) 937-2865

Joly, Gérard
2619, Dandurand #A, Montréal, Québec .... TEL (514) 728-5273

Jorisch, Stéphane
1029, Beaver Hall #505, Montréal, Québec .... TEL (514) 876-1186

Jost, Geneviéve
170, rue Bord de l'eau, St-Eustache, Québec .... TEL (514) 472-3837

Julien, Gaston-Pierre
36, rue Lesage, Repentigny, Québec .... TEL (514) 585-3505

Juteau, Yolande
2054 Jeanne-Mance, Montréal, Québec .... TEL (514) 289-8525

La Perrière, Josée
10, rue Ontario o. #220, Montréal, Québec .... TEL (514) 842-5215

LaBoissiére, Serge
10981, Lacordaire #8, Montréal, Québec .... TEL (514) 324-7594

Labelle, Geneviéve
7449A rue St-Denis, Montréal, Québec .... TEL (514) 525-2508

Labelle, Simon
4302, rue St-André, Montréal, Québec .... TEL (514) 525-8555

Labrie, André
3005, rue St-Laurent #B, St-Romuald, Québec .... TEL (418) 839-5090

Labrosse, Darcia
529, rue Théodore, Montréal, Québec .... TEL (514) 251-0742

Lachapelle, François
6152, rue Hutchison, Outremont, Québec .... TEL (514) 495-2156

Lacombe, Jean
4421, Messier, Montréal, Québec .... TEL (514) 524-9835

Ladouceur, François
3830, place Martin, Brossard, Québec .... TEL (514) 678-8507

Ladouceur, Louise
5390, rue St-Dominique, Montréal, Québec .... TEL (514) 272-3826

Lafaille, Denis
5578 Hadley, Montréal, Québec .... TEL (514) 768-2369

Lafond, Nicole
3575, boul. St-Laurent #533, Montréal, Québec .... TEL (514) 284-0161

Lafortune, Claude
286, rue Gardenville, Longueuil, Québec .... TEL (514) 679-5700

Laframboise, Michéle
250 boul. St-Joseph est #406, Montréal, Québec .... TEL (514) 281-7632

Lafrance, Marie
5987, de l'Esplanade, Montréal, Québec .... TEL (514) 273-1199

Lafrance, Serge
5175, Charleroi #11, Montréal, Québec .... TEL (514) 325-4739

Lafrenière, Anik
2120, rue Sherbrooke est #605, Montréal, Québec .... TEL (514) 522-1254

Lagacé, Paule
10, rue Ontario o. #701, Montréal, Québec .... TEL (514) 844-2738

Lalancette, Monique/LAMO
4457, rue Laval, Montréal, Québec .... TEL (514) 286-4852

Lalonde, Claude
1577, de Maricourt, Montréal, Québec .... TEL (514) 761-6982

Lalumière, Marc
2181, rue Dézéry, app.A, Montréal, Québec .... TEL (514) 525-5458

Lamothe, Raymonde
1903, rue Lionel-Groulx, Montréal, Québec .... TEL (514) 932-4159

Landry, Jean
416, rue Maisonneuve, St-Jean-sur-Richelieu, Québec .... TEL (514) 348-4574

Langlois, Suzanne
1817, boul. Rosemont, Montréal, Québec .... TEL (514) 272-4566

Laniel, Christine
114, rue Principale Sud, Montcerf, Québec .... TEL (819) 449-4776

Laplante, Jocelyn
4853, St-Urbain, Montréal, Québec .... TEL (514) 282-9367

Lapointe, Jac
838 de Montarville, Boucherville, Québec .... TEL (514) 449-3021

Laverdière, Benôit
2479, Quesnel, Montréal, Québec .... TEL (819) 934-6156

Laverdure, Daniel
5775, rue Frontenac, St-Hyacinthe, Québec .... TEL (514) 773-0172

Lavertu, Annic
276B Lakeshore, Pointe-Claire, Québec .... TEL (514) 426-2680

Lavigueur, André
271, rue Roy, Lemoyne, Québec .... TEL (514) 672-7022

Le Minh Cuong/LMC
65 Vanier, Châteauguay, Québec .... TEL (514) 699-1067

Lebrun, Raymond
4358, rue de Lanaudière, Montréal, Québec .... TEL (514) 526-9996

Leclair, Daniel
7136, des érables #1, Montréal, Québec .... TEL (514) 593-8509

Leclerc, Béatrice
594, Rang St-Jean, St-Patrice-de-Beaurivage, Québec .... TEL (418) 596-2942

Leduc, Bernard
1121, rue Ste-Catherine o. #500, Montréal, Québec .... TEL (514) 844-0074

Leduc, Madeleine
4523, boul. St-Michel, Montréal, Québec .... TEL (514) 529-6244

Lefebvre, Lyne
1150 de la Commune o., Montréal, Québec .... TEL (514) 845-3866

Lefebvre, Paul
376, Victoria, Montréal, Québec .... TEL (514) 489-7211

Lefebvre, Yolaine
4282 C, rue Fullum, Montréal, Québec .... TEL (514) 434-6620

Légaré, Jean-Claude
8, Mgr Miville, Lévis, Québec .... TEL (418) 835-1132

Léger, Jean-Louis
2640, rue Daudet, Laval, Québec .... TEL (514) 667-0477

Lemieux, Michéle
3514 Delormier, Montréal, Québec .... TEL (514) 525-6594

Lessard, Marie
5155 Bordeaux, Montréal, Québec .... TEL (514) 524-5383

Levert, Mireille
5245 Durocher, Outremont, Québec .... TEL (514) 270-4917

Lévèsque, Alain
223 Laval, Montebello, Québec .... TEL (819) 423-8525

Litalien, Christiane
880 rue Francis, Longueuil, Québec .... TEL (514) 442-4299

Longpré, Alain
5031 rue Sherbrooke o. #4, Montréal, Québec .... TEL (514) 489-1172

Loranger, Ginette
7821 A, rue Henri-Julien, Montréal, Québec .... TEL (514) 277-3975

Lortie, Stéphane
7351,de Lanaudière, Montréal, Québec .... TEL (514) 271-9885

Lumbago
2116 Gauthier, Montréal, Québec .... TEL (514) 521-3992

Mérienne, Claude/Opérant Suzanne Bousquet
CP 1876 Place d'Armes, Montréal, Québec .... TEL (514)738-7191

Mérola, Caroline
1592, boul. Gouin est, Montréal, Québec .... TEL (514) 389-0106

Madore, Lise
100, Hall #101, Ile des Soeurs, Québec .... TEL (514) 769-8713

Malo, France
192, Highfield, Mont St-Hilaire, Québec .... TEL (514) 446-1941

Marceau, Josée
4579, rue Parthenais, Montréal, Québec .... TEL (514) 598-7866

Marchand, Xavier
4588, Coloniale, Montréal, Québec .... TEL (514) 326-1113

Marion, Denise
790, rue DeRoussillon #10, Longueuil, Québec .... TEL (514) 677-2545

Marquis, Huguette
11, Route de Beaumont, St-Charles, Bellechasse, Québec TEL (418) 672-6065

Martin, Jean-Louis
4060, boul. St-Laurent #310, Montréal, Québec .... TEL (514) 845-8502

Martin, Raymond
1360, boul. Décarie #42, Montréal, Québec .... TEL (514) 744-6084

Massicotte, Alain
1121, rue Ste-Catherine o. 4e étage, Montréal, Québec .... TEL (514) 843-4169

Mather, Christine
3590, Bedford #24, Montréal, Québec .... TEL (514) 325-6712

McDonnell, Patrick/Medical Illustration
3420 Westmore, Montréal, Québec .... TEL (514) 483-5489

Merola, Caroline
1592, boul. Gouin est, Montréal, Québec .... TEL (514) 389-0106

Messier, Richard
5322, rue St-Urbain, Montréal, Québec .... TEL (514) 277-8624

Metz, Frédéric
Universite du Qué. a Montréal, CP 8888-Succ A, Montréal TEL (514) 987-3921

Meunier, Yvan
4420, boul. Lévesque est #209, Laval, Québec .... TEL (514) 664-3348

Michel, Jules
4030, rue St-Ambroise #220, Montréal, Québec .... TEL (514) 933-2802

Monette, Lise
4567, rue Boyer, Montréal, Québec .... TEL (514) 522-5788

Mongeau, Marc
263, Empire, Greenfield Park, Québec .... TEL (514) 672-2345

Mongeau, Sylvain
646, rue Bord-de-l'eau Rang, Ste-Dorothée, Laval, Qué. ..... TEL (514) 689-6651

Monté, Robert
1421, rue Bishop #304, Montréal, Québec .... TEL (514) 849-6421

Montesano, Sam
2075, University #400, Montréal, Québec .... TEL (514) 982-0204

Montpetit, Louis/Mollo Studio
5187, rue de Lanaudière, Montréal, Québec .... TEL (514) 526-8100

Montréal Creative Centre/Centre Créatif de Montéal
407, rue Dowd, Montréal, Québec .... TEL (514) 861-6323

Morel, René
1224, Alexandre de Sève, Montréal, Québec .... TEL (514) 527-9032

Morency, Paule-Andrée
C.P. 31, St-Denis sur Richelieu, Québec .... TEL (514) 739-3371

Morin, Josée
5031 rue Sherbrooke o. #4, Montréal, Québec .... TEL (514) 489-1172

Nadeau, Therese
8561, Casgrain, Montréal, Québec .... TEL (514) 388-1068

Nantel, Jean-Marc
4848, de l'Esplanade, Montréal, Québec .... TEL (514) 272-0912

Normandin, Luc
5031, rue Sherbrooke o. #9, Montréal, Québec .... TEL (514) 489-1172

O'Bomsawin, Diane
1465, rue Rachel, Montréal, Québec .... TEL (514) 842-9698

Othot, Renée
5198, rue Byron, Montréal, Québec .... TEL (514) 483-1829

Otis, Steve
2213, Des Pruches #8, Charlesbourg, Québec .... TEL (514) 622-6964

Ouellet, Daniel
8362, Pl. Croissy, Anjou, Québec .... TEL (514) 352-9187

Ouellet, Johanne
515, Chemin Ste-Foy, Ste-Foy, Québec .... TEL (418) 687-5334

Ouellet, Odile
5711, rue Durocher, Montréal, Québec .... TEL (514) 270-4899

Ozenne, Jean-François
4309, rue Boyer, Montréal, Québec .... TEL (514) 954-1709

Papa, Carlo/Advertising Plus Ltd
4950 Queen Mary Rd #305, Montréal, Québec .... TEL (514) 739-3339

Paquet, Ginette
1650, Place de Gryon, Terrebone, Québec .... TEL (514) 492-4443

Paquet, Stéphane
633, Haute-Rivière, Chateauguay, Québec .... TEL (514) 692-0472

Paquin, Yves
36, rue Calais, Gatineau, Québec .... TEL (819) 561-5267

Paradis, Johanne
7242 Bloomfield, Montréal, Québec .... TEL (514) 276-2934

Parent, Richard
4560, St-Hubert, Montréal, Québec .... TEL (514) 522-8330

Pariseau, Pierre-Paul
9067 Place de Montgolfier, Montréal, Québec .... TEL (514) 849-2964

Parrinello, Carmen
4288 A, Fullum, Montréal, Québec .... TEL (514) 522-1557

Payne, John R.
10769, rue Berri, Montréal, Québec .... TEL (514) 389-2484

Pelletier, Bernard
266, de la Flore, St-Nicolas, Québec .... TEL (418) 648-7772

Pépin, Johanne
99 McLaren, Valleyfield, Québec .... TEL (514) 371-4413

Pépin, Pierre
752, rue Nérée-Tremblay, Ste-Foy, Québec .... TEL (418) 656-1544

Perkins, Stephen
3981, boul. St-Laurent #810, Montréal, Québec .... TEL (514) 288-6635

Perreault, Josée
334, Terasse St-Denis #503, Montréal, Québec .... TEL (514) 845-3005

Pifko, Sigmund
1121, rue Ste-Catherine o. #500, Montréal, Québec .... TEL (514)849-3916

Pilon, Alain
4324, boul. St-Laurent 1e étage, Montréal, Québec .... TEL (514) 287-1632

Pilon, Guy R
6731 2e av. Rosemount, Montréal, Québec .... TEL (514) 872-6607

Pilon, Louis
1098 Casavant, Chomedy-Laval, Québec .... TEL (514) 682-6083

Pilon, Michel
7992 Papineau, Montréal, Québec .... TEL (514) 374-7839

Poliquin, André
264, rue de Montigny, Mont St-Hilaire, Québec .... TEL (514) 467-2774

Pomminville, Louise
1800 ch. de Caribou #111, Longueuil, Québec .... TEL (514) 468-4638

Pratt, Pierre
3768, rue St-André, Montréal, Québec .... TEL (514) 523-0076

Proulx, Gaetan
6585, 12e Avenue, Montréal, Québec .... TEL (514) 374-3433

Prud'Homme, Jules
1620, rue Van Horne #9, Montréal, Québec .... TEL (514) 279-5475

Quinn, Pamela
245, av. Dorval #14, Montréal, Québec .... TEL (514) 636-1079

Racicot, Hélène
20, rue du Rhone #812, St-Lambert, Québec .... TEL (514) 672-5868

Ranco, Marilyn-Ann
211 av. Outremont, Outremont, Québec .... TEL (514) 495-2943

Renaud, Marie
4166, rue St-Denis #105, Montréal, Québec .... TEL (514) 499-0108

Reno, Alain
4324, boul. St-Laurent, Montréal, Québec .... TEL (514) 849-1760

Rhéault, Daniel
1447, rue Montcalm, Montréal, Québec .... TEL (514) 522-2420

Rhéault, Jean-Louis
7400, rue de Chambois, Montréal, Québec .... TEL (514) 342-5023

Richard, Marc
3222 Masson, Montréal, Québec .... TEL (514) 728-1447

Richard, Mario
6246, Delorimier, Montréal, Québec .... TEL (514) 382-5660

Ro, Daniel
1447, Montcalm, Montréal, Québec .... TEL (514) 522-2420

Robert, François
4479, rue Delorimier, Montréal, Québec .... TEL (514) 523-6212

Roberts, Bruce
60 De Brésoles #205, Montréal, Québec .... TEL (514) 849-1001

Robichaud, Daniel
1337, rue Victoria, St-Lambert, Québec .... TEL (514) 672-8436

Rolland, Brigitte
6016, av. de l'Esplanade, Montréal, Québec .... TEL (514) 274-0578

Rosen, David
4642, rue Esplanade, Montréal, Québec .... TEL (514) 842-0722

Ross, Clarence
716 Anyon, Greenfield Park, Québec .... TEL (514) 671-1504

Rossini, Paul
221, St-Joseph o., Montréal, Québec .... TEL (514) 273-5427

Roux, Paul
172, rue Lamarche #303, Gatineau, Québec .... TEL (819) 568-4965

Roy, Louise
94, av Cedar, Pointe-Claire, Québec .... TEL (514) 694-6781

Roy, Nelly
4575, rue St-Denis, Montréal, Québec .... TEL (514) 843-8504

Ryan, John
3340, Ridge Rd, Huntingdon, Québec .... TEL (514) 264-2231

Sabourin, Jacques
4132 rue de Mentana, Montréal, Québec .... TEL (514) 524-1895

Saint-Aubin, Bruno
69, St-Jean, Ste-Thérèse, Québec .... TEL (514) 623-0469

Saint-Onge, Daniel
4650, rue Dupuis #11, Montréal, Québec .... TEL (514) 737-2043

Saint-Pierre, Caroline
271, av. Greene, Montréal, Québec .... TEL (514) 989-9503

Santa Lucia, Frank
440, St-Pierre, Montréal, Québec .... TEL (514) 499-1133

Sauer, Thiery
4675 Delorimier, Montréal, Québec .... TEL (514) 527-5069

Sawyer, Pierre
20, Lanouette #102, Cap-de-la-Madeleine, Québec .... TEL (819) 375-3816

Scott, Susan
35 Prospect, Montréal, Québec .... TEL (514) 933-7039

Sekeris, Pim
350, rue Prince Arthur o. #D811, Montréal, Québec .... TEL (514)287-1864

Seyer, Martine
4699, rue Chabot, Montréal, Quebec .... TEL (514) 525-7634

Simard, Jasmin
334, Terasse St-Denis #503, Montréal, Québec .... TEL (514) 845-3005

Simard, Rémy
5051, rue Marquette, Montréal, Québec .... TEL (514) 526-9065

Simard, Yves
378, Laurier, Granby, Québec .... TEL (514) 287-9219

Simon, Eric
20, rue Bates 3e étage, Outremont, Québec .... TEL (514)277-4391

Sirois, Pierre
1469, rue Bourbonnière, Longueuil, Québec .... TEL (514) 596-1882

Slutsky, Erik
4324, boul. St-Laurent, Montréal, Québec .... TEL (514) 843-5284

Smith, Lynn
1245, rue St-Marc #14, Montréal, Québec .... TEL (514) 933-2063

St-Onge, Daniel
4650, av. Dupuis #11, Montréal, Québec .... TEL (514) 737-2043

St-Pierre, Chantal
1088, Jarry, Greenfield Park, Québec .... TEL (514) 443-4405

Stewart, John W.
4538, rue Drolet, Montréal, Québec .... TEL (514) 849-7805

Strathy, Georgina
206 Coret, Ile des Soeurs, Québec .... TEL (514) 766-2894

Studio Claude Rousseau Inc.
1421, rue Bishop #305, Montréal, Québec .... TEL (514) 842-0885

Studio de la Montagne Communication Visuelle Inc
2105 de la Montagne #300, Montréal, Québec .... TEL (514) 288-7414

Studio en position
110, rue McGill #502, Montréal, Québec .... TEL (514) 393-3310

Studio Krypton/Guy Charrette
CP 5804, Succursale "B", Montréal, Québec .... TEL (514) 289-8601

Studio Michael Fog
221, rue de la Commune o. #200, Montréal, Québec .... TEL (514) 845-9555

Studio Serge Rousseau Inc.
2067 de Murcie, Vimont, Laval, Québec .... TEL (514) 629-7551

Studio St-Louis Inc.
2100, rue Guy #200, Montréal, Québec .... TEL (514) 989-5555

Studio Versatile Ltée
1041, rue Berri, Montréal, Québec .... TEL (514) 842-8908

Sullivan, Colleen
3608, Ste-Famille, Montréal, Québec .... TEL (514) 284-0856

Sylvestre, Daniel
3643, St-Laurent #301, Montréal, Québec .... TEL (514) 987-7668

Tardi, Nicolas
745, Rivière aux Pins, Boucherville, Québec .... TEL (514) 655-1061

Tate, John
164, Poplar Dr., Dollard-des-Ormeaux, Québec .... TEL (514) 684-1906

Therrien, Joseph
1844, rue Champlain, Montréal, Québec .... TEL (514) 524-0144

Thisdale, François
4651, rue Salaberry, Carigan, Québec .... TEL (514) 447-4956

Thouny, Jean-Paul
852, Davaar, Outremont, Québec .... TEL (514)277-8606

Tibo/Guy Badeau
3841 St. Laurent, Montréal, Québec .... TEL (514) 288-5935

Travers, Claude
2295, rue de Chambly, Montréal, Québec .... TEL (514) 521-5102

Tremblay, Céline
770, rue Villeray, Montréal, Québec .... TEL (514) 270-8203

Tremblay, Claire
3035 Route du Port, BGM8, Port St-François, Québec .... TEL (819) 293-4134

Tremblay, Dory
6241, de la Roche, Montréal, Québec .... TEL (514) 272-9665

Tremblay, Yvan
4223, rue Christophe Colomb, Montréal, Québec .... TEL (514) 598-8457

Tremblay, Yvan Illustrateur
1192, Dorion, Montréal, Québec .... TEL (514) 526-8334

Trudeau, Dominic
4814, Henri-Julien, Montréal, Québec .... TEL (514) 982-9358

Trudeau, Pierre M.
2306, rue Ontario est 3e étage, Montréal, Québec .... TEL (514) 522-2062

Trudel, France
455, Osborne, Verdun, Québec .... TEL (514) 761-0669

Turetschek, Alois Guido
755, boul. Montpellier #710, St-Laurent, Québec .... TEL (514) 334-4354

Turgeon, Jean
4145, Blueridge Cr #59, Montréal, Québec .... TEL (514) 937-8748

Turgeon, Pol
5187, rue Jeanne-Mance, Montréal, Québec .... TEL (514) 273-8329

Tyson, Larry
3459 av. Hôtel de Ville, Montréal, Québec .... TEL (514) 842-7872

Vandandaigue, Carole
115, rue Clarence Gagnon, Ste-Rose, Laval, Québec .... TEL (514) 622-4461

Vaudrin, André
1187 Plessis, Montréal, Québec .... TEL (514) 598-7203

Verrall, Paul
601 boul. Strathmore, Dorval, Québec .... TEL (514) 631-9970

Vezina, Jean-François
1261, Shearer #8226, Montréal, Québec .... TEL (514) 951-8296

Vigneault, Louise
2522a, rue Joliette, Montréal, Québec .... TEL (514) 527-0719

Villeneuve, Anne
5352, rue Clark, Montréal, Québec .... TEL (514) 276-5249

Villeneuve, Michel
271, Jacques Cartier nord, Sherbrooke, Québec .... TEL (819) 566-0569

Vinh, Charles
1421, rue Bishop #201, Montréal, Québec .... TEL (514) 845-7374

Weilbrenner, Johanne
875 des Capucines, Ste-Dorothee, Laval, Québec .... TEL (514) 969-1721

Zarawska, M.
6345, Hamilton #3, Montréal, Québec .... TEL (514) 767-2131

SOCIETES — ASSOCIATIONS

ADIQ
407, boul. St-Laurent #500, Montréal, Québec .... TEL (514) 874-3702

AIIQ
19, cours Le Royer o. #305, Montréal, Québec .... TEL (514) 499-1799

CNEDG
19, rue Le Royer o. #305, Montréal, Québec .... TEL (514) 499-0844

La Société des Graphistes du Québec
Pl. Bonaventure CP 1122, Montréal, Québec .... TEL (514) 397-0537

Le Publicité Club de Montréal
1180, Drummond #730, Montréal, Québec .... TEL (514) 875-2565

Promo Marketing Canada Inc.
1350 Sherbrooke St W #8, Montréal, Québec .... TEL (514) 288-5553

TRADUCTEURS (FRANCAIS) — TRANSLATORS (FRENCH)

Abbeloos, Charles J. (Adaptex)
5585, rue Verdi, Brossard, Québec .... TEL (514) 672-5697

Aird Lemieux et Associès
317, Pl. d'Youville, Montréal, Québec .... TEL (514) 844-8307

Belleau, Suzanne
1695, rue Louise, Chomedey, Québec .... TEL (514) 667-2794

Boileau, Chantal
169, Napoléon, Montréal, Québec .... TEL (514) 499-1306

Couture, François
5311, rue Sherbrooke o. #1319, Montréal, Québec .... TEL (514) 487-6767

Demers, Denyse
6300 Pl. Northcrest, #6e, Montréal, Québec .... TEL (514) 342-4382

de Cotret, Pierre René
2198 Regent, Montréal, Québec .... TEL (514) 526-6780

Gervais, Claude
3528, Prud'homme, Notre-Dame-de-G, Québec .... TEL (514) 489-1488

Jo Ouellet Communications
1500, rue Beaulieu #104, Sillery, Québec .... TEL (418) 683-1911

Laberge, Manon
437-A rue Bédard, Lasalle, Québec .... TEL (514) 595-6465

Lemaire, Marie-Claire Inc.
1596, Tournai, Ste-Foy, Québec .... TEL (418) 651-1525

Moise, Daniel
5545 Côte St-Luc #14, Montréal, Québec .... TEL (514) 487-9537

Montè, Guy
297, rue Saint Paul o. #14, Montréal, Québec .... TEL (514) 843-7680

Montpetit, Charles
4282C, rue Fullum, Montréal, Québec .... TEL (514) 525-4565

Penabad-Casas, Thomas
PO Box 52, Stn Place Du Parc, Montréal, Québec .... TEL (514) 845-3052

Simonnot, Frédéric
7675, 22e Av., Montréal, Québec .... TEL (514) 495-4459

TRADUCTEURS (ANGLAIS) — TRANSLATORS (ENGLISH)

Allen, Wade
335 av. Clarke #22, Westmount, Québec .... TEL (514) 934-4898

Bates, Marguerite
Adaptations Bureau, Vieux-Montréal, Québec .... TEL (514) 849-5812

Clark, Jennifer
3644, av. de Musèe #41, Montréal, Québec .... TEL (514) 844-9083

Penabad-Casas, Thomas
PO Box 52, Stn Place Du Parc, Montréal, Québec .... TEL (514) 845-3052

Smith, George S.
25, av. Glengarry, Montréal, Québec .... TEL (514) 738-0607

Thomas, Syd
2300, rue St-Mathieu #811, Montréal, Québec .... TEL (514) 937-0852

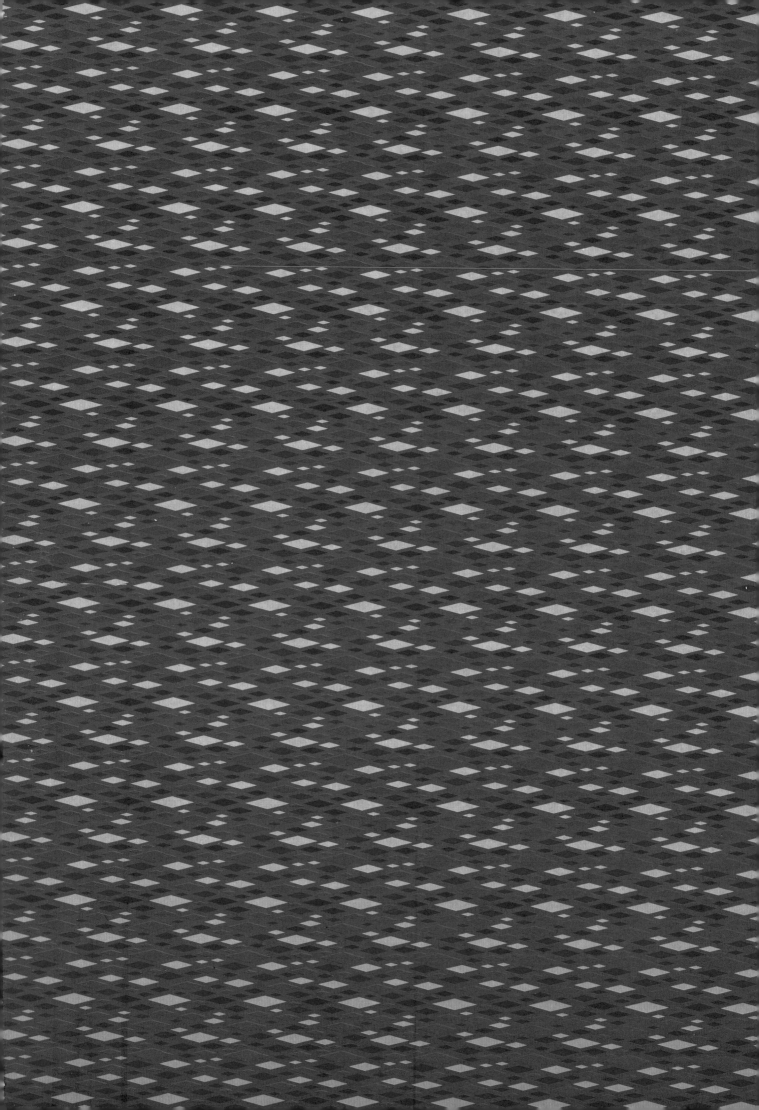